Handbook for the Coalmining Industry
in the European Community

Firedamp Drainage

Published by the Coal Directorate
of the Commission
of the European Communities

Authors:

José Boxho (B) · Pierre Stassen (B)
Gerhard Mücke (D) · Klaus Noack (D)
Christian Jeger (F) · Louis Lescher (F)
Eric John Browning (GB) · Richard Dunmore (GB)
Ieuan Handel Morris (GB)

Verlag Glückauf GmbH · Essen · 1980

This book has also been published in French and German:

Captage de grisou ISBN 3-7739-0255-7
Grubengasabsaugung ISBN 3-7739-0253-0

Results of research work financed by the European Coal and Steel Community (ECSC).

Printed in Germany · Satz und Druck: F. Flothmann GmbH & Co, Essen
Einband: Bercker, Graphischer Betrieb GmbH, Kevelaer
ISBN 3-7739-0254-9

Foreword

Since the beginning of common coal research under the terms of Article 55 of the ECSC-Treaty, close attention has been paid by the High Authority of the European Coal and Steel Community and, subsequently, by the Commission of the European Communities, to problems of firedamp control and its repercussions on safety in the Community's coal mines.

The Commission of the European Communities is therefore pleased to present this Handbook on Firedamp Drainage which combines the results of research and practice and which has been written in a true spirit of European co-operation by experts from the different coal-producing countries of the Community.

The preparation of the Handbook was initiated by the ECSC Experts Committee on Firedamp and Ventilation, which created a working group to establish the text. The group comprised Messrs:

C. Jeger
L. Lecher — Centre d'Etudes et de Recherches des Charbonnages de France

G. Mücke
K. Noack — Steinkohlenbergbauverein

I. H. Morris
E. J. Browning
R. Dunmore — National Coal Board

J. Boxho
P. Stassen — Institut National des Industries Extractives

F. Kindermann — Commission of the European Communities

The Commission of the European Communities wishes success to this work and would like to express its gratitude to the authors.

October 1979

Karlheinz Reichert

Director of the Coal Directorate
of the Commission
of the European Communities

Contents

CHAPTER 4

Firedamp Drainage Monitoring, Control and Experience

CHAPTER 5

Introduction

It is sometimes stated in the literature that firedamp drainage techniques are very old. We do not support this view. Admittedly, in previous centuries several attempts were made to drain firedamp emitted from blowers, fissures in the strata or old workings, but these attempts were only sporadic and never gave rise to routine firedamp drainage.

Systematic drainage of firedamp began at Mansfeld Colliery in the Ruhr in 1943 but because of the special wartime circumstances the technique was not fully developed for some years. About 1948 tests began again both in the Ruhr and the Saar and from 1949 firedamp drainage began to be used in all the other coalmining countries which are now members of the European Economic Community.

In June 1953, the Council of the Organisation for European Economic Co-operation approved a proposal by the Coal Committee to form an intra-European Technical Assistance Mission on the "Drainage and Use of Methane from Coalmines", in connection with the work of the European Productivity Agency. The purpose of this mission was to collect information likely to help in:

a) Reviewing the steps taken in various European mines to drain firedamp, recording the results obtained, analysing the methods employed according to the special geological features of the deposits, and in comparing and using them for guidance in the future planning of work.
b) Studying the specific problems involved in the drainage of firedamp.
c) Considering the conditions under which firedamp can be used in various economic sectors, with a view to the subsequent development of such uses.

Experts from Belgium, France, Germany, Italy, the Saar, Turkey, the United Kingdom and the United States took part in the Mission. Between 10 May and 4 June 1954 they visited gassy mines in European coalfields where various methods of firedamp drainage were employed, ie the United Kingdom, Belgium, Germany, France and the Saar. They studied problems of utilising firedamp in these coalfields and also made a number of visits to different industries in Northern Italy where natural gas was already being widely used. At the end of their enquiries the experts drew up a report entitled "Drainage and Use of Methane from Coal-fields". This report was published in Paris in 1956 by the European Productivity Agency of the Organisation for European Economic Co-operation. Because at that time techniques were developing so rapidly, the experts decided as early as 1958 to publish an addendum to the 1956 report to disseminate the knowledge acquired on each aspect and on the progress made in different techniques. Together these publications in a way constituted the first European Firedamp Drainage Handbook.

Twenty years later, the Committee of Experts on Firedamp and Ventilation appointed by the Commission of the European Communities to monitor research financed by the latter considered that the time had come to draft a new European Firedamp Drainage Handbook. During those twenty years, the Coal Directorate of the ECSC had organised a number of meetings of investigators from the various countries concerned with such matters. Research in progress and those meetings enabled knowledge of strata pressures and the emission and drainage of firedamp together with calculation and surveillance of drainage systems, to be extended and deepened. By frequent contact, investigators and practising engineers now have a clearer insight into the various problems, and the Experts consider that this is a particularly opportune moment for the preparation of a new Firedamp Drainage Handbook for the Coalmining Industries of the European Community.

This Handbook differs in format from the first. It contains five chapters:

1. Basic Principles of Firedamp Drainage,
2. Methods of Firedamp Drainage,
3. Planning, Calculation and Setting Up of Gas Drainage Networks and Extractor Stations,
4. Firedamp Drainage Monitoring, Control and Experience,
5. Utilisation of Drained Firedamp.

The last chapter is short because the widely diversified methods of utilising drained firedamp employed twenty years ago have lost some of their significance in recent years. The rapid expansion of natural gas networks across the whole of Europe has meant that high quality firedamp can be supplied to many former consumers such as the chemical industry, steelworks, distributors of town gas etc. Consequently, the principal direct use of firedamp occurs at or near the centre of production with firedamp being burnt in colliery and power-station boilers or drying kilns. In view of the scarcity and cost of energy, however, these applications are still attractive and are again on the increase.

There must be no doubt, however, that the main reason for firedamp drainage continues to be for safety, because it makes a substantial contribution to the improvement and safety of underground mining by reducing firedamp concentrations in return airways, working areas and travelling roadways of the mine. It also provides increased safety during the working of high-output faces, because it is practicable to extract large quantities of gas which would otherwise have to be mixed with large volumes of air. It would be extremely difficult to circulate such large quantities of air through most working places without raising clouds of dust, inconsistent with health standards currently in use.

Chapter 1

Basic Principles of Firedamp Drainage

1. Characteristics of Firedamp. Liberation of Firedamp from Coal and Rock. Problems Raised by the Presence of Firedamp: Percentage Limits

1.1 Origin and Characteristics of Firedamp in Coal Mines

Firedamp is a gas resulting from the transformation of vegetable waste, and is mainly contained in coal. It may also be found in smaller quantities in the intervening rocks, either by migration from coal to reservoir rocks (such as coarse sandstones) or because the rocks themselves (such as carbonaceous shales) contain a certain proportion of organic matter.

It is generally composed of:

▷ methane (CH_4): 90 to 95 %

▷ and often a small amount of carbon dioxide gas (CO_2): up to 5 %.

Certain measures contain a higher proportion of carbon dioxide, 30 to 50 %, even 100 % in exceptional cases.

Firedamp contains heavier gases of the paraffin series (ethane, propane, butane etc.) in traces or in small quantities. The proportion of these constituents may be greater (20 to 30 %) in very special deposits which are close to natural gas fields, oil bearing shales or sands. Firedamp also frequently contains nitrogen and very small quantities of carbon monoxide (CO) and hydrogen sulphide (H_2S). Sometimes hydrogen (H_2) may be present, especially in old workings.

Tables 1.1 and 1.2 indicate the main physical properties of the individual gases found in firedamp.

1.2 Liberation of Firedamp from Coal and Adjacent Strata

Firedamp is contained in strata in two forms:

▷ free gas in the fissures and pores of the coal and in other rock,

▷ gas adsorbed on the internal surface of the coal.

Table 1.1 Physical Properties of Methane.

Chemical Formula:	CH_4	
Molecular Structure:	H—C(—H)(—H)—H	
Molecular Weight:	16.042 kg/kmol	
Molecular Volume:	22.36 m^3/kmol	(at 273 K and 101.3 kPa)
Density:	0.7168 kg/m^3	(at 273 K and 101.3 kPa)
Specific Weight:	7.034 N/m^3	(at 273 K and 101.3 kPa)
Specific Gravity:	0.5545	(air = 1)
Boiling Point:	111.3 K	(at 101.3 kPa)
Melting Point:	90.5 K	(at 101.3 kPa)
Density of Liquid:	415 kg/m^3	
Latent Heat of Vapourisation:	508.2 kJ/kg	(at 111.3 K and 101.3 kPa)
Latent Heat of Fusion:	58.8 kJ/kg	(at 90.5 K and 101.3 kPa)
Critical Temperature:	190.5 K	
Critical Pressure:	463.03 N/cm^2 = 4.63 MPa	
Critical Density:	162 kg/m^3	
Specific Heat:		
at constant pressure:	2.184 kJ/kg K	(at 273 K)
at constant volume:	1.680 kJ/kg K	(at 273 K)
Thermal Conductivity:	0.110 kJ/m h K	(at 273 K and 101.3 kPa)
	0.118 kJ/m h K	(at 293 K and 101.3 kPa)
Dynamic Viscosity:	1.087 nPa s	(at 293 K)
Diffusion Coefficient:	0.196 cm^2/s	(at 273 K and 101.3 kPa)
relative to air:	0.726 cm^2/s	(at 298 K and 101.3 kPa)
relative to hydrogen:	0.292 cm^2/s	(at 307.7 K and 101.3 kPa)
relative to water vapour:	0.292 cm^2/s	(at 273 K and 101.3 kPa)
relative to carbon dioxide:	0.153 cm^2/s	(at 273 K and 101.3 kPa)
relative to methane:	0.174 cm^2/s	(at 293 K and 101.3 kPa)
Solubility in Water:		
litres (at 273 K and 101.3 kPa) dissolved by 1 m^3 water:	55.6 at 273 K and 33.1 at 293 K	
Explosive Limits in mixtures with air (at 293 K and 101.3 kPa):		
lower:	5 % by volume 33 g methane per m^3 methane/air mixture	
upper:	15 % by volume 100 g methane per m^3 methane/air mixture	
Calorific Value:		
Net (lower):	804.926 MJ/kmol 50.169 MJ/kg 35.994 MJ/m^3	(at 298 K)
Gross (upper):	893.155 MJ/kmol 55.671 MJ/kg 39.942 MJ/m^3	(at 298 K)

Table 1.2 Some Physical Properties of Different Gases.

Properties	Methane CH_4	Carbon Dioxide CO_2	Carbon Monoxide CO	Hydrogen Sulphide H_2S	Ethane C_2H_6	Propane C_3H_8	Hydrogen H_2
Molecular weight	16.042	44.01	28.01	34.08	30.07	44.09	2.016
Density (kg/m^3)	0.7168	1.98	1.25	1.54	1.36	2	0.09
Specific gravity relative to air	0.5545	1.53	0.97	1.17	1.05	1.55	0.07
Boiling point K at 101.3 kPa	111.3	194.5	83	211.2	184.7	230.8	20.2
Lower Explosive Limit (% vol at 293 K and 101.3 kPa)	5	—	12.5	4.3	3	2.1	4
Upper Explosive Limit (% vol at 293 K and 101.3 kPa)	15	—	74.2	45.5	12.5	9.35	74.2
Calorific Value (MJ/m^3 at 288 K)							
upper	37.11	—	11.86	23.50	64.53	96.61	11.94
lower	33.38	—	11.86	21.63	58.93	88.96	10.07

1.2.1 Free Gas

The quantity of free gas C_v (evaluated at 273 K and 101.3 kPa) depends on:

▷ the porosity of the media,

▷ absolute pressure and temperature.

$$C_v = v \frac{p}{p_0} \frac{273}{T} \quad \text{[1.1]}$$

where:

C_v quantity of gas in m^3/t

v porosity in m^3/t

p absolute pressure in kPa or in mbar

p_0 standard atmospheric pressure (101.3 kPa or 1013 mbar)

T absolute temperature in K (273 K is 0 °C).

It should be noted that the in situ pressures may be very high and of the order of 3000 to 4000 kPa for certain measures.

The following table gives an indication of the quantities of firedamp likely to be contained in rock fissures and pores (free gas).

Rock	Quantity of gas C_v in m^3/t at 298 K and 101.3 kPa			
	p: 100	1000	2500	5000 kPa
coal (v = 0.02)	0.02	0.18	0.45	0.90
porous sandstone (v = 0.03)	0.03	0.27	0.68	1.36
shale (v = 0.002)	0.002	0.018	0.05	0.09

The free gas in coal makes up a small fraction, usually 5 to 10 %, of the total gas content (free gas + gas adsorbed).

Porous sandstones are liable to contain more free gas than do stressed coals, whereas for shales the quantities are 10 times less. For example in situ coals whose total firedamp content (free and adsorbed) is 20 m^3/t, may have a free firedamp content of 3 m^3/t. For certain sandstones on the other hand the in situ content may be up to 4 m^3/t.

It should however be noted that the effective volume v of the pores filled by free gas is affected by the pressure of the overlying rock and the moisture content of the coal or rock. So v can vary between 0.01 and 0.11 m^3/t for coal, and 0.004 and 0.04 m^3/t for sandstone.

The term free gas includes gas contained in faulted zones or other natural discontinuities which form "reservoirs".

1.2.2 Adsorbed Gas and the Factors Affecting the Quantity Adsorbed

The greater part of gas contained in coal in situ is held at the surface of the coal pores and microfissures in adsorbed form as a monomolecular layer.

The quantity of firedamp C_p adsorbed by the coal is very high, since the internal surface area of the coal is very large (of the order of 90 m^2/g). For instance, a coal containing 27 % of volatile matter can adsorb at 299 K up to 20 m^3/t (which corresponds to an internal surface area of 95 m^2/g, based on methane molecules of 0.4 nm diameter in a monomolecular layer).

Adsorption is a reversible physical phenomenon which is adequately described by Langmuir's equation:

$$C_p = C_{p\infty} \frac{k_c\, p}{1 + k_c\, p} \qquad [1.2]$$

where:

C_p the quantity adsorbed at pressure p

p the absolute gas pressure

$C_{p\infty}$ and k_c constants depending on the nature of the gas, the temperature, the nature of the adsorbant surface.

Adsorption Isotherm

This is the curve giving the quantity of gas adsorbed C_p as a function of the pressure p of the gas at a given temperature (example in Figure 1.1).

For low absolute gas pressures (p less than 100 kPa) C_p is almost directly proportional to p. For higher gas pressures ($>$ 5000 kPa) C_p shows practically no further increase with pressure.

In virgin seams, 80 % of the cases measured gave in situ gas pressures from 400 to 4000 kPa, with occasional pressures of up to 5000 kPa (Figure 1.2).

One practical use is that the isotherm and the in situ pressure provide an indirect method of estimating the total gas content of the coal. For details of the direct and indirect methods, see Chapter 3, Appendix 3.1.

Effect of the Nature of the Gas

At a given partial pressure and temperature, carbon dioxide is much more readily adsorbed than methane. Methane itself is more readily adsorbed than nitrogen (see Figure 1.1).

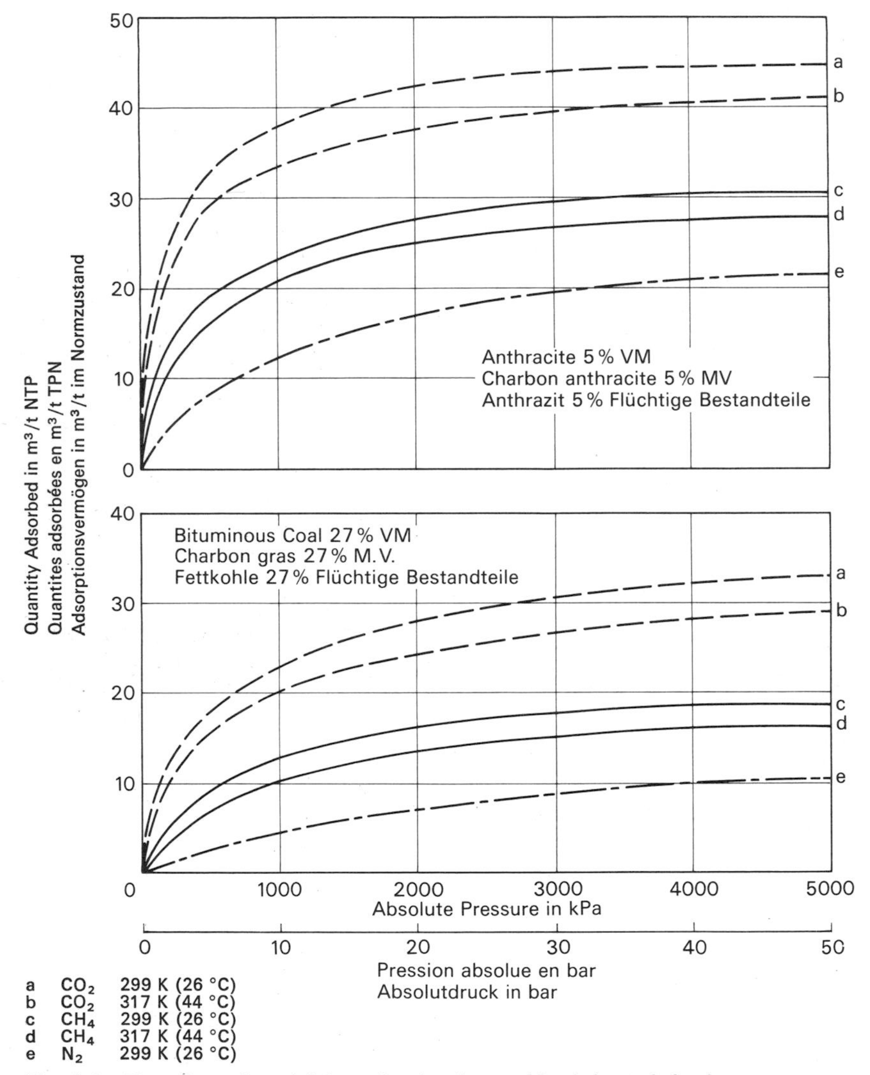

a CO_2 299 K (26 °C)
b CO_2 317 K (44 °C)
c CH_4 299 K (26 °C)
d CH_4 317 K (44 °C)
e N_2 299 K (26 °C)

Fig. 1.1 Two Examples of Adsorption Isotherms (Coal dry, ash free).

Effect of Temperature

At the same equilibrium pressure the quantity of gas adsorbed decreases as the temperature increases (Figure 1.1): starting from 299 K it falls 0.8 % per degree for bituminous coal, and 0.6 % per degree for anthracite.

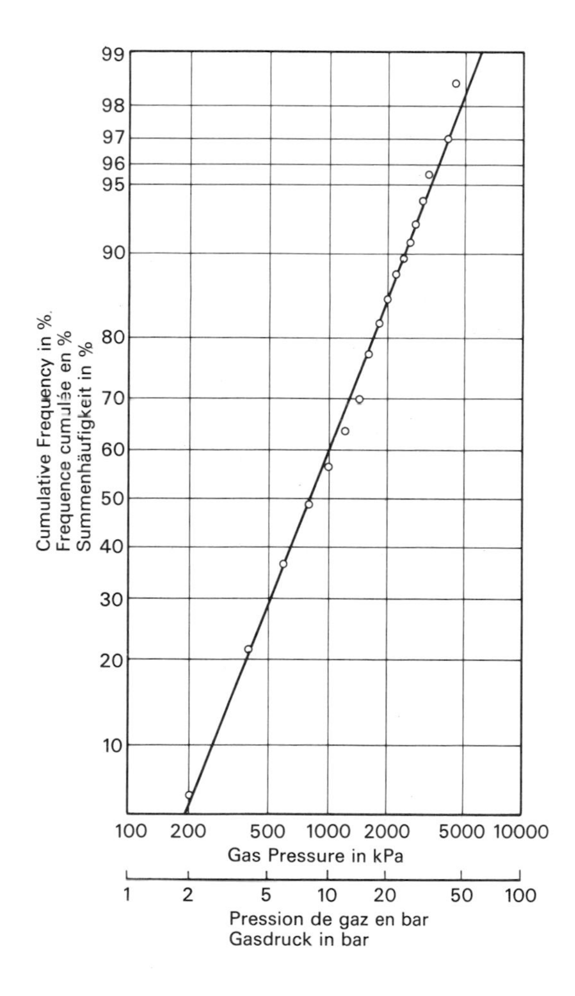

Fig. 1.2 Cumulative Frequency of Gas Pressure in Undisturbed Seams in the Ruhr.

Effect of Moisture

The quantity of methane adsorbed decreases when the natural moisture of the coal increases.

At the same in situ methane pressure, a naturally moist coal is less gassy than if it were naturally dry. In the absence of a direct measurement of the effect of moisture, Ettinger's formula gives an approximate value:

$$\frac{C_{p\ moist}}{C_{p\ dry}} = \frac{1}{1 + 0.31\ H} \quad \text{. . . . . [1.3]}$$

where:

H moisture content in %

$C_{p\ moist}$ gas content of moist coal in m^3/t

$C_{p\ dry}$ gas content of dry coal in m^3/t.

This formula, represented in Figure 1.3 is valid up to 4 to 5% moisture. Above this moisture level, saturation occurs and the ratio is then almost constant.

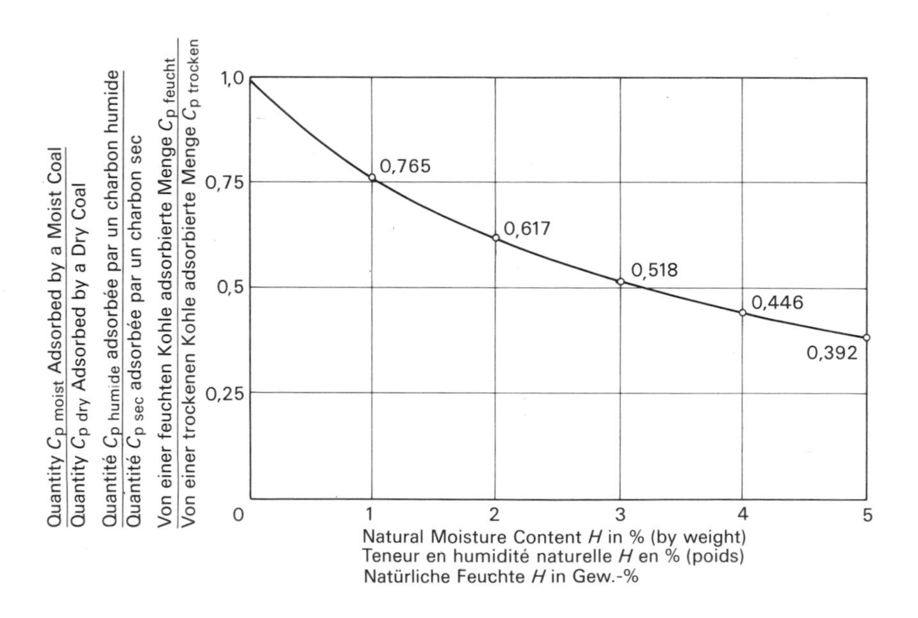

Fig. 1.3 Influence of Natural Moisture on the Adsorption of Methane by Pure Coal.

A large part of natural moisture is held to the internal coal surfaces by adsorption. Infused water is able to release only part of the free gas in the time between infusion and coal winning, reducing the quantity of gas contained by only a few percent.

Influence of Rank

At given pressure and temperature, the quantity of gas adsorbed by dried coal is at a minimum between 20 and 40% volatile matter content (Figure 1.4). In fact it is the adsorption capacity $C_{p\,\infty}$ which is a minimum (Figure 1.5) and k_c decreases regularly with increasing volatile matter content (Figure 1.6).

In the German coal mining industry, average adsorption isotherms have been established for practical use, showing quantity of methane adsorbed by the coal as a function of methane pressure and rank (Figure 1.7).

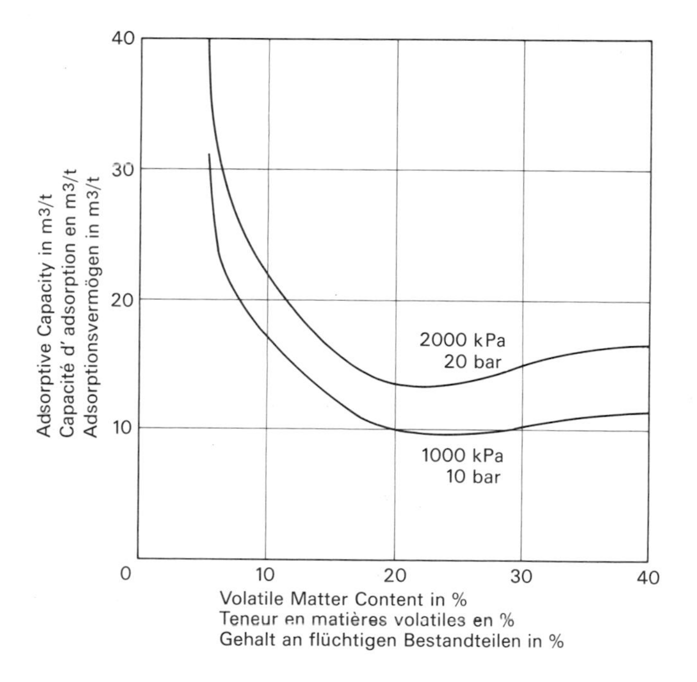

Temperature 303 K;
Values corrected to zero moisture using Ettinger formula;
above 4 % Moisture, constant 4 % correction used.

Fig. 1.4 Variation of Dry Adsorptive Capacity with Volatile Matter Content.

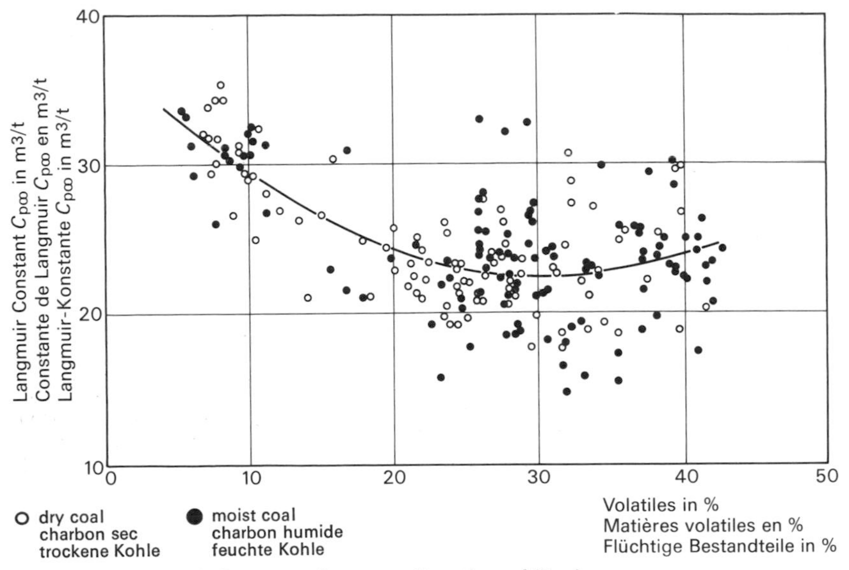

Fig. 1.5 Langmuir Constant $C_{p\infty}$ as a Function of Rank.

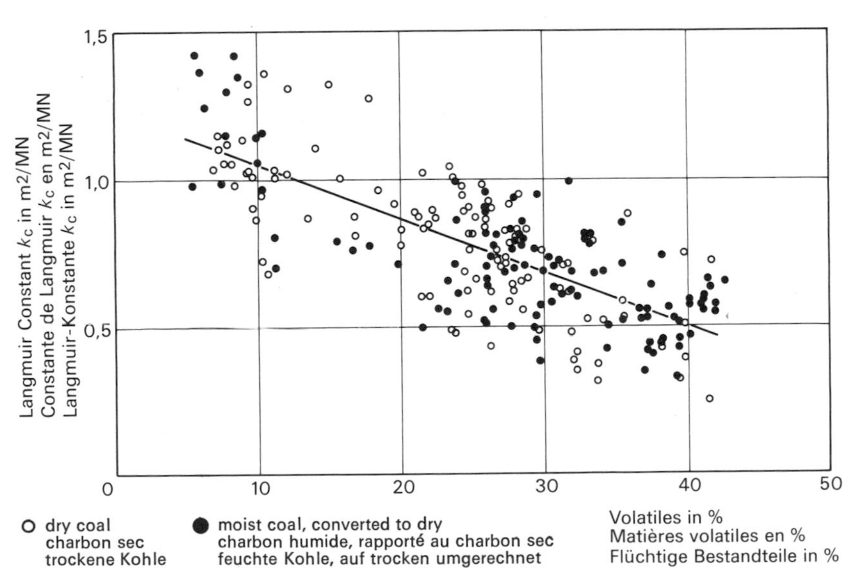

Fig. 1.6 Langmuir Constant k_c as a Function of Rank.

Effect of Ash Content

The gas is only adsorbed by carbonaceous matter.

$$\frac{C_{p\ \text{pure coal}}}{C_{p\ \text{ashy coal}}} = \frac{1}{1 - 0.01\ a} \quad [1.4]$$

where:

a actual ash content %
(if there is some carbonate in the coal, *a* is corrected to take account of the decomposition of this at the time of ash determination. In this case, frequently $a = 1.1\ a'$, where a' is the measured ash content).

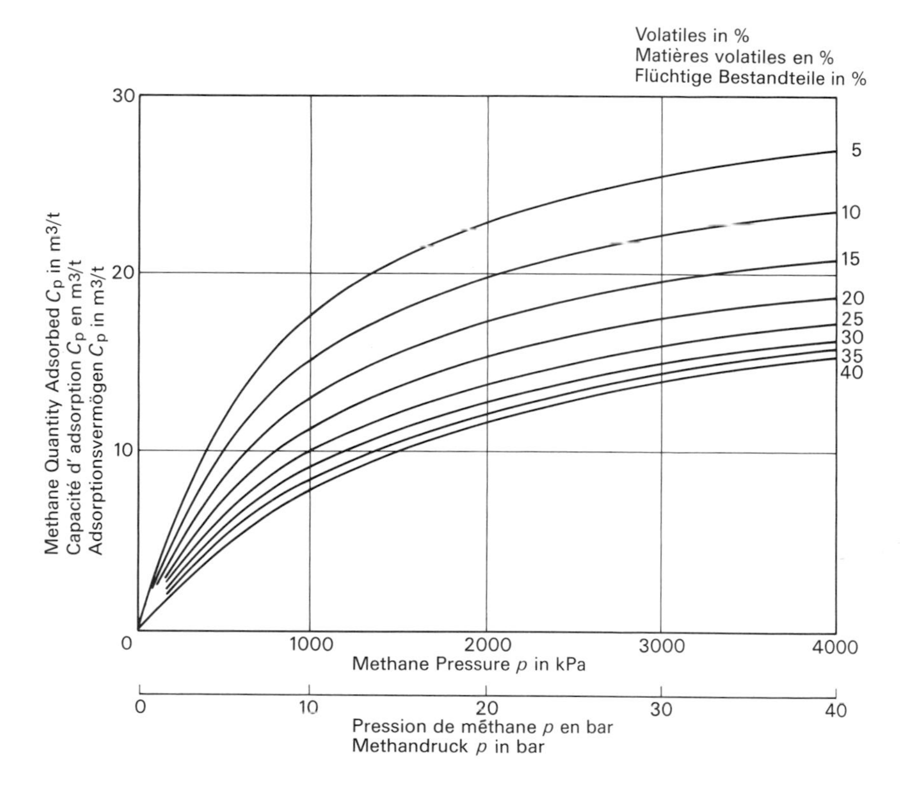

Fig. 1.7 Mean Sorption Isotherms for Dry Coal from 5 to 30 % Volatiles, Temperature 303 K.

1.2.3 Desorption

This is the release of firedamp from coal (the reverse of adsorption). It occurs when mining relaxes and fractures the ground. Firedamp which enters the airstream through the fractures caused by working consists largely of firedamp desorbed, the remainder being free gas from pores and microfissures.

The desorbable content of the coal is the quantity of gas given off when the coal passes from equilibrium with gas at seam pressure to equilibrium with gas at atmospheric pressure in normal conditions (Figure 1.8).

Desorption Kinetics

For a spherical particle of diameter d, the degree of desorption r at the end of time t is given by:

$$r(t) = \frac{q_1^0(t)}{q_1^0(\infty)} \approx \sqrt{1 - \exp\left(-\frac{4\pi^2 D}{d^2}t\right)} \quad \text{[1.5]}$$

where:

$q_1^0(\infty)$ quantity of gas which can be liberated between pressure p_1 and atmospheric pressure p_0 ($p_0 < p_1$) after infinite time

$q_1^0(t)$ quantity of gas liberated after a time t when the pressure moves quickly from p_1 to p_0

d equivalent particle diameter in cm; $d = \frac{6V}{A_0}$

- V particle volume and
- A_0 its surface area

t time in seconds

D diffusion coefficient in cm^2/s.

The coefficient of diffusion D:

- ▷ increases with temperature $\left(\frac{D_{323\,K}}{D_{298\,K}} \approx 2 \text{ to } 4 \text{ for } CH_4\right)$;
- ▷ depends on the initial and final gas contents;
- ▷ depends on the nature of the gas;
  at ambient temperature D_{CH_4} is of the order of 10^{-10} cm^2/s.

If t is not too great $\left(t < \frac{d^2}{D\pi}\right)$ one can write:

$$\frac{q_1^0(t)}{q_1^0(\infty)} \approx \frac{12}{d}\sqrt{\frac{Dt}{\pi}} - \frac{12\,Dt}{d^2} \quad \text{[1.6]}$$

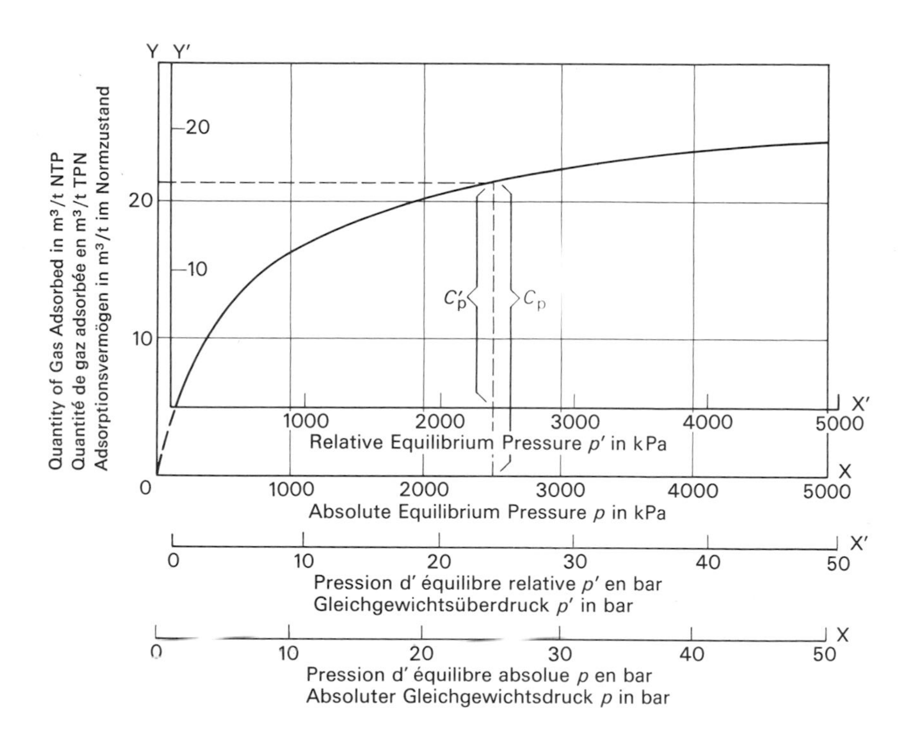

C'_p desorbable gas content for relative pressure
la concentration désorable en fonction de la pression d'équilibre relative
in Abhängigkeit vom Gleichgewichtsüberdruck p' desorbierbarer Gasinhalt

C_p total gas content at absolute pressure
la concentration totale en fonction de la pression d'équilibre absolue
in Abhängigkeit vom absoluten Gleichgewichtsdruck p gesamter absorbierter Gasinhalt

Fig. 1.8 Graphical Representation of Desorbable and Total Gas Contents.

Note:

Certain research workers maintain that the law in $\sqrt{t}$ does not always hold. In Great Britain an empirical equation is used:

$$\frac{q_1^0(t)}{q_1^0(\infty)} = 1 - \exp\left(-\left(\frac{t}{t_0}\right)^n\right) \quad \ldots\ldots\ldots\ldots \quad [1.7]$$

where:

t_0 the time for desorption of 63 % of the gas

n $^1/_3$ for bituminous coals

n $^1/_2$ for anthracites.

Effect of Particle Diameter

The theoretical 90% degassing times for different particle sizes using equation [1.5] are:

Particle diameter	1 μm	10 μm	100 μm	1 mm	1 cm	1 m
Time for r = 0.9	4.6 s	10 min	13 h	1 month	15 years	150 000 years

Initial Desorption

At the start of desorption while $r(t)$ remains below about 25%, it can be stated from equation [1.6] that whatever the particle shape,

$$r(t) = \frac{q_1^0(t)}{q_1^0(\infty)} \approx \frac{12}{d}\sqrt{\frac{Dt}{\pi}} = \frac{2A_0}{V}\sqrt{\frac{Dt}{\pi}} = k_1\sqrt{t} \quad \ldots\ldots \quad [1.8]$$

because Dt is much lower than $\sqrt{Dt}$ (D much less than 1 and t small) where $k_1 = \frac{2A_0}{V}\sqrt{\frac{D}{\pi}} = \frac{12}{d}\sqrt{\frac{D}{\pi}}$ and may be determined experimentally.

On the other hand if equation [1.7] applies:

$$r(t) = \frac{q_1^0(t)}{q_1^0(\infty)} = k_2 t^n \quad \ldots\ldots \quad [1.9]$$

and k_2 may be determined experimentally. According to this equation therefore, desorption initially follows a law in $\sqrt[3]{t}$ for bituminous coals and $\sqrt{t}$ for anthracites.

Equations [1.8] and [1.9] are used to calculate the quantity of firedamp released during the first 3 to 4 min of desorption when using the direct method for gas content measurement (cf Chapter 3, Appendix 3.1).

For longer periods, it is necessary to return to equations [1.5], [1.6] or [1.7], the latter having the advantage of using coefficients which are easily measured.

This method is not applicable in the case of gas mixtures (eg CO_2 and CH_4) where the rates of desorption are different.

1.3 Problems Caused by Firedamp

The presence of firedamp in mine atmospheres poses important problems of safety. Methane forms explosive mixtures with air in the range between 5 and 15% at atmospheric pressure.[1] The maximum limits of concentration in airways are laid down by national mining regulations. The quantities of firedamp liberated by mining vary with the rate of coal extraction; this means that, at constant airflow, the stipulated maximum may set a limit to production.

Firedamp drainage is one of two ways (the other being ventilation) of ensuring that the highest possible production rates may not be constrained by the gas content in airways.

2. Purposes of Drainage

The principle objective is the improvement of safety by reducing the firedamp content of the ventilation.

Drainage is used to capture as much of the firedamp as possible before it enters the mine ventilation. For safety reasons minimum firedamp content is specified for the drained gas. These limits are shown in Appendix 4.5.

The complementary objective is to recover a gas with a high calorific value, to be utilised as fuel either locally or sold. For utilisation purposes it is desirable that the collected gas is consistently rich in methane. It should be noted that:

▷ the economic objective behind firedamp drainage usually takes second place, except in the case of drainage from abandoned mines, a practice which has grown in recent years, and that

▷ experience has shown that conditions favourable to utilisation need not conflict with the main objective of safety. Efforts to maximise drainage have helped to bring down the firedamp content in the ventilation to a level well below the safety limits. On the other hand efforts to obtain a gas rich in methane have led to the improved sealing of airway sides skirting waste areas. This helps to avoid the formation of dangerous mixtures near these sides by unexpected emissions of firedamp from waste areas.

---

[1] If the mixture contains hydrocarbons of a higher rank than methane (eg ethane, propane), hydrogen or carbon monoxide, the lower and upper explosive limits are altered (lower limit decreased, upper limit increased) and the range of explosibility is widened.

3. Emission of Firedamp around the Workings and Flow of Firedamp towards them[2]

3.1 Permeability of Unfissured Ground. Effect of Stress on the Permeability of the Coal

The permeability of intervening strata is generally low and may be considered to be practically unaffected by stress, at least in the cases where fractures are not produced. For coal, permeability diminishes under the effect of compression and increases under that of tension because the pores and fissures naturally tend to close in the first case and to open in the second. If the permeability of the compressed coal before excavation is close to that of the other strata, the permeability of the relaxed coal is clearly greater.

Although the phenomenon is not always completely reproducible, it has been possible by means of laboratory measurements to establish an order of magnitude for variations in the permeability of coals subjected to hydrostatic stress. Between 0 and 30 MPa, the permeability of certain coals may vary by a ratio of 100 to 1 or even 1000 to 1.

In coal measures, firedamp is located predominantly in the seams and thin bands of coal. What has just been said in relation to permeability under stress explains why generally no circulation of gas is possible in virgin areas in European conditions. The permeability of the compressed coal is too low to allow any internal migration of firedamp which would be significant on a human time-scale, and the unfractured surrounding rock layers form impermeable barriers between the coal seams (except for certain sandstones). Firedamp only flows towards the workings from the zones which are relaxed and fissured or simply relaxed, as a result of mining operations.

3.2 Relaxation and Fissuring Around the Workings

All mine workings induce a modification of the stress pattern in the ground around them. This changed stress pattern produces fissures in

---

[2] The conventional description presented in Sections 3 and 4 is that which would be given by a majority of experts in the field. However other views exist, notably those of Airey (Chapter 3 Appendix 3.1) who discounts the concept of permeability in this context and prefers to treat gas emission in terms of the flow of gas from a seam considered as a system of discrete blocks; as the stress induced by the working intensifies, the block size decreases and the rate of emission increases. He takes resistance to flow in the crack system surrounding the blocks to be negligible compared with the internal resistance controlling the rate of emission from each block.

a zone enveloping the excavation, but this fissured zone is not as extensive as the whole zone in which the stress has changed. These changes are generally characterised by a zone of relaxation[3] enveloped by a zone of compression[4]. Fissures can form in the compression zone or in the relaxed zone but they open only in the relaxed zone.

In considering an elemental part of the zone around an excavation, the characteristics and rate of fissuring do not depend only on its distance and position relative to the excavation, or on the shape and size of the excavation and on the initial stress levels which depend upon the depth, and the proximity of other workings; they also depend on the thicknesses and nature of the strata.

Because of the natural structure of coal, the fissuring of a seam can develop strongly in certain conditions even though there is little or no fissuring of the surrounding strata.

Firedamp contained in the seams desorbs if it is able to flow towards the workings. This condition is produced where seams are relaxed and open fissures develop in the strata between those seams and the workings; the right conditions also obtain where there is a working or drivage passing through the relaxed part of a seam.

3.3 Fissuring and Relaxation of the Ground Around a Face. Emission and Flow of Firedamp

3.3.1 Fissuring and Relaxation of Zones Around a Face

Around a face we will distinguish three groups of zones as shown in Figure 1.9.

The first group comprises the zones nearest the excavation where the beds fracture into blocks which are displaced relative to each other (normally referrred to as Z1 in the roof and Z'1 in the floor). Even when the strata takes load again, at least at first, the fissures and voids in these zones do not close completely. This group constitutes a very permeable region around the working. Since the floor zone is very small or often does not exist, the roof zone is clearly more important (Z'1 has been omitted from Figure 1.9). For a typical caved face, the thickness of this roof zone is 3 to 8 times the face height depending on

[3] Relaxation at a point means that in at least one direction the elemental stress is less than that which existed before the excavation. In other directions the stresses may be (according to position) greater than, equal to or less than the initial stresses.

[4] In the compression zone the stresses at a point are greater than the initial stresses, whichever direction is considered.

the strength of the fractured beds; the thickness is less for stowed faces. The voids existing in this zone constitute a reservoir of firedamp which, at a time of falling barometric pressure or changes of ventilation, can release firedamp which increases the general body concentration or causes the formation of layers.

The much larger second group (Z2 in the roof and Z'2 in the floor) comprises zones completely enveloping the first. In these zones the rocks fracture and the beds separate from each other. When the ground recompresses, the natural microfissures partially close bringing together the sides of the fissures and the broken pieces so that even if the permeability does not return to its initial low value, it is considerably reduced.

In the floor one may put the limit of the zone Z'2 at about 50 m below the face.

In the roof, in virgin ground, the zone Z2 can have two configurations depending on the size of the working relative to a certain critical size:

a) When the size of the working is less than the critical size, the vertical limit of the caving and the fissured zone is reached quickly. The ground around the caved zone forms an arch above which there is practically no subsidence nor fissuring of the strata. Therefore if the

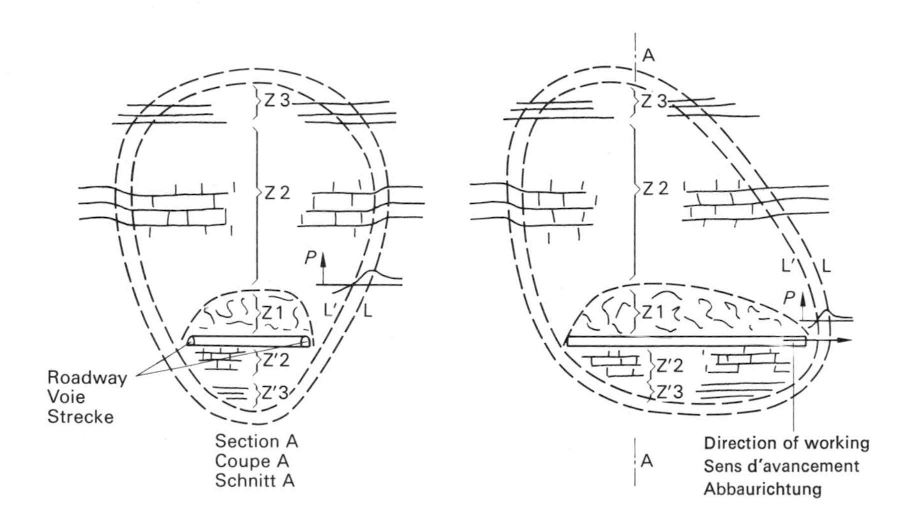

Fig. 1.9 Relaxed Zones Around a Working.

working is in virgin ground and if its size is less than the critical size, the zone Z2 contracts and closes in the same way as the floor arch does.

b) If the working is greater than the critical size there is a progressive extension of the subsidence up to the surface and there the lateral limits of the fissured zone extend beyond the edges of the waste. Therefore if the working is larger than the critical size, either alone or in combination with old neighbouring workings, the zone Z2 opens out. Its height is a function of time, but the rate of vertical extension diminishes and beyond a certain height becomes insignificant, so that during the life of a face there is a practical upper limit for the zone Z2. The height of this limit above the face is probably over 100 m. In addition, as this zone increases in height, the weight of the ground increases proportionally within the zone and compresses its lower part, decreasing its permeability.

In virgin ground the heights of the zones Z1 and Z2 depend on such factors as:

- ▷ the working thickness of the seam,
- ▷ whether the waste is caved or stowed,
- ▷ the length of face,
- ▷ the presence or not of adjacent panels.

If there are old workings above the face the system of fissures of zone Z2 generally overlaps with that of the zone Z'2 in the floor of the old working and the emission of firedamp from the roof is then less than if it had been in virgin ground.

Below the zone Z'2 in the floor and above the zone Z2 in the roof (when the face is in virgin ground) there exist zones Z'3 in the floor and Z3 in the roof where the ground is relaxed but where the rocks are hardly fissured. This relaxation is sufficient for coal seams to become permeable and gas to escape providing there are outlets such as roads or boreholes.

3.3.2 The Distribution of Permeability in the Relaxed Zone

In the zones Z1 and Z'1 permeability is high and can be considered isotropic; dislocation of the ground, expecially in the roof makes the movement of gas in all directions equally probable irrespective of the nature of the strata.

By contrast in zones Z2 and Z'2, the permeability is anisotropic, being greater parallel to the bedding plane than normal to it. The fissures resulting from the fracture of intervening rocks in these zones are more widely spaced than in zones Z1 and Z'1 and this spacing increases with the distance from the worked seam. In strata with well defined bedding planes, numerous bed separations may be observed.

It should be noted that in the coal, the opening of these fissures is assisted by the degassing of the seam. As it loses gas the coal contracts. The reduction in volume adds to the effect of the destressing and causes a widening of the fissures. The phenomenon is reversible — adsorption is accompanied by swelling of the coal but it is evident that desorbed gas, which has found an escape route in the fissures of the surrounding rock during the relaxed phase, is no longer there to be readsorbed when the seam is recompressed. This is why the permeability of recompressed coal is never as low as that of virgin coal.

The zones Z3 and Z'3 are characterised by zero permeability across the bedding planes, whereas the permeability in the plane of the coal seams remains sufficiently high to allow the escape of gas if it finds a flow path (eg borehole) crossing the seam.

3.3.3 Firedamp Flow

As the workings advance, the gas contained at high pressure in the coal fissures flows along the breaks crossing the intervening rocks towards the region of lower gas pressure, ie towards the face, the waste and the gate roads. The fall in gas pressure induces desorption which will continue either until the gas pressure in the relaxed coal approaches that of the air pressure in the mine workings (where the relaxed coal is still linked up to them), or until recompression of the strata has closed the fissures again (150 to 250 m behind an advancing face).

Only part of the relaxed zone comes into being as a result of one day's advance of the face and only part of the firedamp from this newly relaxed region is released during this period. There are several reasons for this:

▷ The fissures in this added portion develop gradually.

▷ The resistance of the fissures, at least in the case of the longest flow paths, slows down the emission.

▷ The emission rate is limited by the desorption kinetics of the coal.

The result is a smoothing of the firedamp flow rate in both the airstream and the firedamp drainage despite the intermittent nature of coal production.

3.4 Relaxed Zone and Fissuring around Roadways. Extent of the Degassing Zone

While a roadway is being driven, an enveloping relaxed and fissured zone is formed around it. In a direction perpendicular to the axis of the roadway the growth of this envelope, which is basically a function of time, falls off rapidly. The maximum radius of this envelope, attained after 3 to 5 months, is between 3 and 4 times the diameter of the roadway, depending on the thickness of the seam and the strength of the partings between the seam and the surrounding strata.

The firedamp which enters the roadway comes in part from the broken coal during the time it remains in the working, and the rest from the relaxed seams intersected by the fissures around the roadway. Often only the seam in which the roadway is driven is affected.

If the roadway is driven in virgin ground, the relaxed zones of the seams intersected by the fissured region around the drivage extend only a few metres beyond this region. Thus, in a roadway of 10 to 20 m^2 cross-section driven in a seam, the virgin gas content may be found at a depth of 12 to 20 m into the sides when the lateral growth of the envelope has ceased. Within two months of passage of the face of the heading, 70 to 80 % of the total degassing from the roadway surroundings has already occurred. The total emission of firedamp into the roadway is limited and most of this emission usually occurs within some 150 m of the face, the distance increasing with the rate of drivage. In addition the average flow of firedamp is related to the rate of advance and to the gas content of the seam.

By contrast if the seams influenced by the drivage are located in a zone previously relaxed by another working but not degassed (zone Z3 or Z'3 previously defined) or only partially degassed (base of zone Z'2 or top of zone Z2) degassing occurs from a greater distance in these seams, well beyond the boundary of the fissured envelope formed by the roadway itself. (Some measurements have shown a reduction of gas content up to more than 100 m into the strata.) In this case the quantity of firedamp coming into the road is greater (possibly as much as 5 or 6 times) than if the drivage were in virgin ground. However, the degassing takes place essentially over the same period and therefore over the same range of distances behind the face of the heading as for virgin ground. In this case also, the average flow of firedamp is related to the average rate of drivage and to the initial gas content of the seams (virgin gas content in zones Z3 and Z'3, residual content in zones Z2 and Z'2). In the driving of such roads the firedamp concentrations can be high even with good ventilation, and sometimes it is necessary to install drainage to maintain advance rate.

4. Potential Drainage Zones Around Faces and Prediction of Drainage Yield

4.1 Potential Drainage Zones Around Faces

4.1.1 Drainage of Firedamp migrating towards the District Airways

The maximum rates of desorption and emission occur in zone Z1 (and Z'1) and in the most relaxed and most fissured parts of zones Z2 and Z'2. It is these zones that have the potential for drainage and it is desirable to drain at the earliest opportunity, ie as near as practicable to the coal face.

4.1.1.1 Drainage from the Roof

Lower Limit of the Drainage Zone

The system of fissures which enlarges the sphere of influence of drainage cavities — boreholes in particular — interconnects not only with these cavities but also with the ventilation system.

It is almost impossible to drain firedamp from zone Z1 because this zone is very permeable and its permeability is such that below a certain

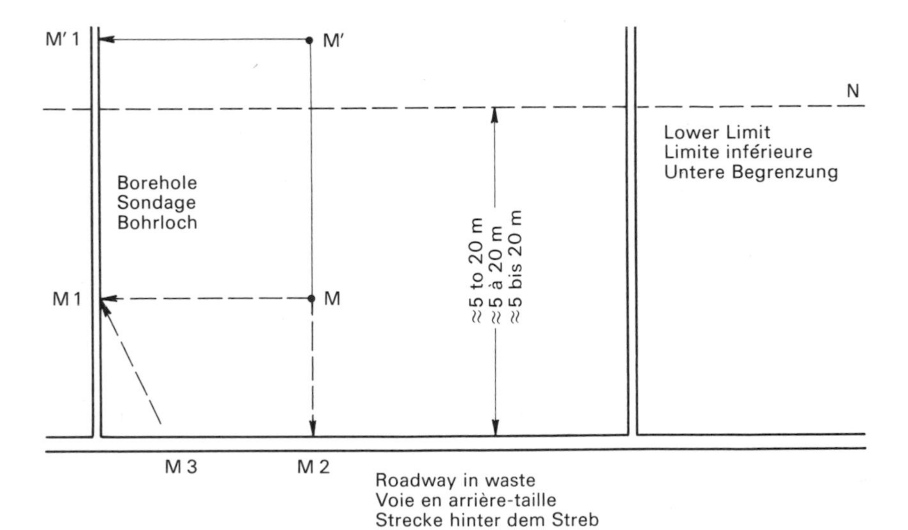

Fig. 1.10 Lower Limit of Roof Drainage.

level N in Figure 1.10 the firedamp under pressure at a point M finds the least resistant route to join the ventilation circuit at M2 rather than to join the drainage at M1. If suction is applied in order to encourage flow into the drainage, air will be drawn in at M3. The height of N above the worked seam is between 5 and 20 m for caved faces depending on the strata. In stowed faces this height is much less (a few metres).

For drainage boreholes drilled from the roadways standpipes ideally should extend to N; the bottom of drainage holes drilled from overlying workings should not come below N.

Upper Limit of the Drainage Zone

Firedamp from seams situated up to a hundred metres above the working migrates towards the face or the gates. It is not necessary for drainage holes to extend this distance to drain the firedamp from these seams. Generally, drainage efficiency is not improved significantly by extending the length of the boreholes more than 50 m above the level of the working unless thick compact rocks separate the seams disturbed above this level.

Forward Limit of the Drainage Zone

In roof strata the forward limit of the destressed zone from which gas can be drained slopes back over the waste from a position several metres ahead of the face. The distance back depends on the height, and at the lower limit of drainage (level N in Figure 1.10) emission generally commences above the face or even further back.

▷ Position of boreholes for districts with caving:

In advancing faces, in order to prolong the life of the drainage boreholes drilled from the gates, holes are drilled from behind the face line, possibly angled towards the face over the waste in such a way that the end of the standpipe is a little behind the face line. If holes were drilled ahead of the face line, drainage would not start any earlier and the standpipe could be nipped by ground movement which occurs at the edges of the caved area.

In retreat faces where the roadways are drawn off, the drainage boreholes may be drilled only from roads in front of the face. These holes may be drilled towards the face so that they reach the face line and generally in this case they are shut off as soon as the end of the standpipe is passed by the face, since there may be nipping of the standpipe and inleakage of air. Sometimes boreholes have been maintained in service after the face has passed.

▷ Position of boreholes for districts with stowing:

Damage to standpipes is less likely when stowing is used rather than caving. The siting of boreholes behind advancing faces requires less precautions with stowing; in retreat faces, boreholes can be left in service behind the face, provided that there is a drainage pipe to each borehole or group of boreholes.

Rear Limit of the Drainage Zone

At a certain distance behind the coal face, the zone Z1 is completely degassed, the permeability of the zone Z2 decreases and at the same time gas pressures fall off causing a drop in drainage flow rates. If the absolute pressure in the boreholes is not raised by regulating the borehole valve, air leakage will increase.

Eventually the flow rate from each borehole becomes insignificant and leaving such boreholes connected to the drainage range increases the probability of the borehole drawing more air than firedamp. The distances at which this happens varies but is normally between 70 and 150 m, except close to the starting line of a face where boreholes often have a very long life. Regular measurements of purity at each borehole give the information necessary for drainage control and show when boreholes should be removed from service.

Lateral Limit of the Drainage Zone

In the plane of the worked seam the relaxed zone may extend some 20 metres into the ribsides.

In the neighbourhood of the face line there is a narrowing of the relaxed zone in the roof; as the face moves away this zone becomes wider at every level.

To be effective, a borehole drilled from a gate should be inclined over the waste so that it drains the firedamp as soon after its release as practicable which is when the maximum flow usually occurs.

In other methods, the roof drainage channels (boreholes drilled from overlying roadways, drainage roadways) must pass over the waste.

4.1.1.2 Drainage from the Floor

Upper and Lower Limits of the Drainage Zone

In the floor, air can be drawn into boreholes down to a depth of 2 to 5 m below the waste. This gives the minimum length of standpipe which must be used in floorholes or the maximum height of boreholes drilled from underlying roadways.

The emission of firedamp is a maximum in the zone of high permeability which extends to about 20 m under the waste and often the most effective boreholes are those which drain from the upper part of this zone. Boreholes drilled from gate roads should be in a plane perpendicular to the road and at an angle below the horizontal such that they finish at least 15 m below the waste. Holes drilled upwards from underlying roads should stop about 5 m under the waste.

In certain cases it is desirable to use longer boreholes in order to drain gas from deeper seams, particularly when these seams are very gassy and densely grouped in the destressed zone (Z'2 and Z'3).

Forward and Rear Limits of the Drainage Zone

The observed extent of maximum gas pressure and the onset of gas emission under a working are shown in Figure 1.11. At 16 and 38 m below a face, as shown in Figures 1.12 and 1.13, there is significant emission of gas for only a short distance behind the face line. Figure 1.14 deduced from residual gas content measurements, indicates where

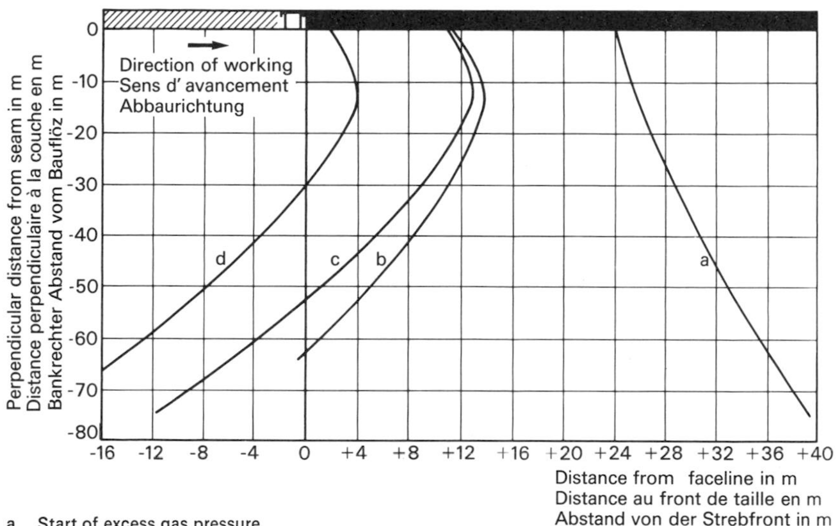

Fig. 1.11 Excesses of Gas Pressure in the Floor of Workings.

emission begins, the position of maximum emission and the rear limit where the emission tails off.

With caved advancing faces, floorholes from gate roads are drilled as close as practicable behind the face, or sometimes even in front of it because, in the floor, there is much less risk of nipping standpipes.

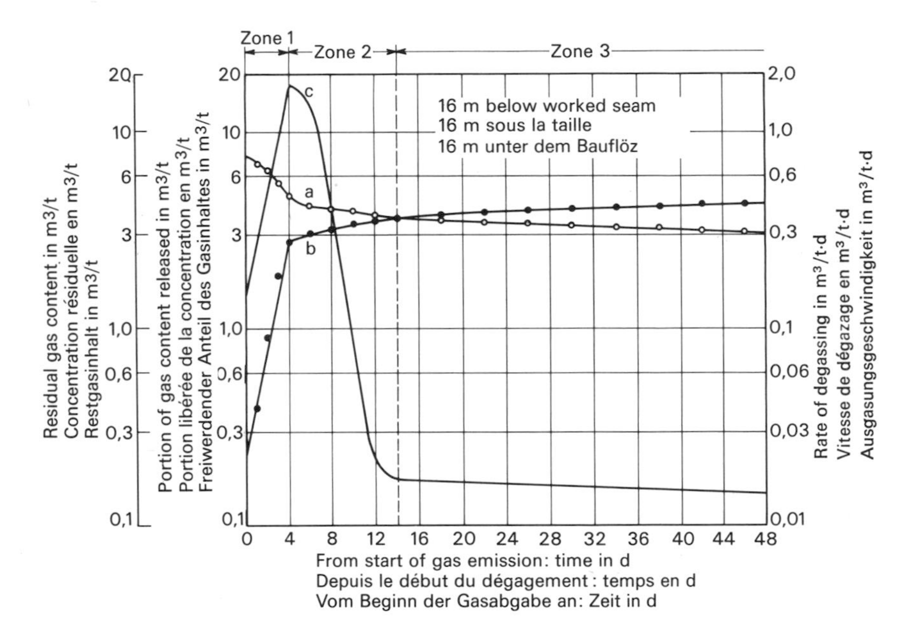

a Residual gas content in m^3/t
Concentration résiduelle en m^3/t
Restgasinhalt in m^3/t

b Proportion of gas content released in m^3/t
Part libre de la concentration en m^3/t
Freiwerdender Anteil des Gasinhaltes in m^3/t

c Rate of degassing in $m^3/t \cdot d$
Vitesse de dégazage en $m^3/t \cdot d$
Ausgasungsgeschwindigkeit in $m^3/t \cdot d$

Fig. 1.12 Evolution of Gas Emission in Drainage Borehole 2, Matthias 2 seam.

With retreat faces, drainage holes drilled in the floor should be directed towards the face so that the bottom of each hole is several metres in front of the face when it is first put into use. It is normally possible to keep floorholes in service longer than roofholes but at times, they can be left in use behind the face, provided the services are available.

The life of floorholes is generally greater than that of roofholes but downholes are often filled with water which considerably reduces their effectiveness and life.

Lateral Limits of the Drainage Zone

In the floor of workings the relaxed and fissured zone gets narrower with depth; in contrast to the roof, this narrowing also exists behind the face. Floorholes drilled from the gate roads should be directed towards the middle of the waste and are frequently drilled in a plane perpendicular to the roadway.

4.1.2 Degassing in Advance of Working in a Zone Relaxed but not Degassed by a previous Face

As already described, in seams situated in the relaxed zones Z′3 in the floor or Z3 in the roof, firedamp remains trapped unless it is able to migrate towards workings or boreholes. This can be used to advantage for degassing the seams before working.

Because in the majority of cases seams are worked in descending order it is usually in the floor zone Z′3 that degassing in advance can be practised; when working is in ascending order the zone Z3 is generally well above future faces.

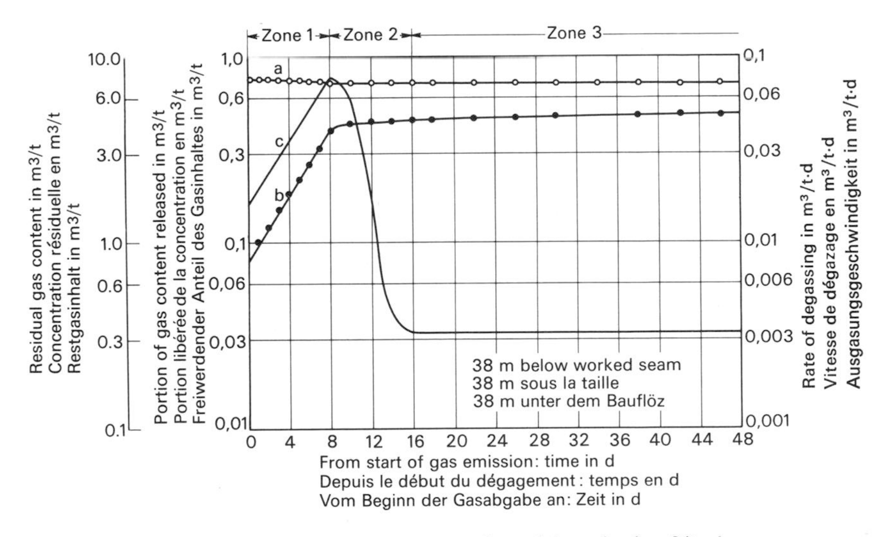

a Residual gas content in m^3/t
Concentration résiduelle en m^3/t
Restgasinhalt in m^3/t

b Proportion of gas content released in m^3/t
Part libre de la concentration en m^3/t
Freiwerdender Anteil des Gasinhaltes in m^3/t

c Rate of degassing in $m^3/t \cdot d$
Vitesse de dégazage en $m^3/t \cdot d$
Ausgasungsgeschwindigkeit in $m^3/t \cdot d$

Fig. 1.13 Evolution of Gas Emission in Borehole 10 seam A.

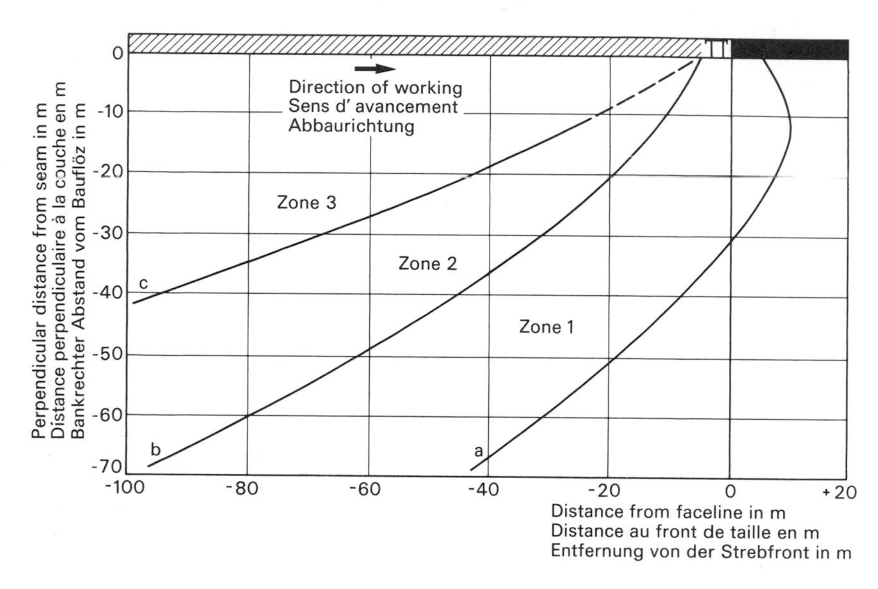

a Forward limit of degassing
Limit avant de la zone de captage
Vordere Grenze des Ausgasungsraumes

b Maximum degassing
Dégagement maximum
Maximale Ausgasung

c Transition to residual degassing
Limite arrière de la zone de captage
Übergang zur Restausgasung

Fig. 1.14 Zoning of Gas Emission in the Floor.

4.2 Prediction of Drainage Yield. Effectiveness and Efficiency of Drainage

Prediction methods (see Chapter 3 Appendix 3.1) enable an estimate to be made of the total quantity of firedamp which will be liberated per tonne of coal extracted by evaluation of the quantity of firedamp originating from:

▷ the roof (seams up to, and sometimes more than, 100 m in the roof release a large part of their firedamp);

▷ the worked seam (on average 50 % of the firedamp from the worked seam, sometimes more, sometimes less);

▷ the floor (seams within 50 m in the floor release a percentage of their gas, the amount reducing with distance from the worked seam).

Having obtained this quantity, called the 'predicted specific emission' the theoretical quantities which can be drained per tonne of coal extracted can then be estimated. In these estimations it is assumed that:

▷ in the roof the liberated firedamp can be drained from seams located more than 20 m from the working;

▷ all the gas released in the floor can be drained.

The following notation is used:

s predicted specific emission in m^3/t
s_t part of s coming from the roof in m^3/t
s_f part of s coming from the seam being worked in m^3/t
s_m part of s coming from the floor in m^3/t
s_{tc} drainable part of the gas coming from the roof in m^3/t
$s_{tc} = (s_t - s')$,
s' representing the firedamp liberated in the first 20 m of the roof in m^3/t
S actual specific emission in m^3/t.

a) Predicted Effectiveness of Drainage

The theoretical effectiveness of drainage η_{th} is defined as:

$$\eta_{th} = \frac{s_{tc} + s_m}{s} \qquad [1.10]$$

This value obviously depends on the method of prediction. Because in practice drainage performance depends on the means which can reasonably be used, and on the quality of drainage management, theoretical values are seldom achieved. Allowing for a realistic fraction to be captured, the predicted effectiveness of drainage is defined as:

$$\eta = \frac{x\, s_{tc} + y\, s_m}{s} \qquad [1.11]$$

where x and y are the fractions which can be drained from roof and floor respectively.

Except in certain cases, application of existing techniques enables drainage of typically 80 % from the roof and 40 % from the floor, which gives:

$$\eta = \frac{0.8\, s_{tc} + 0.4\, s_m}{s} \qquad [1.12]$$

The predicted effectiveness of drainage can be divided into a roof fraction: $\eta_1 = \frac{0.8\, s_{tc}}{s}$ and a floor fraction: $\eta_2 = \frac{0.4\, s_m}{s}$.

At the planning stage, the balance of drainage and ventilation can be determined since the following inequality must be satisfied:

$$(1-\eta)\frac{\beta\, s\, P_0}{86\,400\, Q_a}\, i < \frac{c_L}{100} \qquad [1.13]$$

where:

- η predicted effectiveness of drainage
- Q_a air flow in m^3/s
- c_L limiting concentration in the ventilation in % CH_4
- s predicted specific emission in m^3/t
- P_0 forecast daily production in t/d
- i coefficient of irregularity; this is the ratio, established over a long period for comparable previous workings:

$$i = \frac{c_{MS}}{\bar{\bar{c}}} \qquad [1.14]$$

where:

- c_{MS} value of daily maximum concentration which is only exceeded in 5 % of cases (anomalies excluded)
- $\bar{\bar{c}}$ mean of daily average concentration

- β coefficient making allowance for non-working days:

$$\beta = \frac{n_0}{n} \cdot \frac{\text{(average emission over working days)}}{\text{(average emission over calendar days)}} \qquad [1.15]$$

if i has been determined on working days n_0 (France) or

$$\beta = \frac{n_0}{n} \qquad [1.16]$$

if i has been determined by calendar days n (Germany).

Using inequality [1.13], s and c_L being known, it can then be decided if the airflow Q_a is adequate for the forecast production P_0 without drainage (ie $\eta = 0$). If it is not adequate, it will be necessary to recalculate with drainage either from the roof alone when $\eta = \eta_1$, or if practicable from both roof and floor when $\eta = \eta_1 + \eta_2$; it can then be established whether the inequality [1.13] can be satisfied. It may be found that even with maximum drainage this cannot be done. It may then be necessary to reconsider the ventilation and/or production objectives P_0.

b) Actual Effectiveness of Drainage

During the working of a district, the volumes of firedamp removed by the ventilation (V_a) and by the drainage (V_c) are measured, thus giving the total quantity of gas released. From this the actual specific emission S and the overall effectiveness of drainage τ can be calculated:

$$\tau = \frac{S_c}{S} = \frac{V_c}{V} \qquad [1.17]$$

where:

S_c volume of firedamp drained per tonne of coal worked

V_c volume flow rate of firedamp drained during working

V total volume flow rate of firedamp in the drainage and in the ventilation during working: $V = V_a + V_c$ where

V_a volume flow rate of firedamp into the ventilation.

In all cases a comparison can be made between the effectiveness achieved and the predicted effectiveness and it may be established whether the prediction is correct. So the actual drainage efficiency R_t can be evaluated:

$$R_t = \frac{S_c}{S - s' - s_f} = \frac{\tau S}{S - s' - s_f} \qquad [1.18]$$

for comparison with the predicted drainage efficiency r_t:

$$r_t = \frac{0.8\ s_{tc} + 0.4\ s_m}{s_{tc} + s_m} = \frac{\eta\ s}{s - s' - s_f} \qquad [1.19]$$

NB: The actual values for firedamp released from the first 20 m of roof and from the seam being worked cannot be measured. Hence the calculated values s' and s_f are used in equation [1.18].

5. Conditions for Successful Drainage

Progress made in recent years in the knowledge of the origin, storage and emission of firedamp, as well as in technology, have led to a marked improvement in the effectiveness of drainage. The engineer also now has at his disposal a whole range of techniques to help deal with different situations.

The success of a drainage scheme depends on three fundamental factors:

▷ the design of a suitable drainage system (cf Chapter 3);
▷ the timely implementation of the chosen method (cf Chapter 2);
▷ control of the drainage system once in operation (cf Chapter 4).

5.1 Basic Design Requirements

To establish a drainage scheme it is necessary to know with reasonable accuracy the flows of gas to be expected. To do this, the firedamp emission must be predicted and analysed to indicate the proportions that would come from seams in roof and floor of the working. The prediction and analysis will depend on:

▷ a good knowledge of the stratigraphy (distribution and thickness of seams);

▷ a knowledge of the operational plans of the colliery (position of projected working, planned output, caving or stowing);

▷ an examination of the working plans, paying particular attention to over-working (edges of virgin zones and of zones influenced by old workings and roadways);

▷ knowledge of gas content of the worked seam and of overlying and underlying seams, or a knowledge of specific emission obtained from previous panels in the same seam.

If drainage has been practised in other districts in the same seam, drainage results can be used as a basis for a new scheme, assuming that they are comparable.

5.2 Considerations for the most Suitable Method

An examination of plans at an early stage will enable the best use to be made of the potential offered by underlying or overlying roadways, or even old workings, for firedamp drainage.

Trouble free extraction of drained gas depends upon a correct evaluation of the characteristics and upon the choice of equipment of both drainage system and exhauster plant.

5.3 Control of a Drainage System

The success of a drainage scheme does not depend solely upon the implementation of a borehole pattern or the best siting of drainage galleries. The drainage system must also be adequately controlled:

a) At district level by:

▷ drilling well placed drainage holes of suitable length and inclination, and connecting and disconnecting them at appropriate times,

▷ ensuring that standpipes are airtight,

▷ correct regulation of the suction at each borehole,

▷ installing water traps at suitable points.

b) At colliery level by:

▷ the choice of range sizes adequate for the volumes to be drained,

▷ maintenance of the network (eg checking for air inleakage),

▷ installation of water traps in suitable numbers to prevent blockages,

▷ regulation of district suction where necessary.

In order to optimise suction at each point in the network, regular and frequent measurements must be made by trained personnel with suitable equipment.

Chapter 2

Methods of Firedamp Drainage

The applications of firedamp drainage will be dealt with in order of operational importance:

1. Drainage in working districts.
2. Drainage from old workings.
3. Degassing seams in advance of working.
4. Drainage using surface boreholes.

Within the applications there are several methods which can be used:

a) Underground boreholes.
b) Surface boreholes.
c) Bleeder roadways.
d) Pack cavities.
e) Drainage from behind stoppings.
f) Drainage from abandoned mines.

Methods a) to d) are used for firedamp drainage in working districts, methods e) and f) are used for drainage from old workings (disused districts and abandoned mines) and methods a) and b) may be used to degas seams in advance of working. Because of their particular technical features, surface boreholes are dealt with separately.

1. Firedamp Drainage in Working Districts

Drainage of firedamp is of the greatest importance during production from the points of view of safety and productivity. Around 38 % of British, 25 % of German, 14 % of French and 18 % of Belgian coal output comes from faces with firedamp drainage installations. Without this drainage, some high output faces producing more than say a thousand tonnes per day could be worked only in less gassy parts of seams ($\leqq 10\ m^3/t$) as indicated in Table 2.1.

Table 2.1 Potential Maximum Face Output with Conventional Ventilation Systems for different Drainage Capture Values.

Effective Cross-sectional Area	Air Quantities[c]	Specific Emission	Maximum Face Output (t/d) for Drainage Capture values of			
m^2	m^3/s	m^3/t	0 % [a]	20 % [b]	40 % [b]	60 % [b]
2	9	5	1452	—	—	—
		10	726	1361	1814	2 722
		30	242	454	605	907
		50	—	272	363	544
		70	—	194	259	389
4	18	5	2903	—	—	—
		10	1452	2722	3629	5 443
		30	484	907	1210	1 814
		50	—	544	726	1 089
		70	—	389	518	778
6	27	5	4355	—	—	—
		10	2177	4082	5443	8 165
		30	726	1361	1814	2 722
		50	—	816	1089	1 633
		70	—	583	778	1 166
8	36	5	5806	—	—	—
		10	2903	5443	7258	10 886
		30	968	1814	2419	3 629
		50	—	1089	1452	2 177
		70	—	778	1037	1 555

5 productive days per week, coefficient of irregularity for gas emission 1.5 (see Chapter 1).

[a] Maximum permissible methane concentration in mine air 1 %.

[b] Maximum permissible methane concentration in mine air 1.5 %.

[c] Air quantities based on maximum average air velocity at face 4.5 m/s.

1.1 Underground Boreholes

The most widespread method of firedamp drainage uses cross measure boreholes; for instance, in 1974 in British coalmines some 8000 boreholes were drilled totalling over 320 km in length, through which 91 % of the total quantity of drained gas was captured (Table 2.2).

Table 2.2 Firedamp Drainage Data for the European Community in 1974.

		GFR	UK [a]	Belgium	France	EEC [b]
Deep mine saleable output	Mt	94.876	99.000	8.111	23.600	225.587
Output from districts with firedamp drainage	Mt	23.702	37.619	1.425	3.375	66.121
Proportion of output from drained districts	%	24.98	38.00	17.57	14.30	29.31
Total number of boreholes	—	4 059	7 861	261	679	12 860
Total length of boreholes	m	201 885	320 993	14 585	31 927	569 390
Average length of boreholes	m	49.7	40.8	55.9	47.0	44.3
Total methane drained	Mm^3	575.036	381.031	62.610	152.211	1 170.888
Total drained from old workings	Mm^3	170.001	38.371	32.048 [c]	73.355	313.775
Proportion drained from old workings	%	29.6	10.1	51.2 [c]	48.2	26.8
Quantity utilised	Mm^3	341.896	113.970	59.970	134.066	649.902
Proportion utilised	%	59.5	29.9 [d]	95.8	88.1	55.5
Output per metre borehole from drained districts	t/m	117	117	98	105	116
Methane quantity drained per metre borehole	m^3/m	2 006	1 187	2 095	2 470	1 514

[a] Abnormally low production year; utilisation of gas with less than 40 % inflammable content was not allowed.
[b] Excluding the Netherlands, Ireland and Italy.
[c] Including drainage from abandoned mines.
[d] Only 70 % of total drained methane was brought to the surface of which about 41 % was utilised.

1.1.1 Advantages and Disadvantages of the Method

Advantages

Because of the great depth of workings in Europe, firedamp drainage boreholes are normally drilled underground since they are considerably shorter than boreholes from the surface. Underground drilling machines are lighter and therefore considerably cheaper and easier to assemble than a drilling rig on the surface. The majority of underground boreholes are drilled upwards and are thus kept free of water more easily than surface boreholes are.

Disadvantages

Mine roadways are not always located in areas where drainage boreholes may be required, eg in the case of retreat working. Furthermore

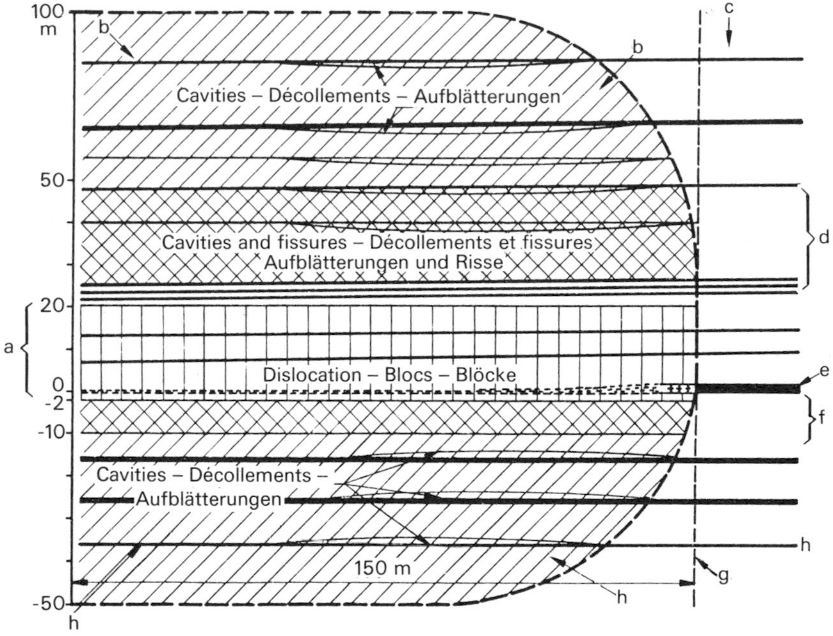

a Zone where there is a risk of the entry of air
b Zone sufficiently relaxed and with fissures or cavities to permit drainage
c Unrelaxed zone
d Generally the most favourable zone for drainage in the roof
e Seam being worked
f Generally the most favourable zone for drainage in the floor
g Line of the face
h Zone which is sufficiently relaxed and with fissures or cavities to permit drainage in some strata

Fig. 2.1 Longitudinal Section showing Gas Emission Zones for a Face.

the size of the drilling machine may be governed by lack of space and hence the length and diameter of underground boreholes may be limited.

1.1.2 Layout of Boreholes in the Relaxed Zone

A rapid and heavy gas emission can be expected to occur mainly in a relaxed zone (Figure 2.1). On the other hand in unrelaxed zones gas is only released into the boreholes very slowly: the quantities involved are usually much smaller but gas emission can persist for a long period of time. Boreholes in the unrelaxed zone are of practical significance when the seam is being degassed beforehand (Section 3).

1.1.2.1 Layout of Roofholes

1.1.2.1.1 General Principles

Since firedamp emission from the undermined roof strata rises directly after the passage of a face (Figure 2.2) drainage boreholes

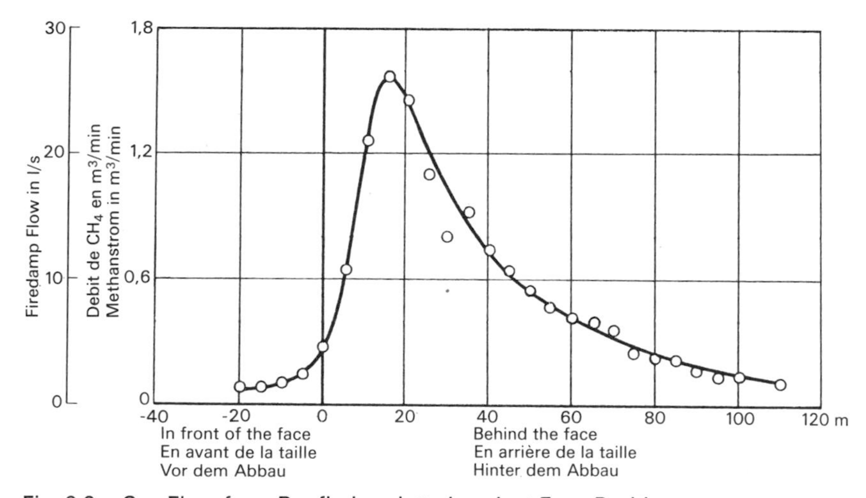

Fig. 2.2 Gas Flow from Roofholes plotted against Face Position.

should usually be drilled in gateroads as close as possible behind the face and at right angles to the centre line of the roadway (shown as Type II in Figure 2.3). Nowadays with conveyor drives and other machinery installed in gateroads and with pantechnicon and material

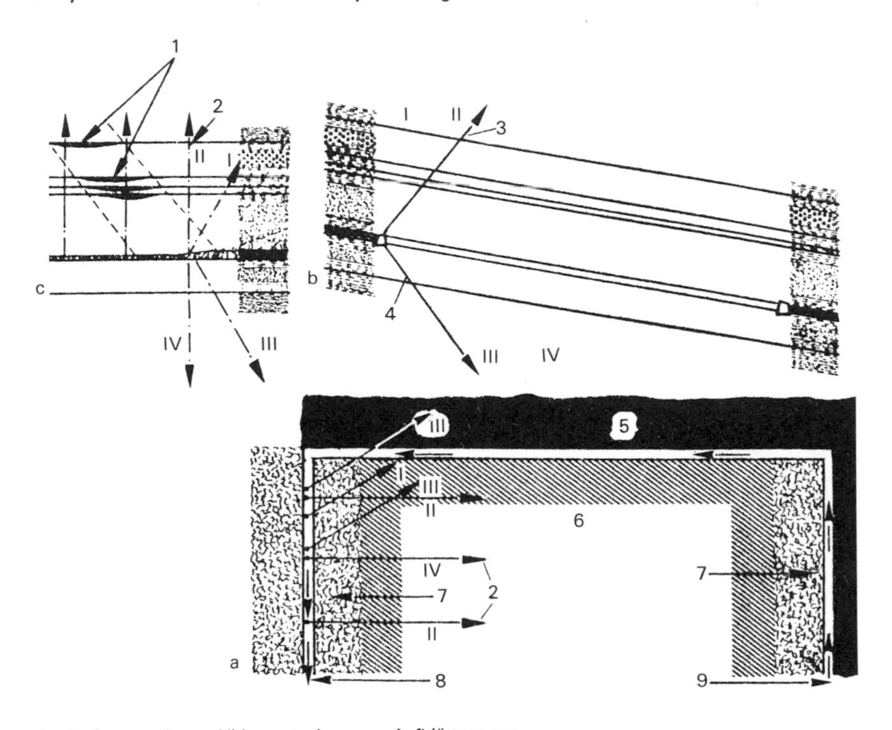

1 Bed separation — Vides entre bancs — Aufblätterungen
2 Borehole — Sondage — Bohrloch
3 Roofhole — Sondage en toit — Hangendbohrloch
4 Floorhole — Sondage en mur — Liegendbohrloch
5 Face — Taille — Streb
6 Caving — Foudroyage — Bruch
7 Pack — Remblai — Versatz
8 Return — Retour d'air — Abwetter
9 Intake — Entrée d'air — Frischwetter

a Plan — Vue en plan — Grundriß
b Cross section — coupe transversale — Querschnitt
c Longitudunal Section — Coupe longitudinale — Längsschnitt

Fig. 2.3 Firedamp Drainage with Cross Measure Boreholes.

handling positions close to the face end, there may be difficulty in setting up a drilling machine near to the face. In some cases this difficulty can be overcome by using a small drilling machine. In order to bring the end of a borehole as near as possible to the front edge of the relaxed zone, boreholes may be made correspondingly longer, shallower and angled forward towards the face (shown as Type I in Figure 2.3).

1.1.2.1.2 Borehole Spacing

Borehole spacing is determined by geological, technical, economic and safety considerations.

Geological Factors

If the rock is penetrated easily, boreholes can be closely spaced; however if the rock is difficult to drill, boreholes may have to be further apart.

If the distance to overlying seams is great, seam density is low and gas flows are small, boreholes may be spaced wider apart. If the distance is small and seam density and gas flows are high, they may be closer together.

Technical Factors

Borehole spacing in some narrow, low roadways may be greater than in wider, higher roadways. Efficient drilling machines and tools may permit closer borehole spacing.

Economic Factors

Borehole spacing may be increased when actual output decreases in relation to the maximum output dictated by gas emission considerations.

Safety Factors

Local high concentrations of methane may be avoided in gateroads by closer borehole spacing, and near face ends by drilling closer to the face.

The proportion of gas drained from a district is generally highest for a given borehole pattern (length, diameter, angle, direction, standpipe) when zones of influence of the individual boreholes meet or overlap (Figure 2.4). If there are gaps between zones, the proportion drained tends to fall and more gas flows into the ventilating airstream. On the other hand if zones overlap too much, the quantity drained may not decrease but the yield per metre of borehole is less, thereby making boreholes less efficient. Therefore borehole spacing and suction should be co-ordinated in such a way that the zones of influence just meet.

One can determine whether borehole spacing in a given drainage system is too close, too great or just right in a number of ways. For example one borehole in a series of productive boreholes may be shut off and the gas flow from the two neighbouring boreholes monitored. If the gas flow increases substantially then it may be deduced that borehole spacing is too close. In another check on borehole spacing,

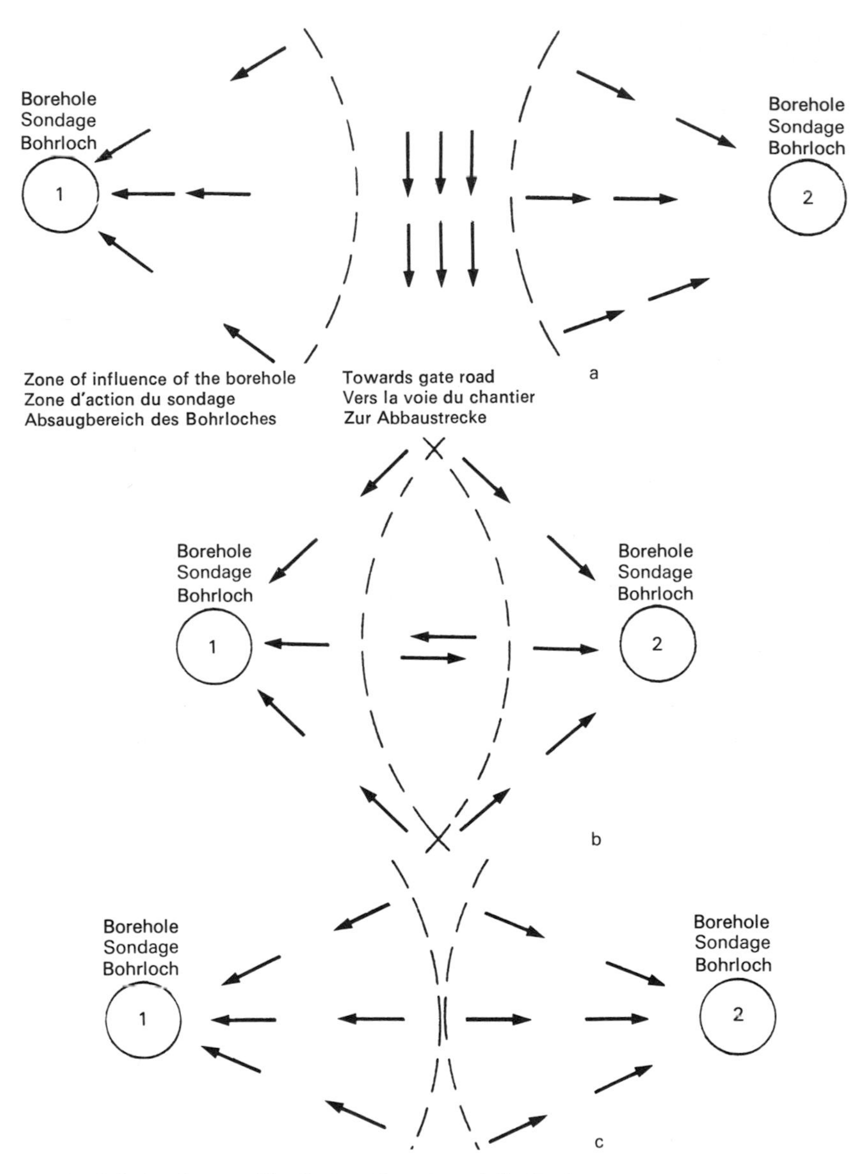

a Borehole Spacing too wide: Firedamp flows towards the Roadway
b Borehole too close: Firedamp yield per m Borehole too small
c An Ideal Borehole Spacing

Fig. 2.4 Selecting an Optimum Borehole Spacing.

methane concentrations in the air between the face and the first productive borehole or between the first and last productive boreholes are carefully checked by taking measurements over roadway cross-sections using portable measuring instruments. If gas flows detected in a length of roadway are clearly related to the catchment area of a borehole, then it may be deduced that borehole spacing is too great.

At present there is no method for accurate prediction of optimum borehole spacing. At the planning stage, therefore, one is obliged to depend on experience gained in previous districts. Generally a borehole spacing of 10 to 25 m is chosen.

1.1.2.1.3 Angle, Direction and Length

Angle, direction and length of boreholes are determined primarily by the distance of gas-producing roof seams from the worked seam and by the distance of the drilling position from the face, since an attempt has to be made to contact gas-producing seams near the front of the de-stressed zone. Experience gained in adjacent districts in the same seam has a decisive influence on angle and direction of boreholes.

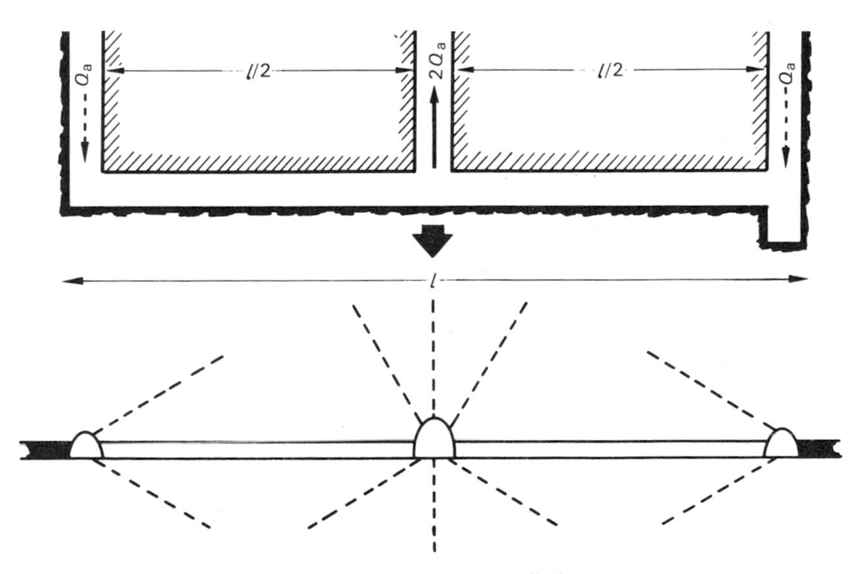

Fig. 2.5 Borehole Pattern for a Face with W-Ventilation.

Care must be taken not to use too shallow an angle because bed separation in immediate roof strata may lead to dislocation of the borehole and extraction of low purity gas. However, boreholes should not be set at too steep an angle, since they might penetrate only the periphery of the destressed zone and fail to contact the main part over the waste where the gas emission is greater.

In principle, gas drainage can be carried out from both gateroads, but if there are only small quantities of gas it is normally limited to the return gate, making use of the ventilation pressure gradients. Particularly good results can be achieved with boreholes drilled over the face start line (Figure 2.8) and in the return airways of districts with W-ventilation (Figure 2.5).

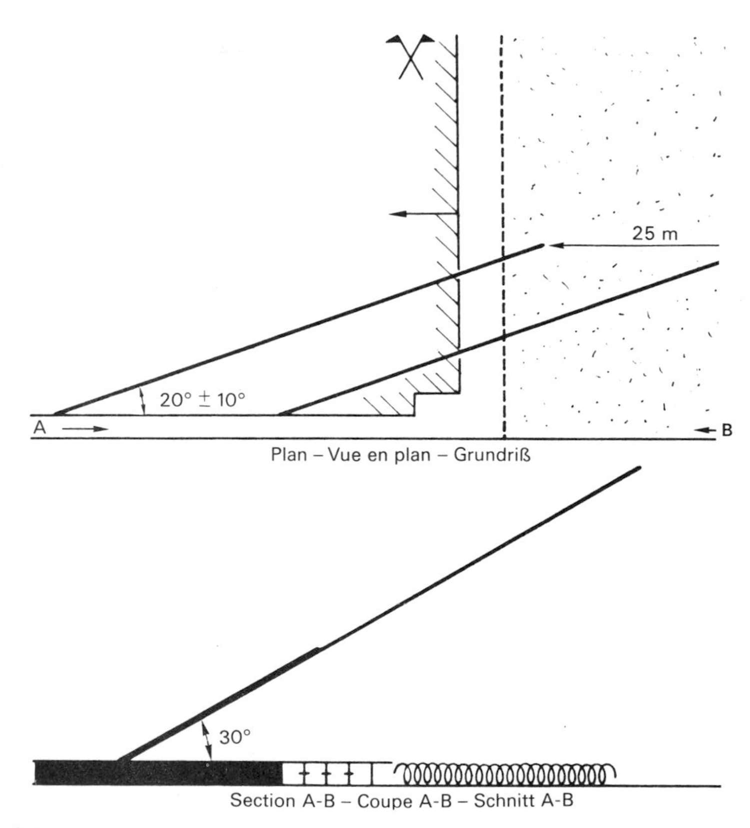

Fig. 2.6 Firedamp Drainage with Individual Roofholes over a Retreating Face. (The borehole will be disconnected a few metres before the face reaches it).

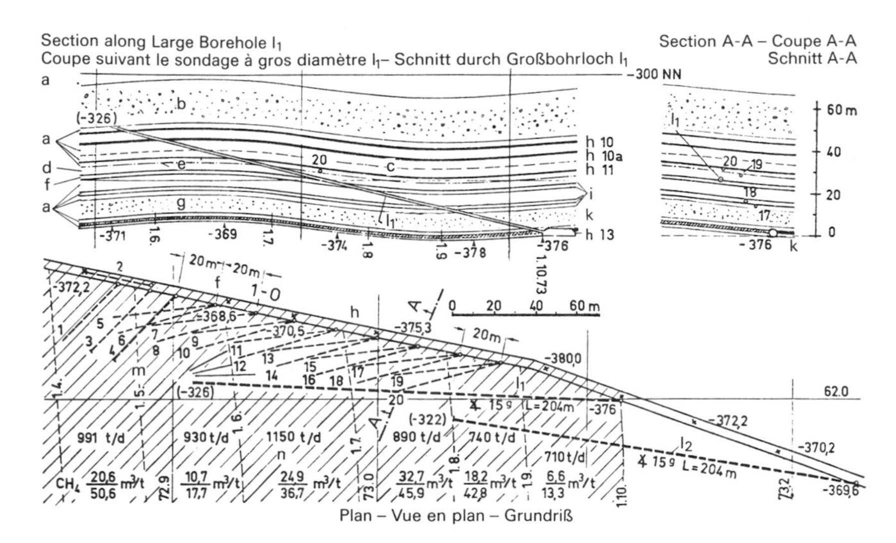

a	Sandy Shale — Schiste gréseux — Sandschiefer
b	Coarse Sandstone to Conglomerate — Grès à gros grains-conglomérats — Grobkörniger Sandstein bis Konglomerat
c	Shale with Coal — Schiste et charbon — Schiefer mit Kohle
d	Sandstone — Grès — Sandstein
e	Mudstone — Tonstein — Tonstein
f	Shale — Schiste — Schiefer
g	Conglomerate and Sandstone — Conglomérat et grès — Konglomerat und Sandstein
h	Seam 13 — Couche 13 — Flöz 13
i	Coal — Charbon — Kohle
k	Tailgate — Voie de tête — Kopfstrecke
I_1	Large Borehole 1 — Sondage à gros diamètre 1 — Groß-Bohrloch 1
I_2	Large Borehole 2 — Sondage à gros diamètre 2 — Groß-Bohrloch 2
m	Boreholes — Sondages — Bohrlöcher
n	Face worked in 1973 — Exploitée en 1973 — Abbau 1973

Borehole Type Type de sondage Bohrloch-Typ	I	II
Direction ∢ Angle de direction Richtungs-∢	13 to 18° 13 à 18° 15 bis 20 gon	22 to 27° 22 à 18° 25 bis 30 gon
Inclination ∢ Angle d'inclinaison Neigungs-∢	32° 32° 35 gon	
Borehole Length Longueur du sondage Bohrlochlänge	≈ 60 m ≈ 60 m ≈ 60 m	

Fig. 2.7 Firedamp Drainage with Roofhole Pattern in Retreat Workings.

Advance Working

Boreholes may be drilled from a position 10 to 20 m behind the face at a forward angle of 45° to the face line. Usually boreholes are drilled parallel to the line of the face. The angle to the horizontal in level seams or seams with low dip is 45 to 55°. In steep seams this angle is related to the gradient of the face. Boreholes may have to be drilled parallel to the face line in thick seams where severe roof stresses may cause drill rods to jam and standpipes to be dislocated.

Retreat Working

Where roadways have been maintained behind the face, it is possible to drill boreholes to the same pattern as in advance workings. Mainte-

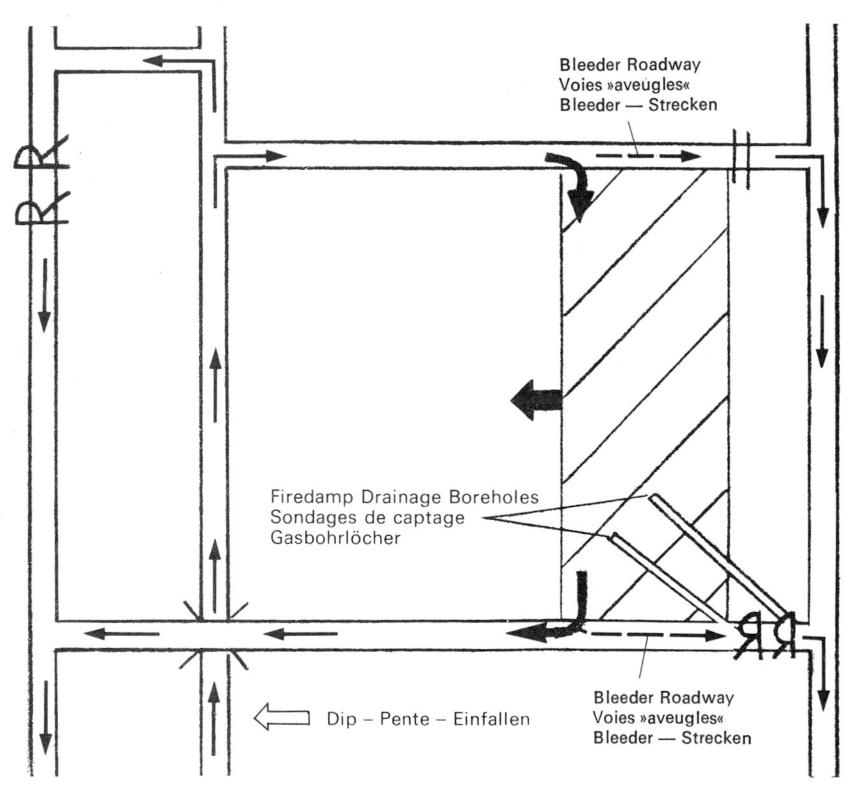

Fig. 2.8 Firedamp Drainage with Roofholes in Retreat Workings with Relatively Low Gas Emission.

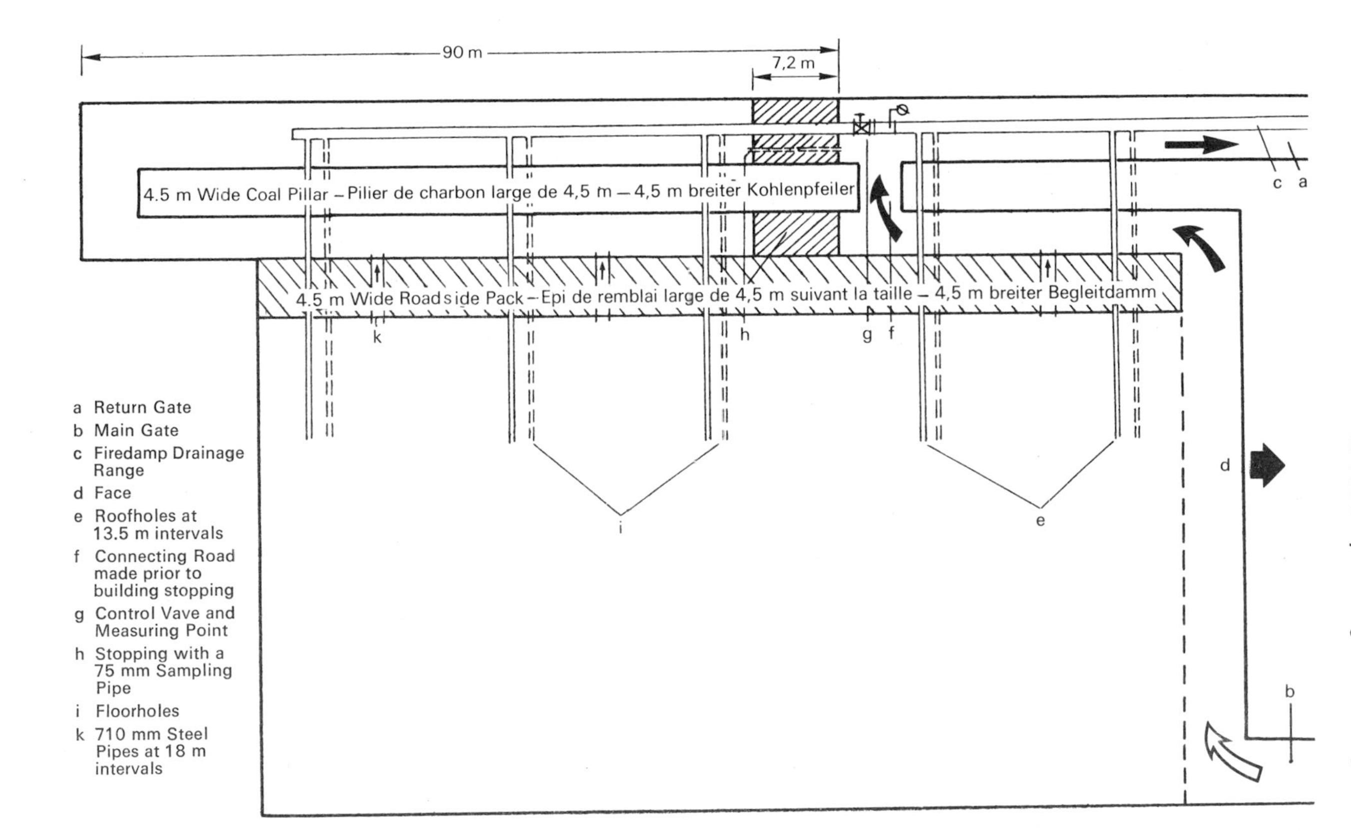

Fig. 2.9 Firedamp Drainage with Boreholes in Retreat Work ngs with High Gas Emission Rates.

nance of a sufficiently long length of roadway for drilling purposes may be a problem. In such cases, boreholes can be drilled ahead of and angled towards the face to reach the de-stressed zone quickly, facilitating drainage before the lower end of the borehole is subjected to severe rock movements and possible dislocation. This may mean that angles are shallower than in advance workings (Figure 2.6). In the Saar a number of borehole patterns have proved successful (Figure 2.7).

If two roadways are driven together, for retreat mining as in some British mines, gas may be drained from the outer gateroad as the face is retreated, using borehole patterns similar to those for advance workings. These holes may be drilled at a shallower angle and are longer because they have to cross the pillar between the two roadways. Figure 2.8 shows a method for seams with low gas emission rates and Figure 2.9 shows a method for seams with higher gas emission rates.

1.1.2.2 Layout of Floorholes

The positioning of floorholes is governed by principles similar to those governing roofholes. Variations exist however because of differences in behaviour of roof and floor strata.

1.1.2.2.1 General Principles

Floorholes may be fewer in number because of less disturbance in the surrounding strata and generally lower gas release. Floorholes may be more difficult to drill and an inflow of water can seriously hamper gas drainage. Unlike gas released from the roof which can cause layering at low air velocities, gas released from the floor mixes easily with air because of its lower density. These factors have meant that generally in the past floorholes have been drilled less often and with less success than roofholes.

However heavy emissions from the floor, such as occur particularly in the United Kingdom, have led locally to an intensification of floor drilling. This has considerably reduced the number and magnitude of floor emissions, achieving a marked improvement in mine safety.

The yield from floorholes is normally lower than from roofholes, but the supply is much richer making it particularly useful for firedamp utilisation schemes.

1.1.2.2.2 Spacing

For reasons mentioned already in Sections 1.1.2.1.2 and 1.1.2.2.1 the spacing for floorholes may be greater than for roofholes. Generally the spacing ranges from 25 to 45 m. There are however reasons for adopting the same spacing for floor- and roofholes.

1.1.2.2.3 Angle, Direction and Length

In France floorholes are usually drilled at relatively shallow angles under the face, to cover the largest possible area of disturbed strata around the working (Figure 2.10); in the other countries angles of 35 to 65° to the horizontal are more common (Figure 2.3, Types III and IV).

Shallow-angled floorholes may have the advantage of being easier to keep free of water than steep holes. They may be successful if the floor strata are very permeable perpendicularly to the bedding planes.

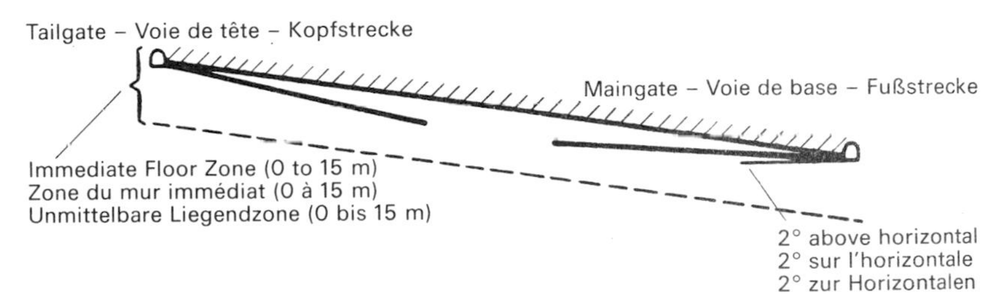

Fig. 2.10 Firedamp Drainage from the Floor.

At greater seam inclinations it may be possible to drill in the floor on a slight incline from the main road thereby facilitating drainage of water. The floorholes are also drilled parallel to or towards the face. The type of working is immaterial to the positioning of floorholes, because they are not damaged as badly as roofholes by the passage of a face.

1.1.2.3 Layout of Boreholes in Overlying and Underlying Roadways

1.1.2.3.1 Boreholes from Overlying Roadways

Gas can also be drained from overlying roadways by floorholes (Figure 2.11) or upholes (Figure 2.12) according to the position of the relevant gas producing seams. The question of whether to attempt to break through to the waste depends on the type of working. In the

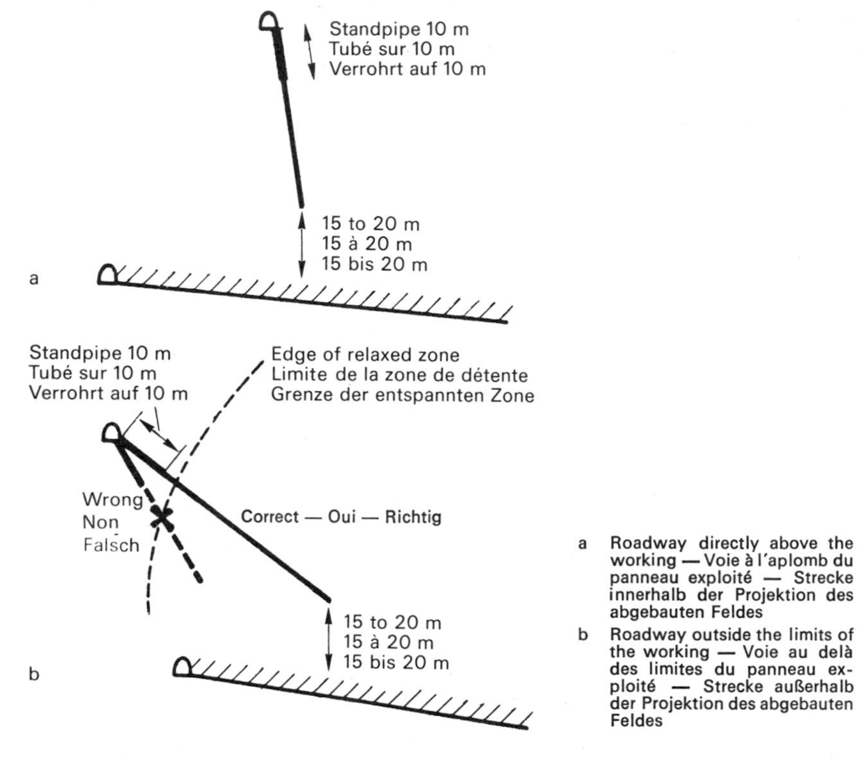

Fig. 2.11 Firedamp Drainage from an Overlying Roadway using Downholes.

case of retreat mining it can be an advantage to drain the waste, whereas with advance working the firedamp content of the air in the waste may be too low for gas drainage. If the overlying roadway lies in a gas-producing neighbouring seam, boreholes within the seam are recommended.

1.1.2.3.2 Boreholes from Underlying Roadways

Conditions most favourable for the drainage of gas with high methane concentrations are obtained when a face is retreating to the dip. Boreholes from an underlying roadway are especially effective for combating firedamp emissions from the floor of the worked seam because they are free of water, and larger areas of the disturbed floor strata can be covered than with conventional floorholes in the worked district. Drilling from an underlying roadway is always towards gas-producing seams, which normally lie above it (Figures 2.13 and 2.14). It is also possible to drill into the waste of a retreat face.

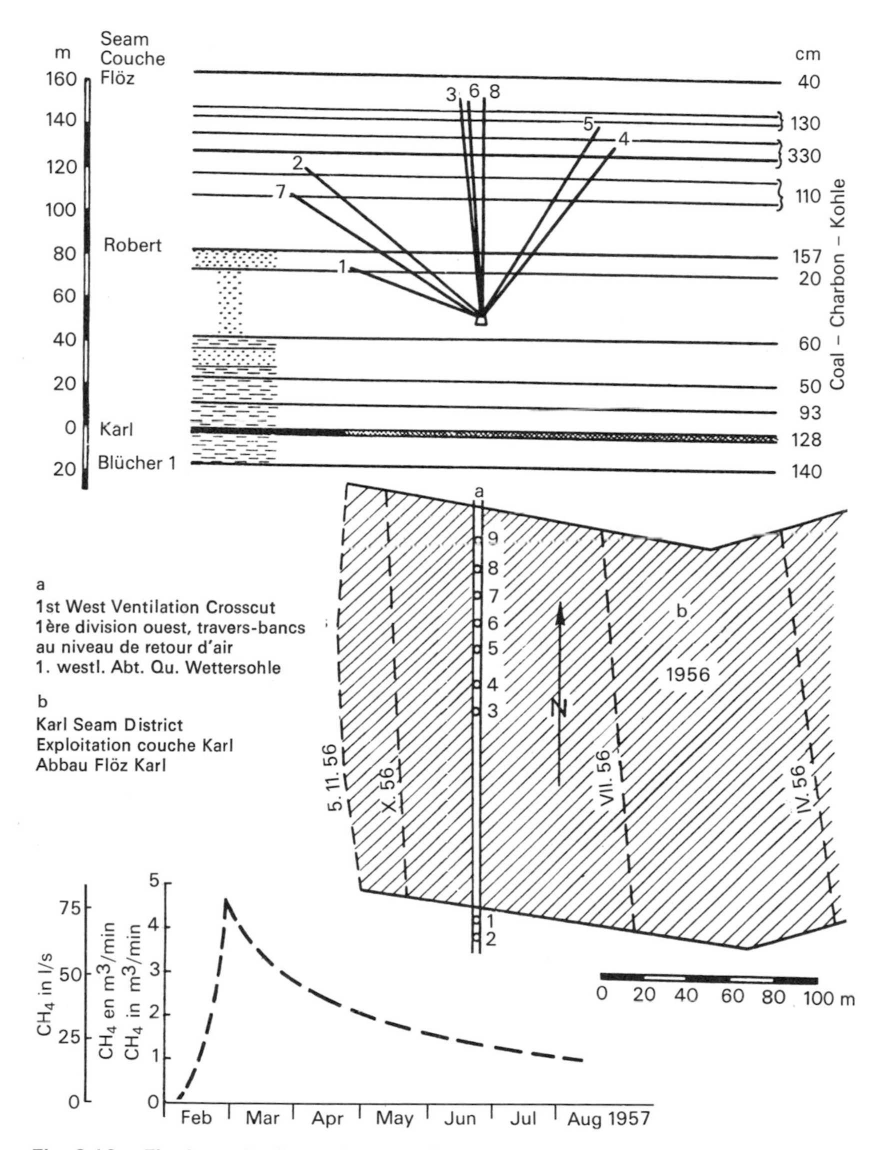

Fig. 2.12 Firedamp Drainage from an Overlying Roadway using Upholes.

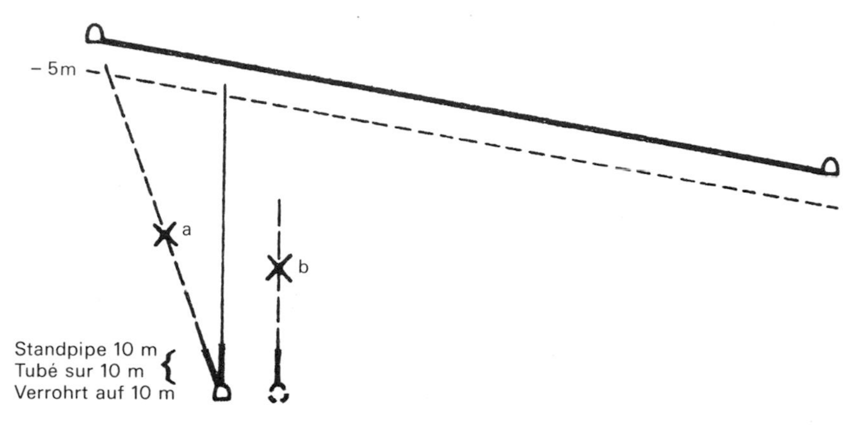

a Wrong: too close to the edge of the relaxed zone.
Non: trop en bordure de la zone détendue.
Falsch: zu nahe an der Grenze der entspannten Zone.

b Wrong: the hole must reach the immediate floor.
Non: il faut atteindre le daisne immédiat.
Falsch: man muß das unmittelbare Liegende erreichen.

Fig. 2.13 Firedamp Drainage from an Underlying Roadway using Upholes.

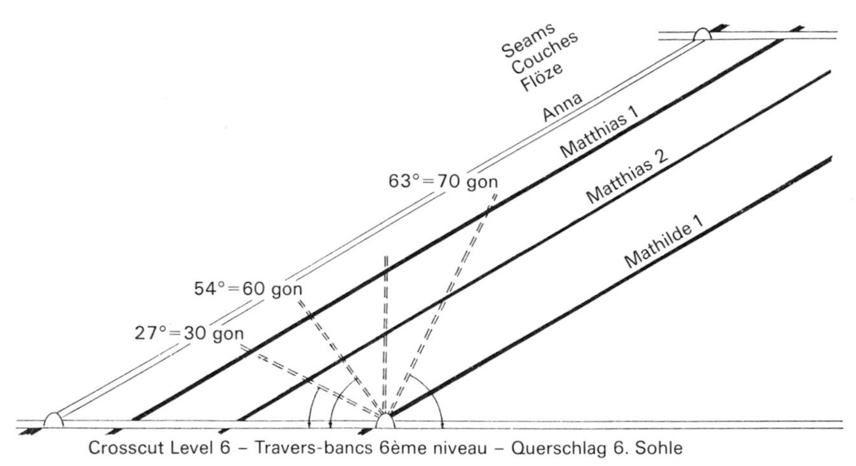

Fig. 2.14 Firedamp Drainage from an Underlying Roadway using Long Boreholes.

1.1.3 Drilling Boreholes

Rotary and percussive drilling machines and combinations of them are used.

1.1.3.1 Borehole Dimensions

Diameters of the Productive Borehole and the Standpipe Length

In the United Kingdom rotary tungsten carbide bits are used to drill gas drainage boreholes. The borehole diameter is usually 50, 60 or 65 mm, and the diameter of the standpipe length is 85 or 115 mm.

In the other countries 75 and 95 mm roller bits have been applied. In mines of the Saar it has been found that the borehole spacing can be increased when using larger diameter boreholes. The drilling equipment usually used in coal mining does not produce boreholes with diameter greater than 100 to 120 mm, when using a maximum rod diameter of 76 mm. It has been established that the diameter of the bit needs to be related to that of the rod. If the rod is too thin, the drill string tends to bend and additional stresses can be caused by oscillation. In current practice 75 mm bits are used with 60.3 mm hollow drill rods and 95 mm bits are used with sturdier 76 mm rods.

The standpipe length has to be big enough for the standpipe, which itself must allow the passage of the drill bit (if required). The standpipe length should be drilled to the final diameter; it is usually disadvan-

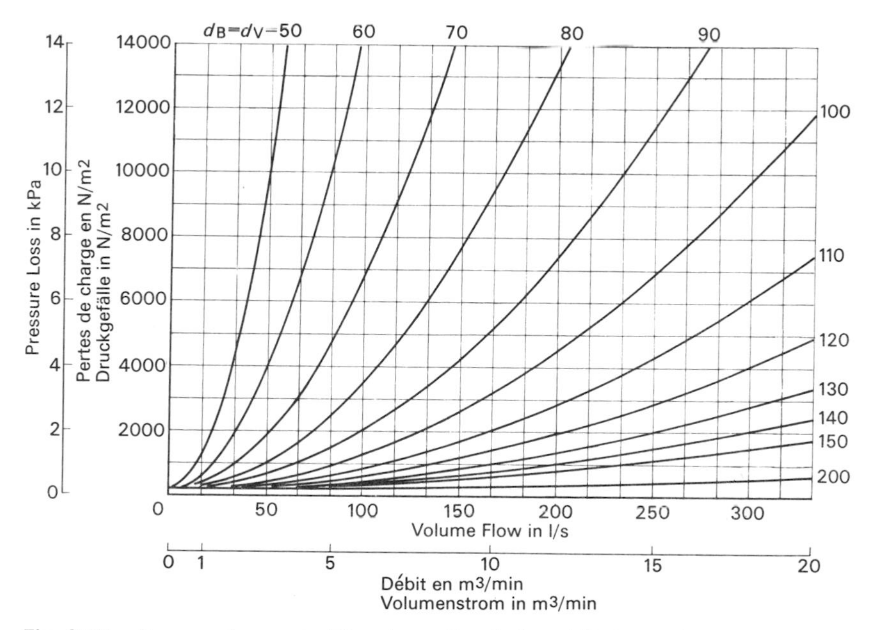

Fig. 2.15 Pressure Losses in 50 m Long Boreholes of Various Diameters Reamed out to Accommodate a Standpipe of the same Bore (key overleaf).

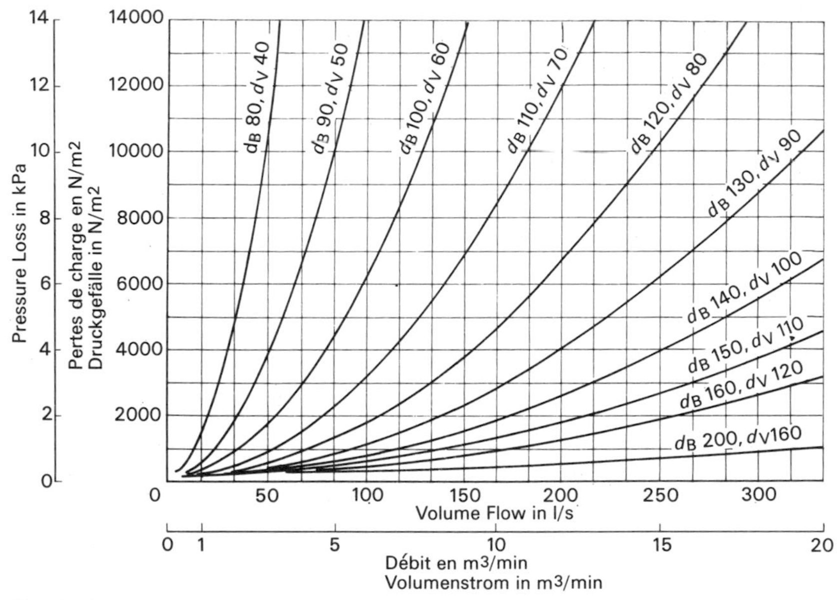

Fig. 2.16 Pressure Losses in 50 m Long Boreholes of Various Diameters Using a Standpipe of Smaller Bore.

Key for Figures 2.15 and 2.16

	Borehole Sondage Bohrloch	Standpipe Tubage Verrohrung
Length in m Longueur en m Länge in m	50	10
Diameter in mm Diamètre en mm Durchmesser in mm	d_B	d_V
Roughness in mm Rugosité en mm Rauhigkeit in mm	5	1

Number of Standpipe Sections Nombre de raccords Anzahl der Verbindungen	5
Borehole Inclination Pente montante du sondage Ansteigen des Bohrloches	45°
Purity of CH_4 Teneur en CH_4 CH_4-Gehalt	100 %

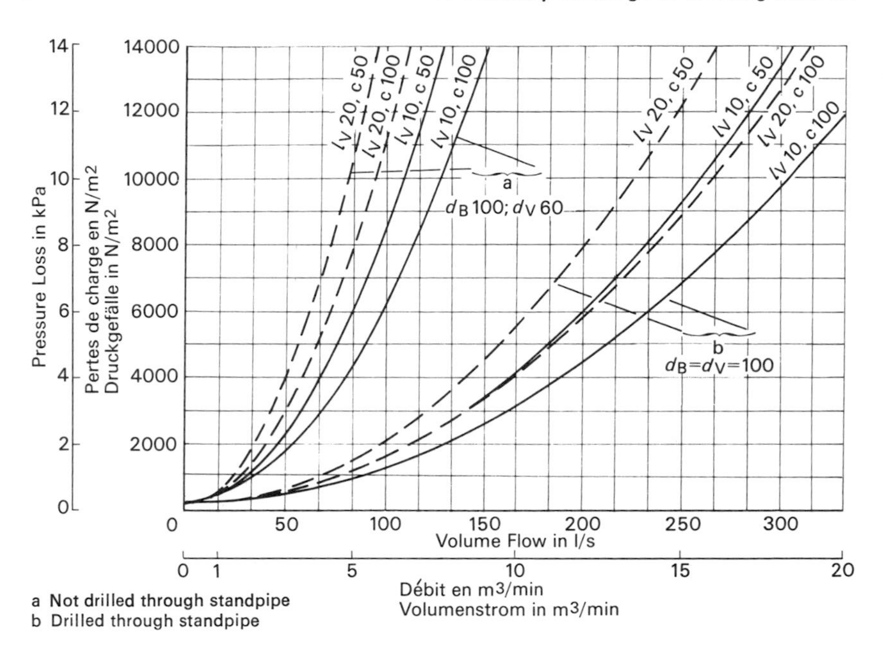

Fig. 2.17 Pressure Losses in 50 m Long Boreholes Showing Effect of Standpipe Length and Diameter and Firedamp Purity.

	Borehole Sondage Bohrloch	Standpipe Tubage Verrohrung
Length in m Longueur en m Länge in m	50	l_V
Diameter in mm Diamètre en mm Durchmesser in mm	d_B	d_V
Roughness in mm Rugosité en mm Rauhigkeit in mm	5	1
Number of Standpipe Sections Nombre de raccords Anzahl der Verbindungen	5 (for) $l_V = 10$ 10 (pour) $l_V = 20$ (bei)	
Borehole inclination Pente montante du sondage Ansteigen des Bohrloches	45°	
Gas Purity % CH_4 Teneur en CH_4 en % CH_4-Gehalt in %	c	

tageous to ream out an existing borehole because of damage to the drilling equipment. Owing to high additional buckling stresses encountered while drilling the standpipe length, special drill rods (guide rods) should be used.

If a standpipe length is not drilled, the borehole cross-section is reduced, resulting in higher pressure losses. It is customary first to drill the standpipe length, insert and secure the standpipe and then continue to drill through it.

Length of Borehole

The optimum length of a borehole can only be determined by assessing the strata section in terms of the position and thickness of gas-producing seams and by probe measurements and drainage tests.

Table 2.2 gives information on average borehole lengths in the countries of the European Community.

Pressure Losses

Pressure losses in a borehole depend on:

- ▷ the roughness of borehole wall,
- ▷ length and diameters of the borehole,
- ▷ length and diameter of the standpipe,
- ▷ gas flow rates.

Movements in roof strata and small pieces of stone falling down the borehole can appreciably increase pressure losses in roofholes. Figure 2.15 plots the pressure loss against diameter and flow when borehole and standpipe inside diameters are the same. Figure 2.16 illustrates a less favourable situation where the standpipe diameter is 40 mm less than that of the borehole. Figure 2.17 shows how changes in the diameter and length of the standpipe affect pressure losses. Data for these figures are to be found in Appendix 2.1.

1.1.3.2 Drilling Equipment

Drilling equipment must be adapted to the space available underground. The weight of the drilling equipment is also of prime importance for mobility reasons. Shortened forms of drilling machines are easier to erect in small roadways.

a) Comparison of Rotary and Percussive Drilling

Advantages of Rotary Drilling

Advantages of the rotary drilling machine are its versatility as regards borehole diameter and roadway size, the relatively simple design and cheapness of drill rods and the relatively small loss of equipment in the event of the drilling bit becoming wedged.

Advantages of Percussive Drilling

The main advantage of percussive drilling machines is their performance in hard rock which cannot be drilled or is difficult to drill with tungsten carbide or roller bits. The percussive drilling machine has been used with success in the conglomerate strata of the Saar and Lorraine coalfields, and the very hard abrasive strata of South Wales.

Disadvantages of Rotary Drilling

In very hard ground rotary drilling may be possible only with diamond bits. Many rotary drilling machines used for firedamp drainage, however, are not suitable for diamond-bit drilling, because neither the drilling speed nor the thrust can be properly controlled. The forces exerted by rotary drilling machines call for firm anchorage of such a machine. Some hydraulic assemblies are limited in usefulness because of the low thrust of the hydraulic stakes.

Disadvantages of Percussive Drilling Machines

In ground subject to heavy weighting, expensive drill rods may be lost in the borehole. The minimum diameter of borehole attainable is generally considered to be 80 mm. The percussive drilling machine requires high compressed air pressure (500 to 600 kPa) which can often be achieved only by using an additional compressor. Rods with separate channels for flushing water and compressed air are relatively expensive. The hydraulic drive on the drill carriage is more liable to break down than the motor of the compressed air rotary drilling machine.

b) Rotary Drilling

Drilling Machines

Gas drainage boreholes of 50 to 145 mm diameter can be drilled with rotary drilling machines. Some of these machines are shown in Figures 2.18 to 2.23 and technical details are given in Table 2.3. Maximum borehole length is about 150 m. Penetration rates with a 75 mm diameter roller bit and 60.3 mm drill rods are 17 mm/s in coal, 7 mm/s in shale, 6 mm/s in sandy shale, and 3 mm/s in sandstone. For 95 to 115 mm roller bits penetration rates may be about 60 % of the above. Such machines are equipped with compressed air or electro-hydraulic drives. Electro-hydraulically powered machines require additional equipment such as protective devices, pumps and

Table 2.3 Details of Rotary and Rotary Percussive Drilling Machines.

		Turmag P IV/6	Turmag P IV/6-K	Korfmann GBV 15/Z	Korfmann GBV 15/ZK	Edeco Mini Hydrack L	Edeco Midget Mini	Victor Minotaur L	Victor Minotaur S	Hausherr DK 9-S (rotary percus-sive)
Frame length	mm	3 020	2 010	3 030	2 430	2 006	1 219	2 134	1 372	3 708
Frame width	mm	600	550	580	580	370	279	330	330	508
Frame height	mm	495	580	400	400	420	356	254	254	508
Frame weight	kg	460	420	600	525	294	185	203	160	760
Stroke	mm	1 700	1 000	1 700	1 100	762	381	762	381	1 600
Power	kW	5.9 [a]	5.9 [a]	7.4	7.4	11	11	7.5	7.5	18.5
Rod speed	rad/s	10.5 [b]	10.5 [b]	5.2/10.5	5.2/10.5	5.2/9.1/19.4	10.5	11.5	11.5	3.1/14.7
Thrust	kN	39.2	39.2	58.9	58.9	42.3	42.3	50.0	50.0	79.7/130.0
Penetration rate	mm/s	100	67 [c]	0 to 250	0 to 250	17 to 133	up to 100	up to 100	up to 100	
Free air consumption	l/s	150	150	300	300	—	—	—	—	200
Flushing water	l/s	0.3 to 1.7	0.3 to 1.7	0.3	0.3	0.9 to 1.5	0.9 to 1.5	0.7	0.7	0.7 to 0.9
Type		com-pressed air [d]	com-pressed air [d]	com-pressed air	com-pressed air	electro-hydraulic	electro-hydraulic	electro-hydraulic	electro-hydraulic	com-pressed air [d]

[a] In electro-hydraulic version 15 kW.
[b] In electro-hydraulic version 0 to 20.9 rad/s.
[c] In electro-hydraulic version 100 mm/s.
[d] Also electro-hydraulic.

Fig. 2.18 Turmag P IV/6 Rotary Drilling Machine with Hydraulic Drive.

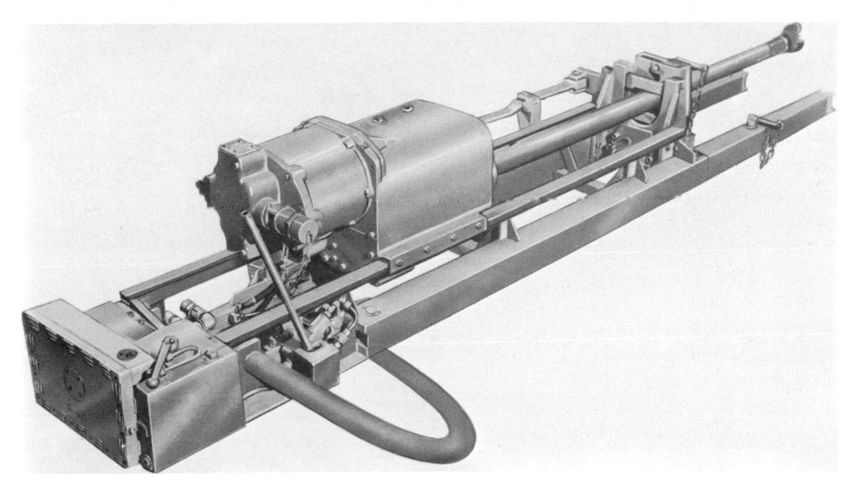

Fig. 2.19 Korfmann GBV 15/ZS Rotary Drilling Machine with Hydraulic Drive.

hoses, which may reduce the manoeuvrability of the machine in small gateroads; it should also be remembered that they may have to be cut off at certain methane levels*.

Drill Rods

Typical diameters of drill rods and bits are given in Table 2.4. It has been found that 51 mm rods, originally developed for 65 mm drill bits, are too weak to be used with 75 or 95 mm roller bits.

---

* Observe national regulations.

Rod lengths generally range from 1100 to 1700 mm, but shorter lengths, eg 762 and 381 mm are in use in the UK. These lengths may be governed by roadway dimensions. When longer drill rods are used the drilling operations has to be stopped less often for rod changing.

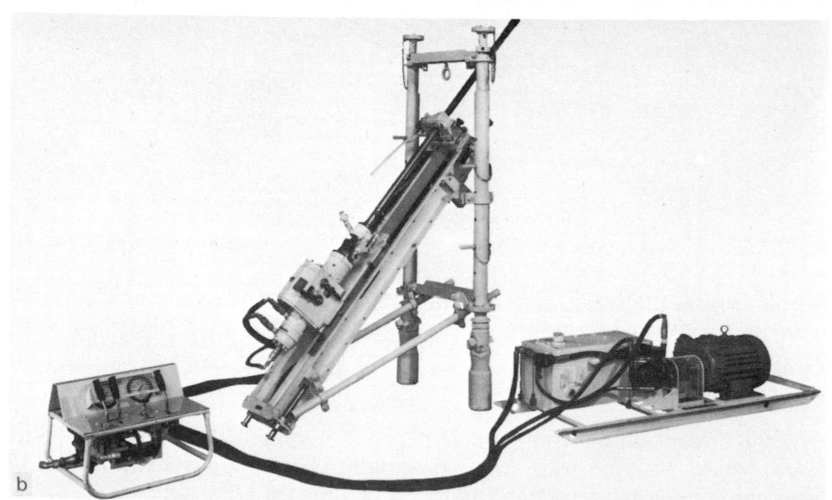

Fig. 2.20 Edeco Mini-Hydrack Drilling Machine Self Propelled (a) and Conventional (b).

Table 2.4 Diameters of Drill Rods and Bits.

Rod Diameter mm	Bit Diameter mm	Type of Bit
41	50	Tungsten Carbide
41	60	
41	65	
41	70	
41	85	
41	115 [a]	
51	60	
51	65	
51	70	
51	115	
51	75	Roller
60 [b]	75 [b]	
60	95	
76 [b]	95 [b]	
76	121	

[a] Also for reaming out. [b] Recommended combination.

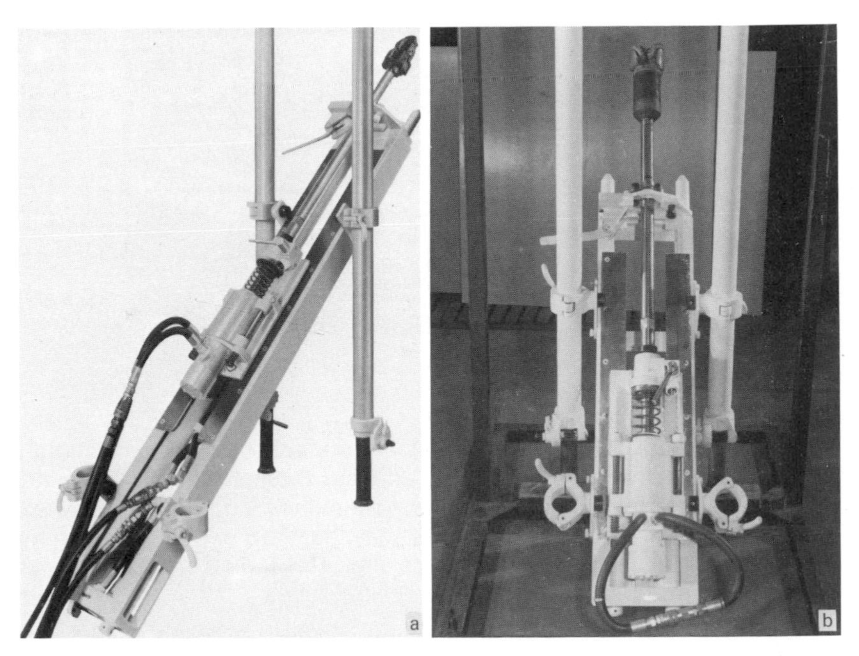

Fig. 2.21 Victor Minotaur Drilling Machine (a) and Victor Mini-Minotaur Drilling Machine (b).

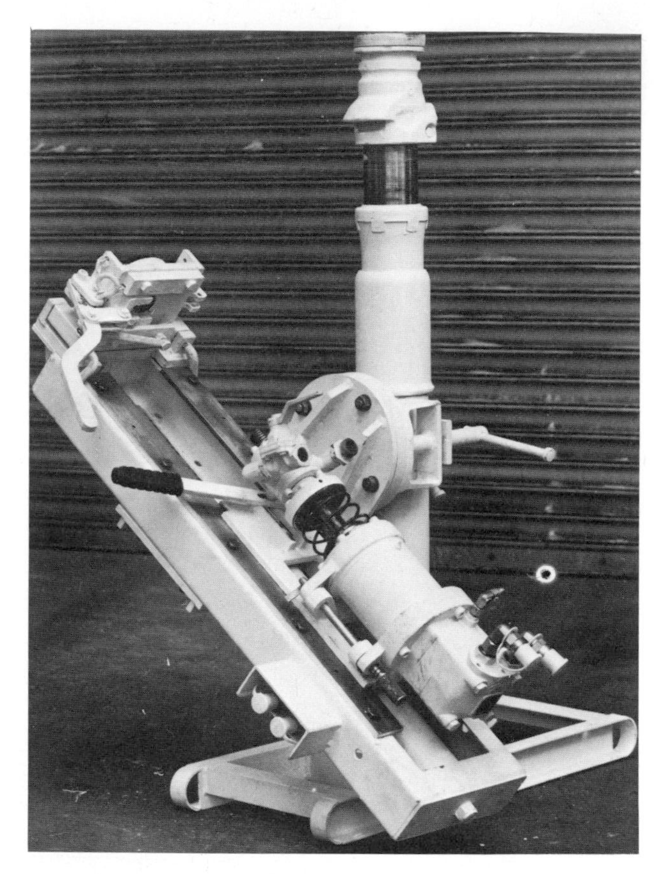

Fig. 2.22 Edeco Midget-Mini Drilling Machine.

Drill Bits

Tungsten carbide bits (Figure 2.24) are suitable for coal and softer rock, are cheaper and may be more efficient than roller bits. Generally they are not suitable for quartzitic sandstones and conglomerates. Because of high friction, such bits may heat up rapidly if flushing breaks down. A long overall service life is obtained in softer rocks because these bits can be reground several times.

Roller bits (Figure 2.24) have minimum diameters of about 75 mm. The most widely used diameter of roller bit for gas drainage purposes is 95 mm. The 75 mm size has a shorter life than the 95 mm partly

Fig. 2.23 Hausherr DK 9 — 68 S Drilling Machine.

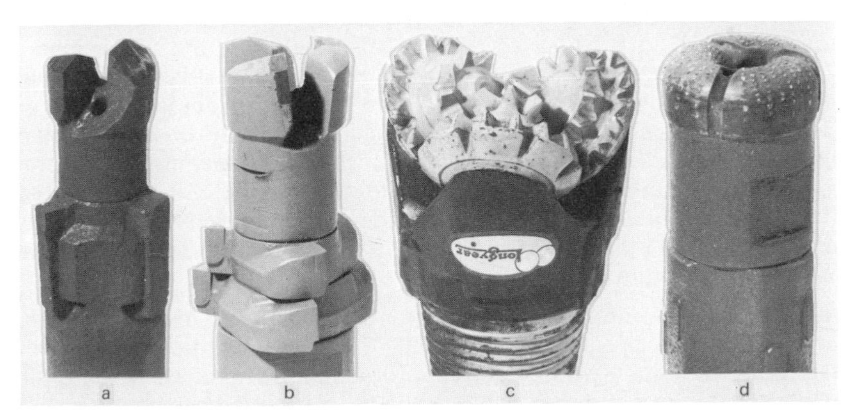

a Tungsten Carbide Bit — Couronne de forage à plaquettes de carbure — Hartmetall-Bohrkrone
b Tungsten Carbide Reamer Bit — Couronne de réalésage à plaquettes de carbure — Hartmetall-Aufbohrkrone
c Roller Bit — Outil à molettes — Rollenmeißel
d Diamond Bit — Couronne de forage au diamant — Diamant-Bohrkrone

Fig. 2.24 Types of Bits for Rotary Drilling.

because smaller bearings must be used. Even in hard rock a roller bit generally lasts until the borehole has been completed, so that the time-consuming process of bit changing is avoided. In the Ruhr one bit normally lasts for two boreholes.

Flushing Heads

Flushing heads are necessary to feed air or water into the hollow rod. Wear on them may be high where seals (O-rings) come into contact with drill cuttings. However, only rarely are flushing heads changed but when it is necessary, it is time-consuming and interrupts drilling.

Water Flushing

This is the most widespread type of flushing and in the UK it is the only approved method.

The advantages of water flushing are highly effective cooling leading to relatively low bit wear, improved penetration by rapid removal of cuttings, and reduced risks of explosive mixtures being ignited in boreholes.

The disadvantages are that wetting of the strata may lead to swelling of certain rocks such as shales and fireclays with occasional problems associated with loss of water to the strata; in addition there may be problems of waste water disposal where drill cuttings are abrasive and flushing water cannot be reused.

Water for drilling is obtained from existing underground water mains and may be fed directly to the water head of the drilling machine. Alternatively, it may be taken from water mains and put into a tank or drum. A water circulating pump (usually electrically driven) is then used to pressurise the water and deliver it to the machine. The water is forced through hollow drill rods to the cutting bit and returns through the annulus between the outside of the drill rods and the sides of the borehole either to a local sump (ie hole in the floor) or to the water tank or drum.

In the case of roofholes, drill cuttings fall away from the bit and are removed partly by gravity and partly by the circulating water. For floorholes adequate water flow is essential to provide a suitable upward velocity since the drill cuttings must be lifted out of the holes. If this is not done, 'secondary drilling' (ie grinding of cuttings) takes place and penetration rates may be reduced to zero. To ensure an adequate water velocity, the cross-sectional area of the annulus between the outside of the drill rod and the sides of the floorhole must not exceed a certain value; if the area were larger, for the same quantity

Table 2.5 Details of Water Circulating Pumps.

		Turmag Type 1	Edeco Slush	Evers & Wall D. 3	Boyles BB7 — 12R	Challenger
Type		Piston Rotary	Double Acting Single Cylinder	Nitrile Triple Diaphragm Type	Double Acting Single Cylinder	Nitrile (Neoprene) Twin Diaphragm Type
Stroke	mm		70	6.35	70	6.35
Bore	mm		63.5	—	63.5	—
Suction Hose Diameter	mm	28	51	31.25	37.5	37.5
Delivery Hose Size	mm	20	37.5	31.25	31.25	25
Transmission		Gear	Vee Belt	Vee Belt	Vee Belt	Gear
Pump	rad/s		20.9 (Usual)	52.4	20.9 (Usual)	52.4
Claimed Maximum Working Pressure	kPa	2100/2450	3500	1400	2450	1400
Claimed Maximum Delivery	l/s	0.75	1.20	1.00	1.20	1.00
Motor	kW	1.5 to 2.2	5.5 to 7.5	5.5	3.7 to 5.5	3.7
Drive		Compressed Air Turbine	Electric or Compressed Air	Electric or Compressed Air	Electric or Compressed Air	Electric or Compressed Air

The water flow and pressure figures refer to pumps in good condition handling clean water.

of water the velocity would be too low. A practical area of annulus is about 0.003 m^2 and this is achieved for example by using a 76 mm standpipe and 41 mm rods, or a 100 mm standpipe and 76 mm rods.

Small water losses may occur mainly at the water circulating pump, water swivel, hose joints, nose piece and rod joints, and allowances are made for them when deciding water pump capacity, or water flow rates needed from a water range. The water quantities circulated in roofholes are usually of the order of 0.5 to 0.9 l/s with pump pressures of 1400 to 1750 kPa depending on the length of uphole. Floorholes may require up to 1.2 to 1.5 l/s against a head of 3500 kPa.

Table 2.5 gives technical information on the water circulating pumps used in the UK.

Air Flushing

On the occasions when air flushing is used, dust is controlled by sucking out the cuttings, eg by the Königsborn system (Figure 2.25).

Fig. 2.25 Königsborn KE 8 Extraction Equipment.

▷ The advantages of air flushing are that it does not affect the surrounding rock and that there is no waste water disposal problem.

▷ The disadvantages are that considerable local heating may occur if a rod breaks; a number of ignitions have occurred during dry drilling arising from dilution of high concentration gas mixtures by the air (Appendix 2.2) and firedamp sucked into the system may lead to an ignition by static electricity generated in the dust-laden air.

Frames

The drill frame provides the support and guidance for the drill motor and for the necessary powered feed; the latter is achieved by either a chain, a toothed rack, a screw or a hydraulic cylinder. Mention of the hydraulic anchoring assembly has already been made in Section 1.1.3.2.

c) Percussive Drilling

Drilling Machines

Percussive machines (Figure 2.26) can drill boreholes 80 to 200 mm diameter. Given sufficient air pressure, penetration is 0.8 mm/s in shale and 1.3 mm/s in sandstone. Important technical data on percussive drills are contained in Table 2.6.

Drill Rods

The drill rods for percussive drilling have two channels, one for water and one for compressed air. Drill rods are 1500, 2000 or 3000 mm long.

Drill Bits

Carbide-tipped cruciform bits are used which can be re-ground.

Frames

Frames perform the same basic functions as for rotary drilling machines. Rotary drilling frames have been used on occasions in an attempt to overcome some of the problems encountered with percussive machine frames.

1.1.4 Standpipes

The standpipe which is inserted into the first part of the borehole is made usually of steel or occasionally plastic* piping; the standpipe is intended to limit the inleakage of air into the gas drainage system and to enable the borehole to be connected to the main drainage range.

---

* Observe national regulations.

Table 2.6 Technical Details of Percussive Drilling Machines.

		Stenuick Supermine 4 ASE 80	Stenuick Supermine 4 ASE 100	Stenuick Supermine 4 ASE 160	Bois Stenuick
Frame length	mm	Stroke + 1 250	Stroke + 1 250	Stroke + 1 250	2 850
Frame width	mm	420	420	420	450
Frame height	mm	730 to 1 050	730 to 1 050	730 to 1 050	600
Frame weight [a]	kg	435, 450, 480	435, 450, 480	435, 450, 480	1 000
Machine weight	kg	19.5	33.5	115	36
Stroke	mm	1 500 2 000 3 000	1 500 2 000 3 000	1 500 2 000 3 000	1 500
Borehole diameter	mm	80 to 85	105 to 115	160 to 180	104 to 135
Rod diameter	mm	70	70, 90	90, 120	90
Drilling machine power	kW	2.9 [c]	2.9 [c]	2.9 [c]	3
Rod speed	rad/s	4.7 to 8.9	4.7 to 8.9	4.7 to 8.9	7.9
Thrust motor power	kW	2.9 [c]	2.9 [c]	2.9 [c]	1.5
Percussive force	kN	61.8 [c]	61.8 [c]	61.8 [c]	
Thrust	kN	14.7 [c]	14.7 [c]	14.7 [c]	40.0
Air consumption	l/s	83 [b] to 100 [c]	83 [b] to 125 [c]	167 [b] to 200 [c]	125 [d]

[a] Depending on stroke.
[b] For an air pressure of 490 kPa.
[c] For an air pressure of 590 kPa.
[d] For an air pressure of 700 kPa.

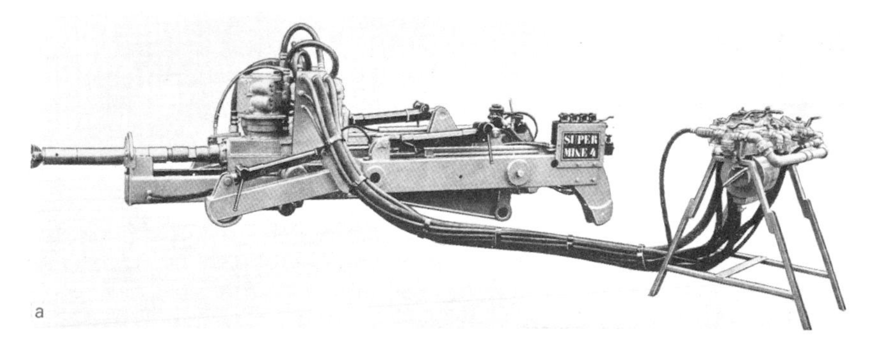

Fig. 2.26 Percussive Drilling Machines Stenuick (a) and Bois Stenuick (b).

1.1.4.1 Drilling the Standpipe Length

Because it is preferable for the standpipe to have approximately the same inner diameter as the productive length of borehole, a larger diameter standpipe length is necessary. This has the advantage of reducing the pressure losses (Figure 2.17). A disadvantage is that drill rods have to be withdrawn to change the bit after only about one-fifth of the borehole has been drilled. The vibrations of the drill rods during drilling may affect the seal between the standpipe and the borehole wall. In the case of roller bits which cannot be used to enlarge a hole, the standpipe length has to be drilled to its full size before drilling the productive length. Enlarging the standpipe length is only possible with carbide bits (Figure 2.24).

A prime advantage of installing the standpipe before drilling the remainder of the borehole is that if firedamp problems arise, gas can be immediately drained through the connection to the main gas range.

1.1.4.2 Diameters of the Standpipe and Standpipe Length

The diameter of the standpipe is related to the diameter of the borehole and to gas flow rates. Thus, with a 95 mm borehole size, a standpipe with a bore of 100 mm and a standpipe length of 143 mm diameter are practicable. Standpipes of 80 mm bore are used occasionally with a standpipe length diameter of 120 mm. If the standpipe length does not have a greater diameter, even smaller standpipes must be used. In some countries standpipes with a bore of 50 mm were formerly used with 65 mm boreholes but they are now considered too small and 75 or 95 mm holes are now used. In the UK the following diameters are common: standpipe lengths 85 or 115 mm, standpipe 51 or 76 mm, productive length 50 or 65 mm.

1.1.4.3 Length of Standpipe

The length of the standpipe depends on:

- ▷ the distance of gas sources from the worked seam,
- ▷ the angle of the borehole,
- ▷ the extent of bed separation planes in adjacent strata,
- ▷ the required purity of the drained gas.

In the case where sources are close to the worked seam, the standpipe is taken to a few metres below the source if it is in the roof, or a few metres above the source if it is in the floor. In such a case the methane released from the neighbouring seam is drained before leakage air is drawn in from the waste of the worked seam.

If a particularly rich methane mixture is needed the standpipe may have to be taken right up to a seam well above the roof of the worked seam.

The strata thickness h to be penetrated by the standpipe section measured perpendicular to the strata, and the angle of inclination α of the borehole are used to determine the borehole length l.

$$l = \frac{h}{\sin \alpha} = f_R h \quad [2.1]$$

The value of the factor f_R can be found in Figure 2.27.

Since the standpipes are installed mechanically, the weight of a long standpipe is of little importance; however the purchasing costs of manufactured pipes can be substantial.

It is important that the connections between individual sections of the standpipe should be secured so that the standpipe sections do not part when being installed or when subjected to strata movement.

1.1.4.4 Sealing

Between Sections of Standpipe

Annular collars or rubber packing are used as a seal between manufactured sections of the standpipe. If standpipes are made at the colliery itself they are screw jointed or may have simple male/female connections.

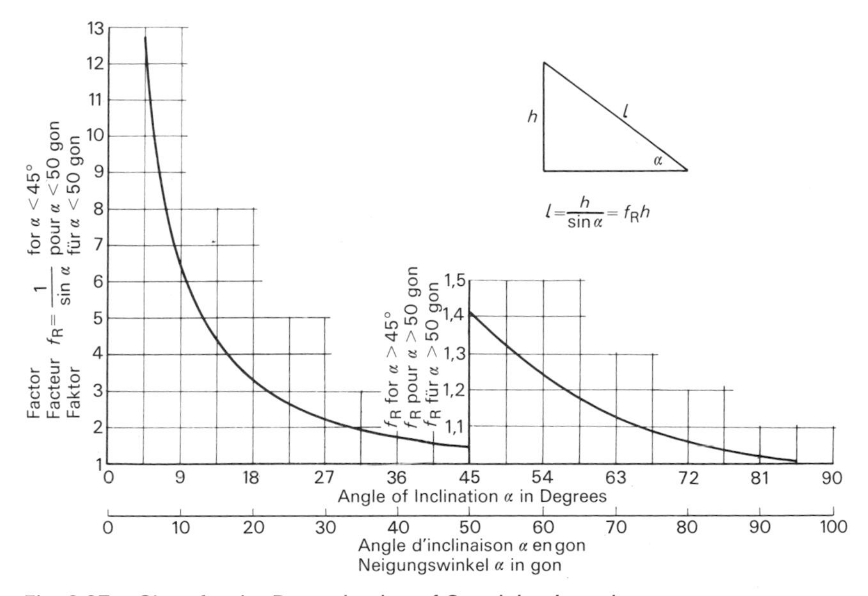

Fig. 2.27 Chart for the Determination of Standpipe Length.

Between the Standpipe and the Borehole Walls

Standpipes as manufactured and used in France and Germany usually have rubber sealing sleeves which are so designed that they are forced against the borehole sides by suction (Figure 2.28). Rubber rings can also be used (Figure 2.29). Care has to be taken to see not only that sufficient sealing sleeves are provided, but also that the whole of the

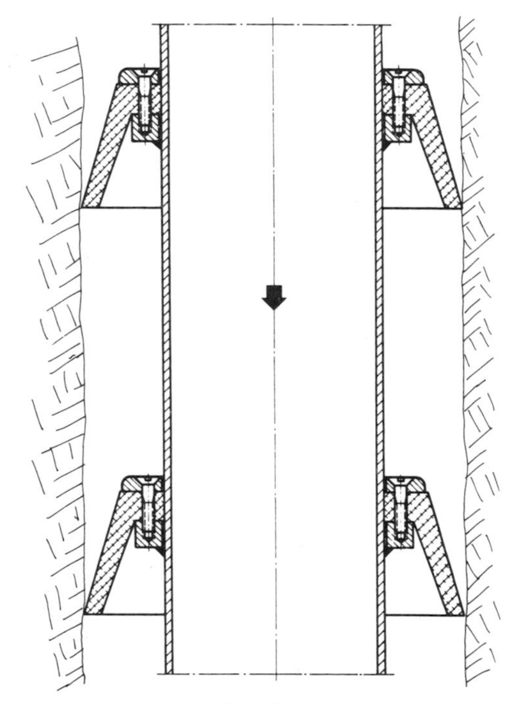

Fig. 2.28 Standpipe Seal using Rubber Sleeves.

standpipe length is sealed against inleakage of air, to ensure that the annular space between standpipe and strata does not act as an easy flow path for air.

In countries other than the UK, punched-out rubber gaskets (Figure 2.30) are used with standpipes made at the colliery itself.

Alternatively, the screwed collar is wrapped with Densotape (Figure 2.31). In the case of a standpipe sealed with Densotape the annular space between the borehole sides and the standpipe is filled during drilling with a slurry of drill cuttings. A relatively modern method

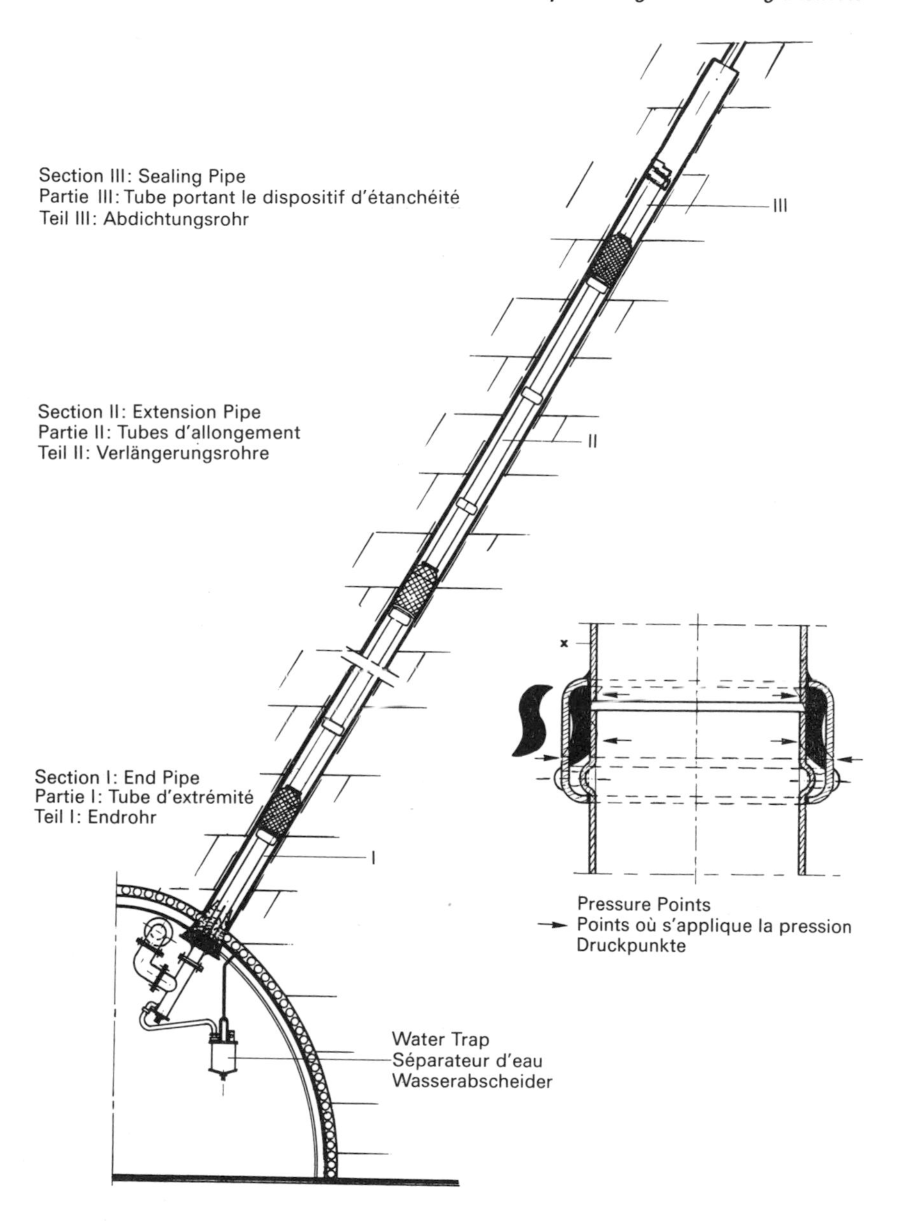

Fig. 2.29 Standpipe Seal with Cellular Rubber Rings. Inset: Quick Connector with a 3 lip seal.

used in the UK entails the sealing of the annular space with an approved synthetic resin (Figure 2.32 and Appendix 2.3). In addition, recent tests carried out in Germany with a view to sealing the annular space with polyurethane*, have been successfully completed (Appendix 2.4).

Sometimes gas drainage holes are sealed with cement (Figure 2.33). This method has a number of drawbacks:

▷ Setting takes too long.

▷ Rock movements may cause brittle cement to crack and break the seal.

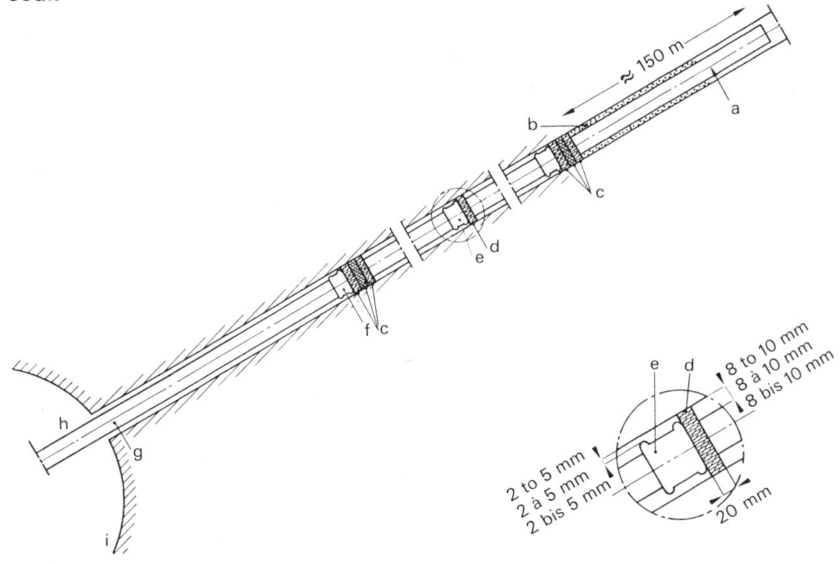

a Final Section of Standpipe — Dernier tube du tubage — Letztes Rohr der Verrohrung
b Cuttings Scraped by the Rings — Cuttings raclés par les anneaux — Durch die Ringe abgeschabtes Gut
c 3 Rubber Rings — 3 anneaux de caoutchouc — 3 Gummiringe
d 1 Rubber Ring at each Intermediate Section — 1 anneau de caoutchouc à chaque tube intermédiaire — 1 Gummiring an jedem Zwischenrohr
e Connecting Socket between Sections — Manchon de liaison entre tubes —Verbindungsmuffe zwischen den Rohren
f Connecting Socket between 1st and 2nd Sections — Manchon de liaison 1er à 2ème tube — Verbindungsmuffe zwischen erstem und zweitem Rohr
g 1st Setcion of Standpipe — 1er tube du tubage — Erstes Rohr der Verrohrung
h 1st Section connected to Drainage Range — 1er tube raccordé au réseau de captage — Erstes Rohr verbunden mit dem Absaugnetz
i Roadway — Galerie — Strecke

Fig. 2.30 Standpipe Seal Using Rubber Rings.

* Observe national regulations.

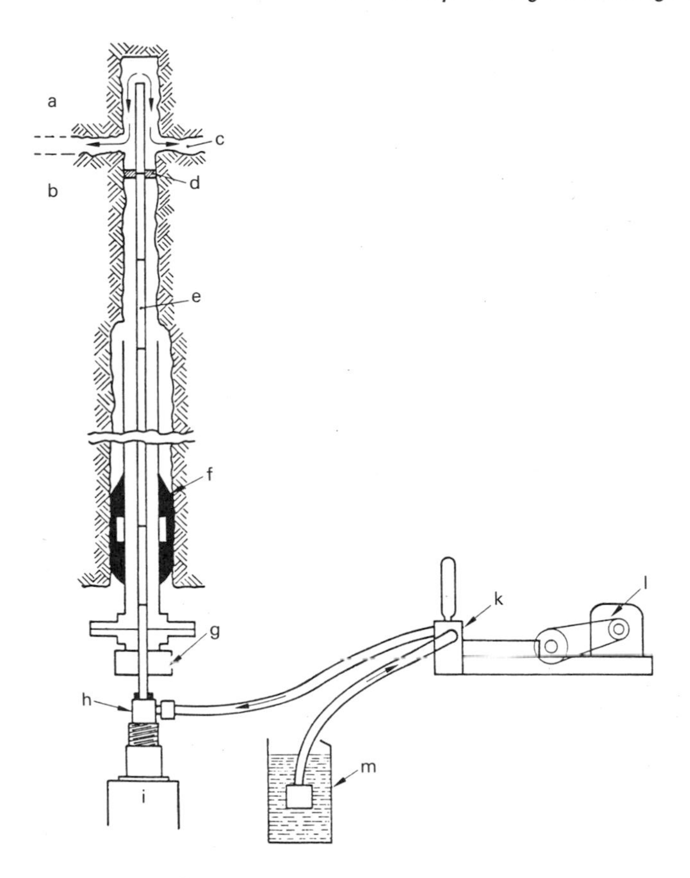

a Sandstone — Grès — Sandstein
b Shale — Schiste — Schiefer
c Remote large Bed Separation Plane or Break — Plan de séparation ou fissure largement ouvert — Unzugängliche Schichtenaufblätterung oder Spalte
d Rubber or Wooden Ring — Anneau en caoutchouc ou en bois — Gummi- oder Holzring
e Drill Rods — Tiges de forage — Bohrstangen
f Densotape Seal — Joint d'étanchéité Denso — Densobinde als Abdichtung
g Valve and Stuffing Box — Vanne et boîte à bourrage — Ventil und Stopfbüchse
h Water Head — Tête d'injection de l'eau — Spülkopf
i Drilling Machine — Sondeuse — Bohrmaschine
k Water Circulation Pump — Pompe d'injection de l'eau — Spülpumpe
l Motor — Moteur — Motor
m Drum Containing 8 % by Weight Bentonite/Water Mixture or approved Alternative — Réservoir contenant un mélange d'eau et de 8 % en poids de bentonite, ou d'un produit analogue adéquat — Faß mit einer Mischung aus 8 Gew.-% Bentonit und Wasser oder mit einer anderen zugelassenen Mischung

Fig. 2.31 Method of Sealing a Large Fissure Using Bentonite/Water Mixture together with a Densotape Standpipe Seal.

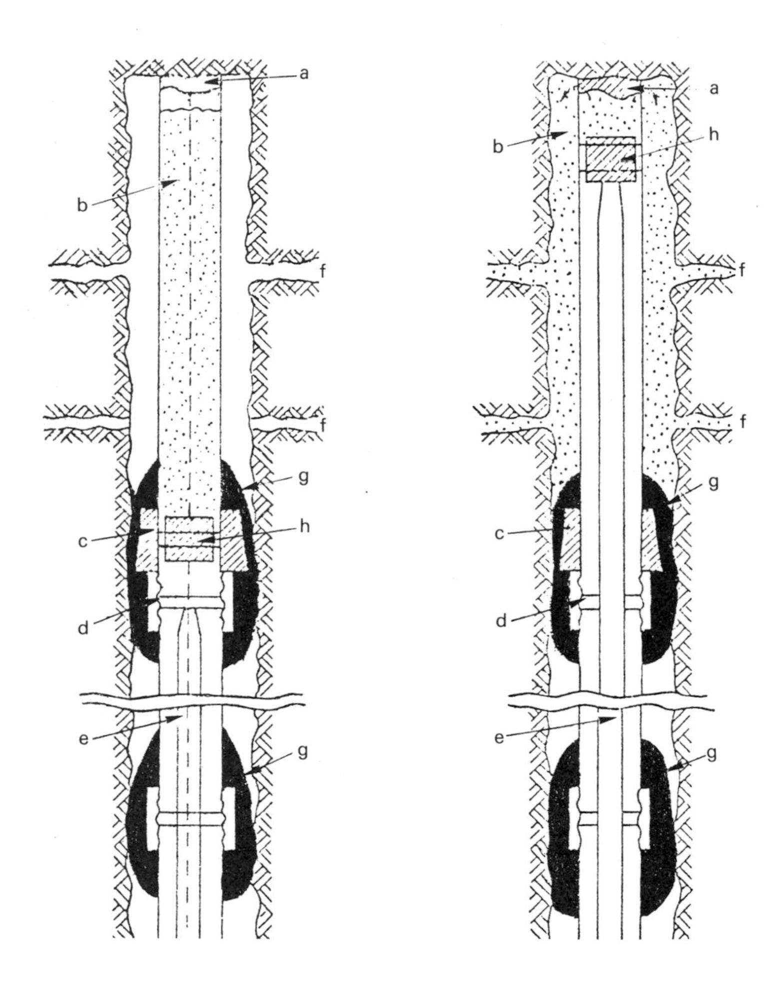

a Resin cap — Capuchon de résine — Harzkappe
b Resin mix — Mélange de résine — Harzmischung
c Resin ring — Anneau en résine — Harzring
d Pipe coupling — Raccord entre tubes — Rohrkupplung
e Drill rod — Tige de forage — Bohrgestänge
f Bed separation planes — Plan de séparation entre bancs —
g Densotape — Joint Denso — Densobinde
h Resin Piston with "O" rings — Piston (pour la résine) avec joints "O-Ring" — Harzkolben mit O-Ringen

Fig. 2.32 Resin Sealing of Standpipes before and after placing Mix.

▷ The rigidly held standpipe can be fractured by rock movement.

▷ Cement can escape through roof fissures.

Because cement is capable of withstanding high pressures, it may be used to best advantage in stable rock, where high pressures are encountered, eg water drainage boreholes.

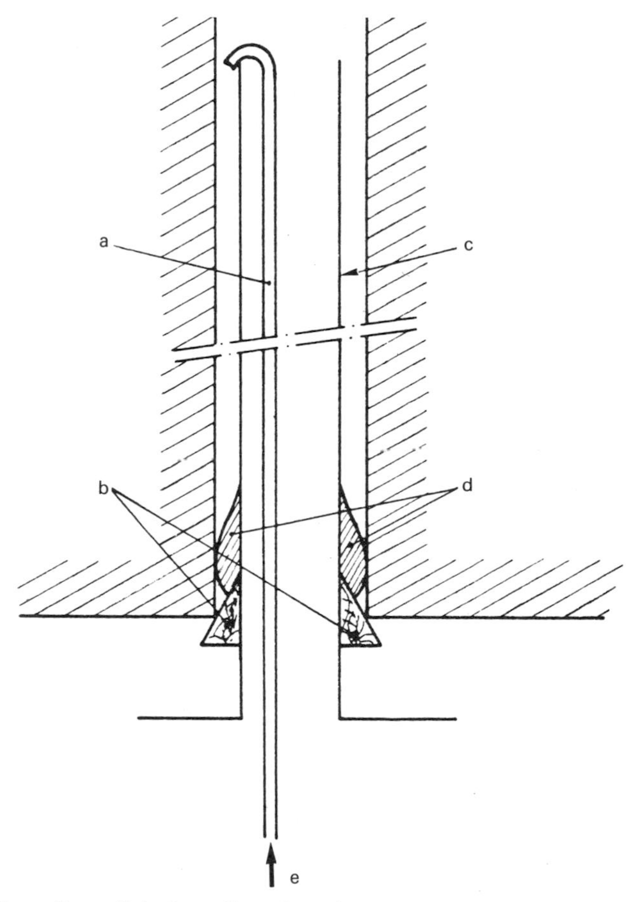

a Injection Pipe — Canne d'injection — Zementiersonde
b Wooden Wedge — Cales en bois — Holzkeile
c Standpipe — Tubage — Verrohrung
d Plug to Retain the Cement — Bouchon de retenue du ciment — Stopfen zum Zurückhalten des Zementes
e Pumped Cement Grout — Pompage du lait de ciment — Hochpumpen der Zementmilch

Fig. 2.33 Cement Sealing of a Standpipe.

Special Sealing Methods

When drilling through large rock fissures, local filling of cavities with a Bentonite/water suspension is practised (Figure 2.31 and Appendix 2.5).

In Belgium a method based on a two-stage cementing operation (Figure 2.34) has been perfected where seams in the roof are very close to the worked seam. Firstly a standpipe of normal length, with perforations at the level of the adjacent seam, is inserted. The annular space between the borehole and the standpipe is then filled with cement up to a point just below the seam. As soon as the borehole becomes affected by ground movements, the perforations are stopped up from inside by a foam rubber stopper while the annular space is further cemented up to the top of the standpipe. In this manner it is possible to drain gas initially from the seam just above the roof of the worked seam, and from the more remote seams before and after the perforations have been closed.

Where air enters the borehole well above the normal standpipe length, a double-standpipe method is sometimes used in the UK. In this case a long smaller diameter steel pipe is pushed up inside the normal standpipe and borehole, sealed against the borehole wall and then

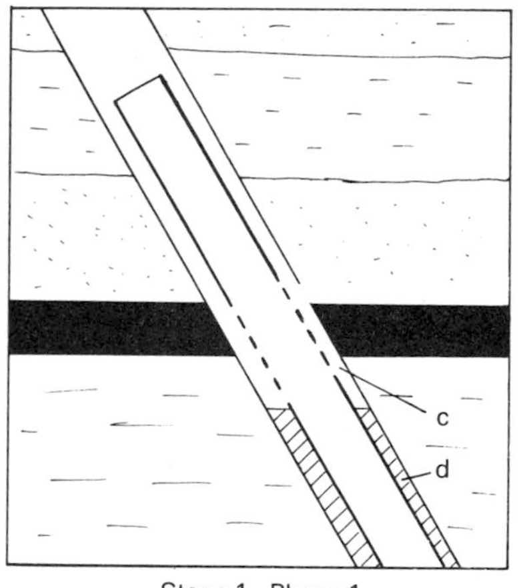

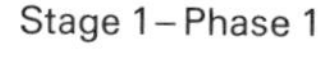
Stage 1 – Phase 1

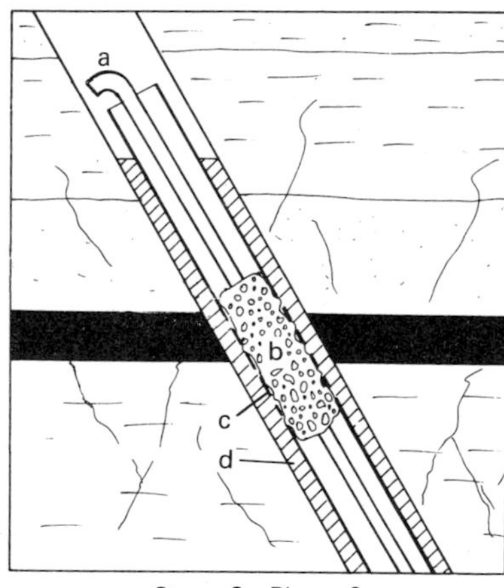

Stage 2 – Phase 2

a Injection pipe — Canne d'injection — Zementiersonde
b Foam Rubber Plug — Bouchon constitué d'une éponge en caoutchouc — Schaumgummistopfen
c Perforated Standpipe — Elément perforé du tubage — Perforiertes Standrohr
d Cement — Ciment — Zement

Fig. 2.34 Standpipe Sealing using a Two Stage Cementing Process.

connected up to the main gas range. By this means it is possible to drain gas from more remote sources with high purity and little air dilution (Appendix 2.6).

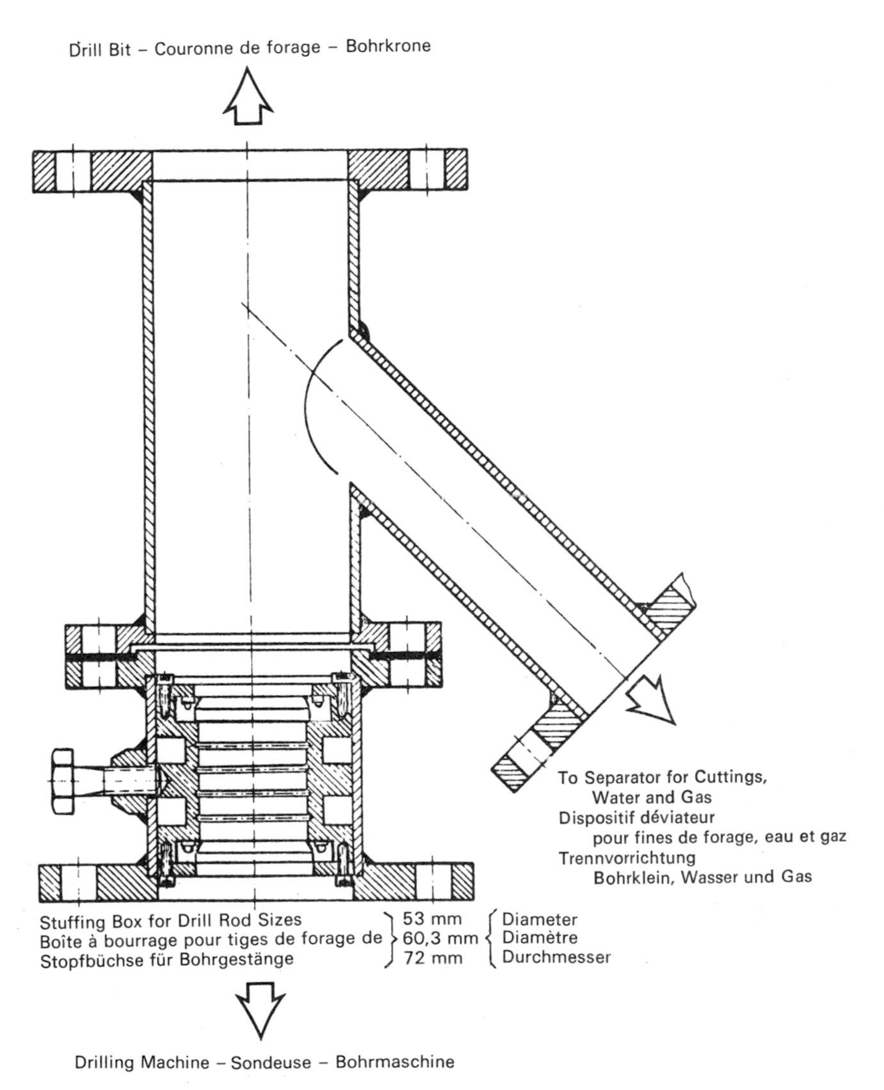

Fig. 2.35 Stuffing Box to allow Firedamp Drainage whilst Drilling.

1.1.4.5 Draining during Drilling

When gas emissions are high, gas may have to be drained during drilling operations and for this purpose a standpipe has to be used. A T-piece attached to the standpipe provides a connection for the

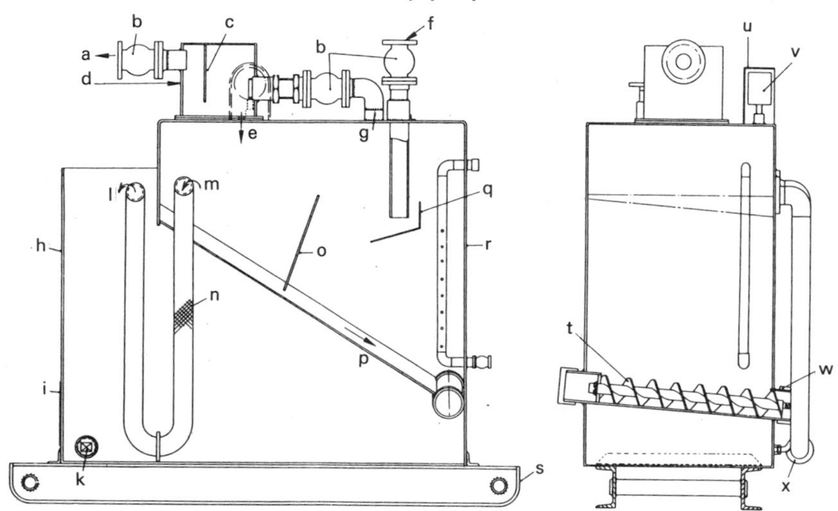

a To Gas Main — Vers la tuyauterie collectrice du gaz — Zur Absaugleitung
b Isolating Valve — Vanne d'isolement — Absperrventil
c Baffle — Chicane — Prallplatte
d Water Separator — Séparateur d'eau — Wasserabscheider
e Water Return to Tank — Retour de l'eau au réservoir — Wasserrücklauf zum Tank
f Water, Gas, Cuttings Inlet from Drill Hole — Arrivée de l'eau, du gaz et des fines de forage, en provenance du sondage — Eintritt von Wasser, Gas und Bohrklein aus dem Bohrloch
g Gas Outlet — Sortie du gaz — Gasaustritt
h Outer open Water Tank — Réservoir à eau externe, ouvert — Äußerer offener Wassertank
i Inspection Hatch — Lucarne d'inspection — Inspektionsluke
k Drain Cock — Robinet de purge — Ablaßhahn
l Water Outlet — Sortie de l'eau — Wasseraustritt
m Water — Eau — Wasser
n Armoured Hose — Flexible armé — Armierter Schlauch
o Internal Baffle — Chicane interne — Innere Prallplatte
p Cuttings — Fines de forage — Bohrklein
q Deflecting Baffle — Déflecteur — Deflektor
r Outer Casing — Carter extérieur — Äußeres Gehäuse
s Skids — Patins — Kufen
t Spiral for removing Cuttings — Vis sans fin d'évacuation des fines de forage — Schnecke zum Abfördern des Bohrkleins
u Protective Cover — Couvercle de protection — Schutzhaube
v Pressure Gauge — Manomètre — Manometer
w Removable Cap — Coiffe amovible — Abnehmbare Kappe
x Retaining Clip — Etrier-support — Halteklemme

Fig. 2.36 Assembly for Separating Gas, Water and Drillings for Low Gas Pressures.

stuffing box and a side connection for drill cuttings, water and gas (Figure 2.35).

In the UK, gas, water and drill cuttings may be separated at normal gas pressures in steel containers (Figure 2.36). For floorholes at which high pressures may be encountered the equipment shown in Figure 2.37 is used.

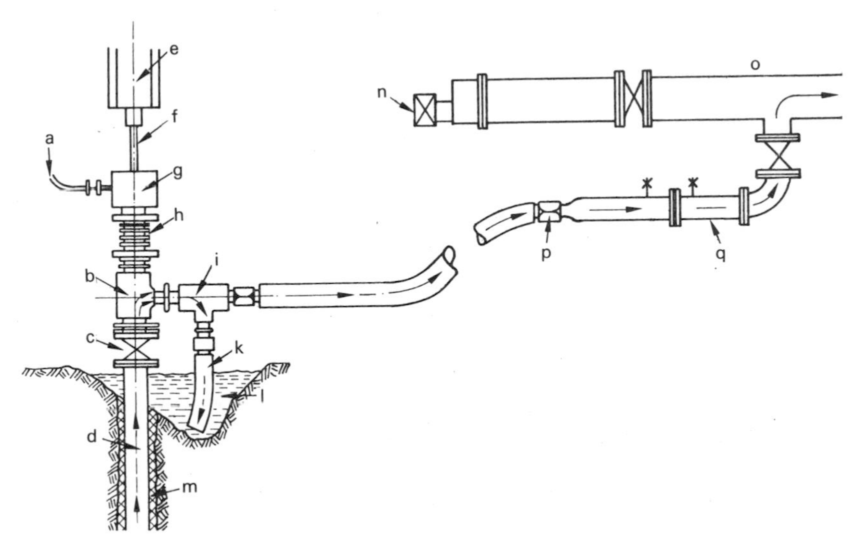

a High Pressure Water Supply — Alimentation en eau sous forte pression — Hochdruckwasser-anschluß
b Simple Tee Piece — Té simple — Einfaches T-Stück
c Gate Valve — Vanne passante — Schieber
d Standpipe — Tubage — Verrohrung
e Drilling Machine — Sondeuse — Bohrmaschine
f Drill Rod — Tige de forage — Bohrgestänge
g Hydraulic Stuffing Box — Boîte à bourrage hydraulique — Hydraulische Stopfbüchse
h Stainless Steel Bellows — Soufflet en acier inoxydable — Balgrohr aus nichtrostendem Stahl
i Three way valve — Vanne à 3 voies — Dreiwegeventil
k Return Water Hose — Flexible de retour pour l'eau — Wasserrücklaufschlauch
l Recirculating Water Sump — Puisard de récirculation de l'eau — Sumpf für Spülwasserumlauf
m Rapid hardening Grout — Scellement à durcissement rapide — Schnellbindender Mörtel
n Water Trap — Piège à eau — Wasserfalle
o Firedamp Drainage Range — Réseau de captage — Gasabsaugleitung
p Pressure Coupling — Raccord sous pression — Druck-Kupplung
q Borehole Equipment — Station de mesure du sondage — Bohrlochmeßstrecke

Fig. 2.37 Diagrammatic Arrangement of Borehole Equipment for Floorholes in Conditions Liable to Sudden Firedamp Emissions.

1.1.4.6 Connecting the Standpipe to the Drainage Range

Gate Valves

Gate valves (Figures 2.38 and 2.39) at boreholes are used to regulate the suction and if necessary to isolate the borehole from the drainage network. Open gate valves should have the same cross-sectional area as the standpipe. It is important that gate valves should not be affected by dirt and corrosion.

Flexible Hoses

Flexible hoses are used to connect boreholes to the firedamp drainage ranges (Figures 2.38 and 2.39), and also to make allowance for

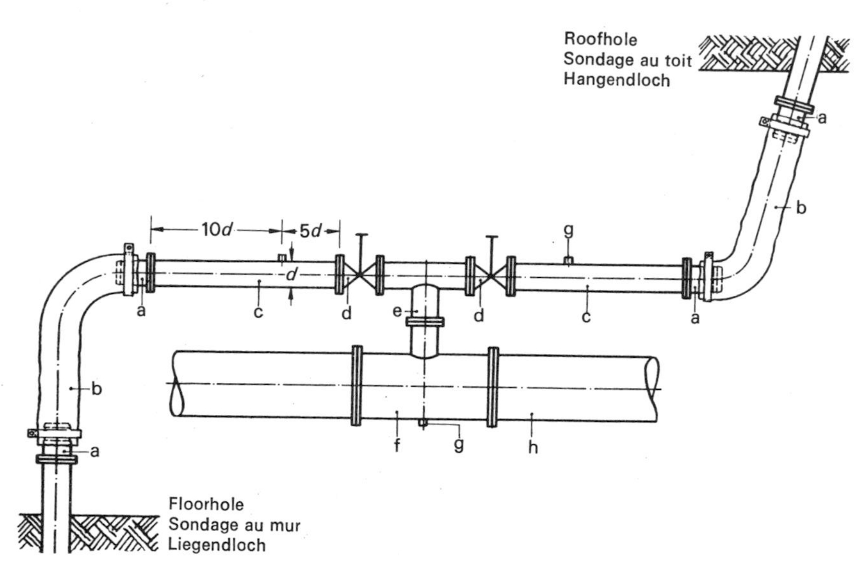

a Hose Adaptor — Douille d'emmanchement du flexible — Schlauchtülle
b Hose with Clamp — Flexible à colliers — Schlauch mit Schellen
c Measuring Section with Socket — Tuyau pour mesures, avec prise — Meßrohr mit Muffe
d Valve — Vanne sphérique — Kugelhahn
e Tee Piece — Té — T-Stück
f Tee with Socket — Té avec prise — T-Stück mit Muffe
g Measuring Point — Prise de mesure — Meßstutzen
h Drainage Range — Tuyauterie collectrice de gaz — Gassammelleitung

Fig. 2.38 Connection of Boreholes to the Drainage Range (German Fittings).

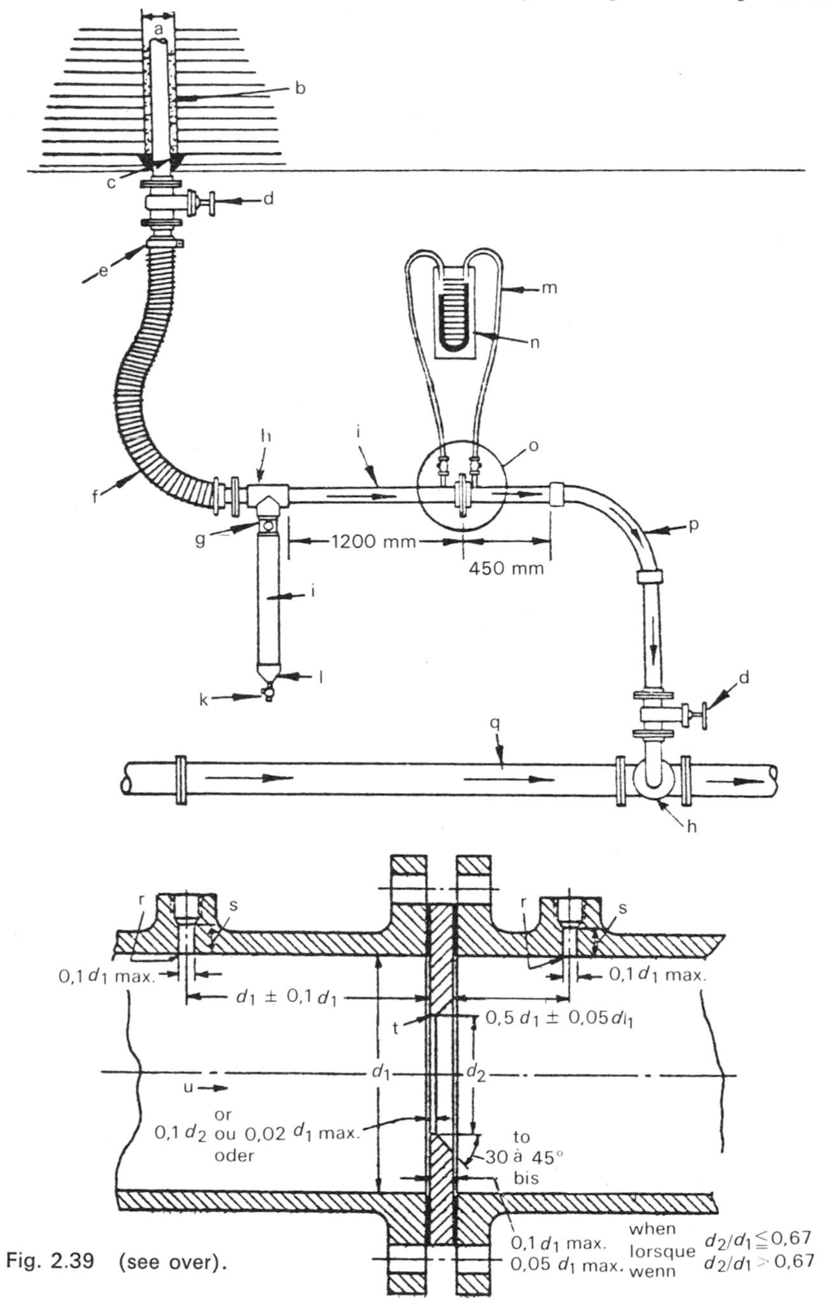

Fig. 2.39 (see over).

strata movement. Wire-armoured hoses do not kink, and may be more difficult to work with. The diameter of the hose should be the same as that of the standpipe. Hose connections are made with special hose clips of several different designs.

Dirt and Water Separator

In Belgian coal mines, combined dirt and water drains are used for boreholes (Figure 2.40). These installations must be regularly checked.

Water Drains

Water drains are most important for the safe and effective operation of gas drainage equipment. Condensation, inflowing strata water or flushing water can collect in the lowest parts of the gas range and interfere with gas drainage. Hence it is necessary to fit water drains at boreholes and at low points of the gas range. They include:

▷ siphon drains (open and closed types),

▷ water traps,

▷ pump drains.

The simplest type is the open siphon drain (Figure 2.41) which normally consists of an outlet pipe extending from a low point in the range to a water tank. The head of water in this down pipe must be

---

a Borehole — Sondage — Bohrloch

b Cement Grout (Alternative mechanical Seal) — Scellement au ciment (variante: mécanique) — Zementmörtel (alternativ: mechanische Abdichtung)
  Densotape — Joint Denso — Densobinde
  Resin seal — Joint à la résine — Kunstharzabdichtung
  Bentonite — Bentonite — Bentonit

c Standpipe — Tubage — Verrohrung

d Fullway Valve — Vanne à plein passage — Schieber

e Hose Clip — Collier du flexible — Schlauchschelle

f Internally reinforced Hose — Flexible renforcé intérieurement — Schlauch mit Innenarmierung

g Valve — Vanne — Ventil

h Tee — Té — T-Stück

i Pipe — Tuyau — Rohr

k Plug Cock for draining water — Robinet de purge à eau — Kükenhahn für die Entwässerung

l Reducer — Convergent — Reduzierstück

m Light Rubber Tubbing — Tubes en caoutchouc tendre — Leichtgummischlauch

n U Gauge — Manomètre en U — U-Rohr-Manometer

o Orifice Plate — Diaphragme — Meßblende

p Bend — Coude — Krümmer

q Gas Main — Tuyauterie de captage — Absaugleitung

r Pressure Hole — Prise de pression — Druckentnahmeöffnung

s Minimum twice diameter of pressure hole — Minimum 2 fois le diamètre de la prise de pression — Mindestens doppelter Durchmesser der Druckentnahmeöffnung

t Square edge — Arête à angle droit — Rechtwinkelige Kante

u Flow — Sens de l'écoulement — Strömung

Fig. 2.39 Connection of Boreholes to the Drainage Range (British Fittings). Above: View over all. Below: Details of Pipe Connections for Individual Boreholes.

greater than the suction in the range, otherwise the tank will be sucked dry. The downpipe must be fitted with a flame trap*. Normal compressed air hoses are strong enough to be used as downpipes.

To prevent evaporation of water and entry of dirt closed siphon-type drains (Figure 2.42) have been developed, which can also act as safety valves by preventing air being drawn in when there is no water in the tank.

Siphon traps are effective only if the suction head in the pipe range is less than the vertical distance to the floor of the roadway. If water is

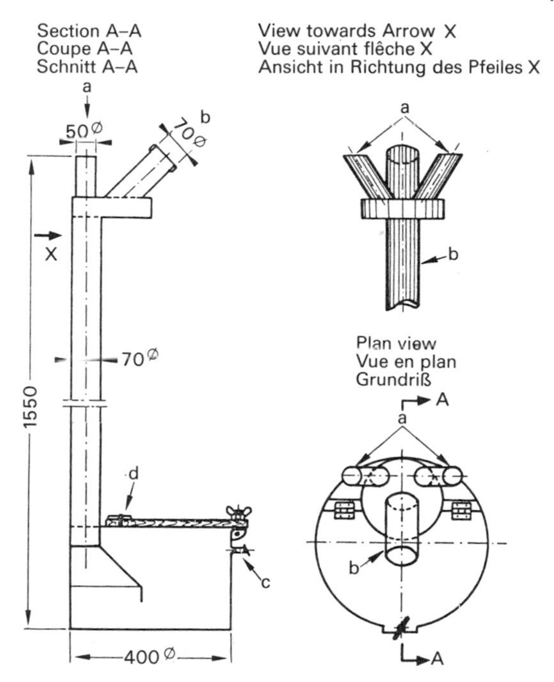

a Connection to the Borehole (it is possible to Couple two Boreholes to the Apparatus at the same Time) — Raccordement au sondage (il est donc possible de raccorder l'appareil à 2 sondages à la fois) — Anschluß an das Bohrloch (es ist möglich, das Gerät an zwei Bohrlöcher gleichzeitig anzuschließen)

b Connection to the Drainage Range — Raccordement à la tuyauterie de captage — Anschluß an die Gasabsaugleitung

c Overflow (Hydraulic Sead formed by the Accumulation of Water) — Orifice de trop-plein (du joint hydraulique formé par l'accumulation d'eau) — Überlauföffnung (hydraulische Abdichtung durch die Ansammlung von Wasser)

d Removable Cover (for the manual Removal of Dirt) — Couvercle amovible (pour l'évacuation manuelle des pierres) — Abnehmbarer Deckel (für die Entfernung der Steine von Hand)

Fig. 2.40 Dirt and Water Separator.

* Observe national regulations.

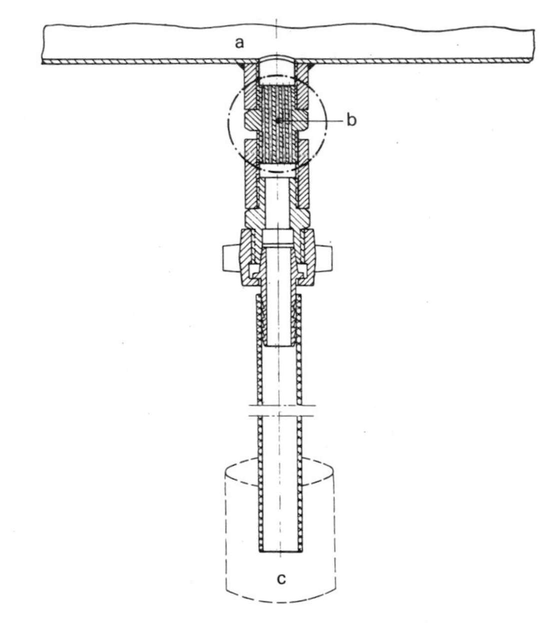

a Drainage Range — Tuyauterie collectrice de gaz — Gassammelleitung
b Flame Trap — Pare-flamme — Flammensperre
c Water Drain — Séparateur d'eau — Wasserabscheider

Fig. 2.41 Open Syphon Type Water Drain with Flame Trap.

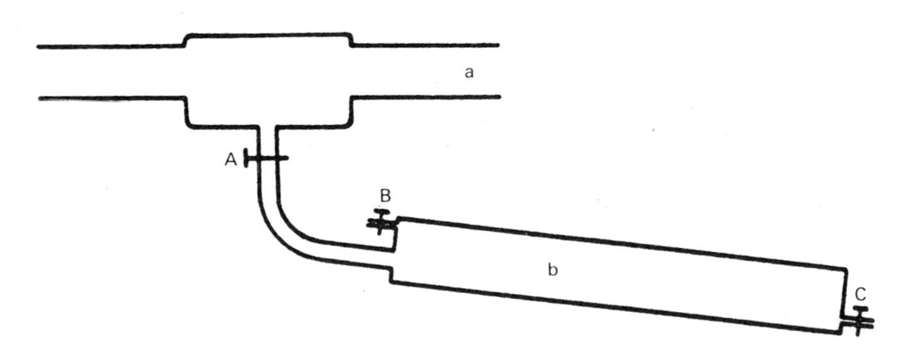

Fig. 2.43 Water Trap.

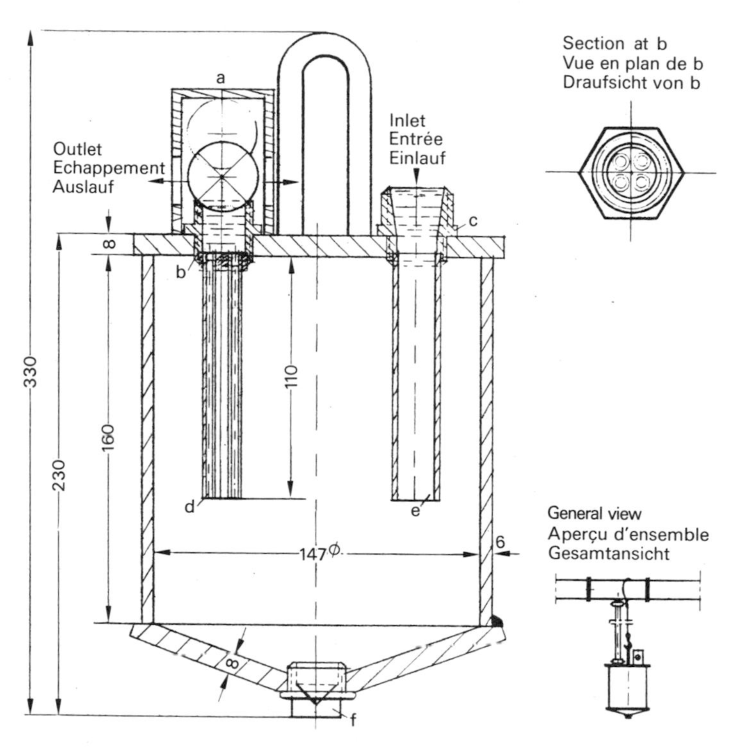

a Rubber covered Iron Ball 30 mm Ø — Bille en caoutchouc à noyau en fer 30 mm Ø — Gummikugel mit Eisenkern 30 mm Ø

b G $^3/_4$ Nipple — Double nipple $^3/_4$" — Doppelnippel $^3/_4$"

c Connecting Nipple G $^3/_4$ — Nipple-raccord $^3/_4$" — Anschlußnippel $^3/_4$"

d Small Tube 3 mm Ø inside — Fin tube de 3 mm Ø interne — Röhrchen 3 mm Ø innen

e 9.5 mm Tube — Tube $^3/_8$" — Rohr $^3/_8$"

f G $^3/_4$ Plug — Bouchon $^3/_4$" — Stopfen $^3/_4$"

Fig. 2.42 Closed Syphon Type Water Drain with Ball Valve.

Table for Fig. 2.43 (opposite).

Taps — Robinets — Hähne	A	B	C
Operating En fonctionnement Bei Absaugung	Open Ouvert Offen	Closed Fermé Geschlossen	Closed Fermé Geschlossen
Draining Lors d'une purge Bei Entwässerung	Closed Fermé Geschlossen	Open Ouvert Offen	Open Ouvert Offen

a Drainage Range under Suction — Conduite de captage en dépression — Unterdruck-Absaugleitung

b Drain Tank — Purgeur sac — Abscheide-Kessel

under high suction, and if siphon traps cannot be used at the bottom of a shaft or other deep mine workings, then water traps (Figure 2.43) must be installed to collect the water. These traps need one connection to the gas range and two cocks. Water level indicators may be fitted. Use can be made of large pipes, old water wagons, steam boilers etc.

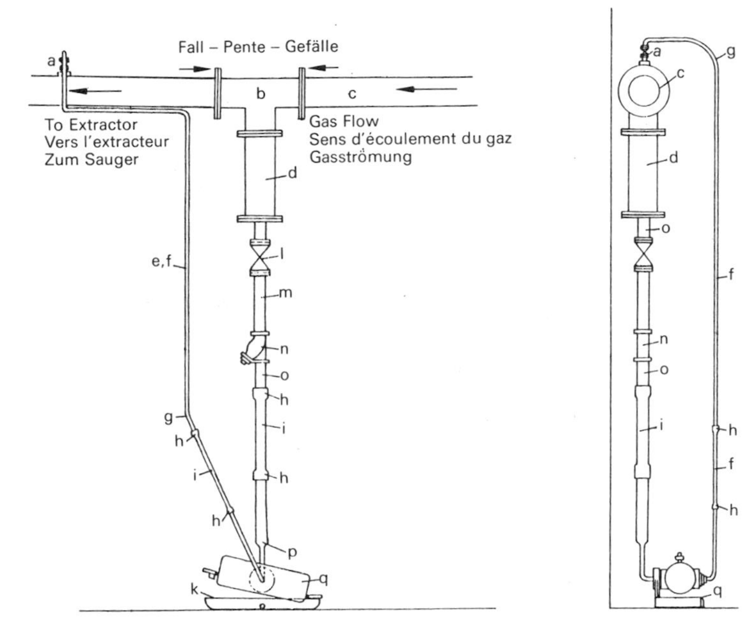

a $^3/_8$ inch Fullway Valve — Vanne de $^3/_8$" à plein passage — $^3/_8$"-Schieber
b Equal Tee — Té à branches égales — T-Stück
c Gas Main — Tuyauterie de captage — Absaugleitung
d Water Receiver — Récolteur d'eau — Wasserbehälter
e Balance Pipe — Tuyau d'équilibrage — Ausgleichsrohr
f $^3/_8$ inch Bore Steel pipe — Tuyau en acier de $^3/_8$" de diamètre — $^3/_8$"-Stahlrohr
g Easy bend — Coude léger — Krümmer
h Jubilee or Hayden clip — Collier «Jubilee» ou «Hayden» — Jubilee- oder Hayden-Schelle
i $^3/_8$ inch Bore Internally Reinforced Rubber hose — Flexible en caoutchouc, $^3/_8$", renforcé intérieurement — $^3/_8$"-Gummischlauch mit Innenarmierung
k Tray must be Level — Le plateau d'appui doit être de niveau — Horizontale Mulde
l 2 inch Fullway Valve — Vanne de 2" à plein passage — 2"-Schieber
m 2 inch Bore Water Inlet Steel Pipe — Tuyau en acier d'amenée de l'eau 2" — 2"-Stahlrohr für den Wassereintritt
n 2 inch Water Strainer — Filtre à eau 2" — 2"-Wassersieb
o 2 inch Bore Steel pipe — Tuyau en acier de 2" de diamètre — 2"-Stahlrohr
p 2 inch/1 inch Reducer — Convergent 2"/1" — 2"/1"-Reduzierstück
q 1 inch Spirax-Ogden Vacuum Trap — Piège à eau, entrée 1", Spirax-Ogden — 1"-Spirax-Ogden-Vakuumbehälter

Fig. 2.44 Automatic Water Trap of the Tipping Type (side and end elevations).

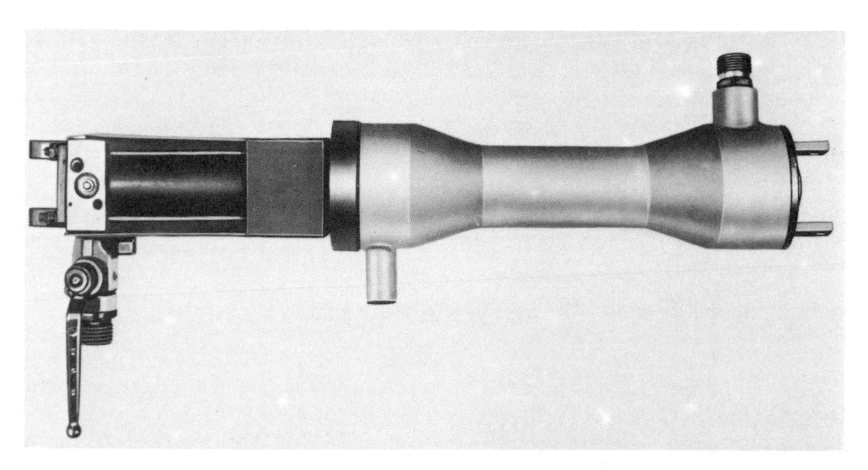

Fig. 2.45 Pump Type Water Drain.

In the UK an automatic water trap is used which works on the see-saw principle, where a tipping movement is caused by the inflow of water from the gas range (Figure 2.44). The trap consists of a cylindrical receiver divided into two separate chambers and pivoted about a central axis. Each chamber has an upper inlet port and a side outlet valve, so arranged that when a chamber is in the upper position the inlet is open to the gas range, allowing water to flow into the chamber, but the outlet valve is closed. The inlet of the lower chamber is closed and the outlet valve is opened simultaneously, allowing water to flow out until the chamber is empty. The chamber tips automatically when the upper chamber contains a certain quantity of water. A compensating pipe ensures that the small quantity of air which is forced out of the upper chamber by the water can flow back into the gas range, thus establishing a pressure equilibrium.

Automatic or manually operated compressed-air driven water pumps (Figure 2.45) have been developed to draw off water collected in the gas range and pump it into a water drain. They require regular servicing.

Measuring Sections

A measuring section (Figures 2.38 and 2.39) is provided at each borehole to determine the flow, suction and concentration of the drained gas. It consists of a straight pipe usually of the same diameter as the standpipe, with a length at least 15 times the internal diameter *d*. A tapping point is provided for measurements at a distance of 10 *d* from the leading edge. Normally G $^3/_4$" sockets with a 19 mm internal thread are welded on the pipe (Figure 2.38). In the UK an orifice plate is fitted (Figure 2.39). All measuring sections should be clearly identified.

Pumps for Deep Boreholes

Gas boreholes which are not self draining may require water to be pumped out of them. However, at present, there is no flame-proof narrow diameter borehole pump available.

1.2 Drainage with Bleeder Roadways (especially driving of the roadways)

In the late 1940s a method of gas drainage was developed in the Saar whereby a roadway was driven, usually to the strike, above the worked seam and wherever practicable in the adjacent gas-producing seam. When necessary cross-measure boreholes were drilled from this roadway to extend the zone of influence. Experience showed that boreholes crossing the face line yielded gas before the working disturbed the roadway. These holes were not connected up to the main gas range. Instead, the roadway was sealed off at its entrance and drainage carried out by means of pipes grouted in the stopping. Currently this method is practised only occasionally in the Saar Coalfield.

1.2.1 Advantages and Disadvantages

Advantages

One of the advantages of this method is that the roadway driven to the strike over the middle of the face acts as a borehole of similar diameter and length, in the middle of the broken roof strata. With retreat mining this method also provides better control of gas emission than bore-holes from gate roads do, because the roadway has a large zone of influence and continues to function even after underworking. Other advantages are that the same heading can be used to drain workings in more than one seam, the cost of individual borehole fittings is reduced or eliminated and face advance is not hampered by the drilling of boreholes. The gas drainage range is not in the district being worked. Provided the bleeder road is sufficiently far above the worked seam high purity gas can be drained, which can be used to enrich gas of a lower quality, thereby improving financial return. Moreover, bleeder roadways in the floor are likely to give better control of gas emission from the floor, and bleeder roads can be used for proving the seam ahead of the face.

Disadvantages

The disadvantages are that the driving of a bleeder roadway in a roof or floor seam means a third gateroad and the additional cost can only be justified if this method is more likely to give higher capture values than other methods, so enabling production to be increased. Additionally the capture in a bleeder road depends mainly on the nature of the strata between it and the worked seam. Moreover, if thick and heavy sandstones or conglomerates (more than 5 m thick) occur in these strata, gas flow from adjacent seams into the bleeder road may be severely delayed or even totally prevented, resulting in increased gas flow into the face air stream.

1.2.2 Layout and Dimensions

Where practicable, the bleeder roadway is driven to the strike over the middle of the face, at a distance of between 20 and 25 m from the worked seam (Figure 2.46). Its cross-section must be such that if necessary it is large enough to accommodate a drilling machine and remain open so that inflowing gas may be drained off even after the roadway has been underworked. Bleeder roads cannot be travelled since they are sealed off.

1.2.3 Equipment

The bleeder roadway must be supported cheaply but adequately to withstand at least one underworking. Roof bolts or steel bars on wooden props are suitable for this purpose.

1.2.4 Stopping Off and Connecting to the Drainage Network

Bleeder roads must be separated from the ventilated workings by solid gas-tight stoppings. The stopping is constructed according to appropriate directives (Appendix 2.7). An effective gas-tight seal can be obtained if a 5 m core of rapid-drying fly ash or stonedust slurry is placed between the supporting walls (Figure 2.47). Good bonding to the rock is obtained by sealing materials. The site for the stopping must be chosen in such a way that it is neither over- nor underworked (Figure 2.48). The drainage pipe through the stopping must be large enough to contend with any unexpected high gas flow. It is also important to have a water drainage pipe fitted with a siphon. A sampling pipe should be provided for cases where gas drainage has to be stopped for a particular reason (eg concealed fire). The drainage pipes in the bleeder road are connected to the drainage network by measuring sections, which can be isolated.

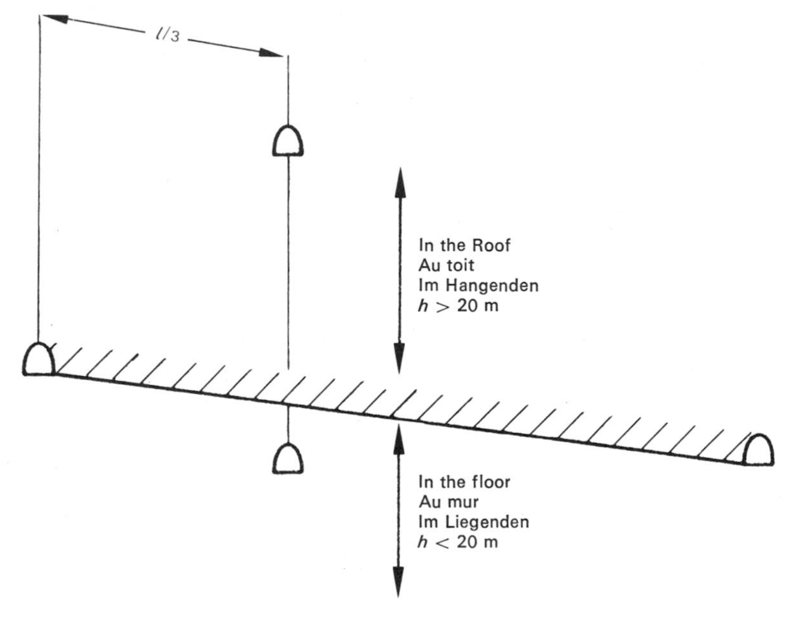

Fig. 2.46 Position of Drainage Roadways in the Roof and Floor.

1.3 Drainage using Pack Cavities

If quantities of firedamp occur in the waste, especially with retreat mining, and they cannot be dealt with by ventilation measures or by firedamp drainage boreholes, mine safety can be increased in some cases by draining through pack cavities, as in the Lorraine.

1.3.1 Advantages and Disadvantages

Advantages

The advantages of this method are that cavity spaces are formed in the waste, from which, using a pipe range, gas can be extracted which would not otherwise be drained (Figure 2.49) and gas emissions on to the face from the waste are prevented.

Disadvantages

The disadvantages are that gas drainage with pack cavities is practicable only where pneumatic stowing is used. Moreover if the waste of a face being worked to the rise fills with water, pack cavity drainage is

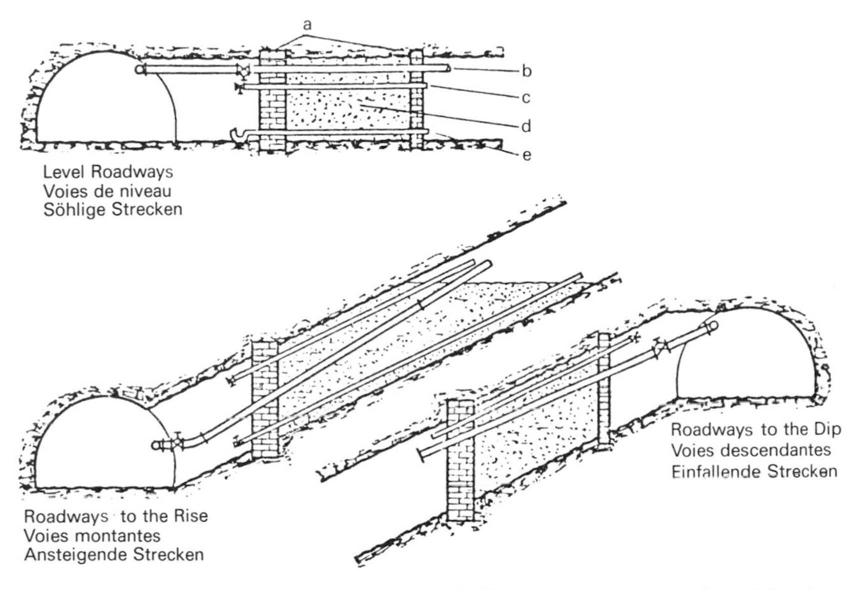

a Retaining Walls (Stone, Gypsum, etc.) — Parois d'appui (roche, gypse, etc.) — Stützwände (Stein, Gips u. a.)

b Drainage Range ≧ 200 mm Nom. Bore — Captage Ø ≧ 200 — Gasabsaugung ≧ NW 200

c Sample Pipe 50 mm Nom. Bore — Tuyau de prise d'échantillons Ø 50 — Probenahmerohr NW 50

d Fly Ash or Stone Dust — Cendres volantes ou poussières de roche — Flugasche oder Gesteinstaub

e Water Drain — Purge — Entwässerung

Fig. 2.47 Stoppings for Drainage Roadways.

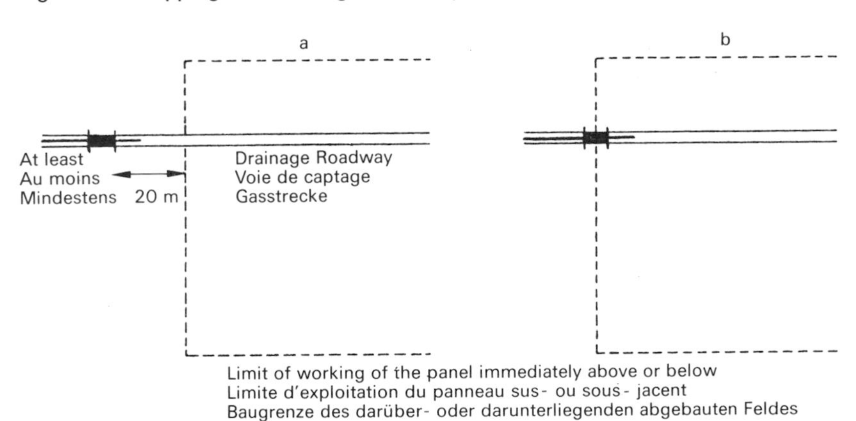

a Correct b Incorrect

Fig. 2.48 Position of the Stopping in a Drainage Roadway.

not practicable. Also since only a low suction can be applied to pack cavities to avoid excessive air inleakage, its zone of influence can be only very small.

1.3.2 Types, Layouts and Dimensions

Pack cavities in the waste of the face are primarily intended to keep that part of the emitted gas not captured by boreholes away from the machinery at the return end of the face. Packs parallel to the face seal off parts of the waste; packs in the direction of advance remain effective somewhat longer.

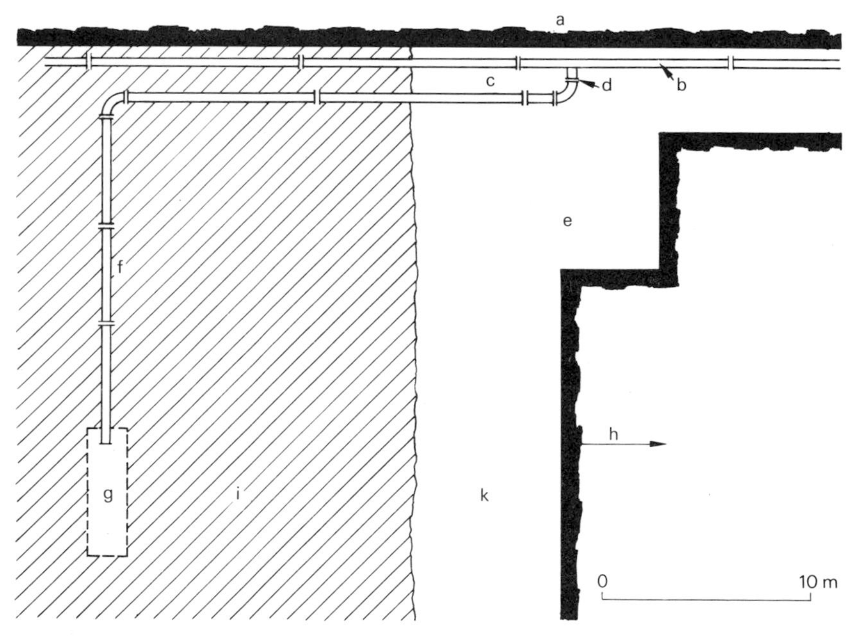

a Rib Side — Amont non exploité — Anstehender Oberstoß
b Drainage Range — Tuyauterie collectrice — Sammelleitung
c Road End — Voie de tête — Kopfstrecke
d Connection made when purity is satisfactory — Le branchement est réalisé lorsque la teneur est jugée satisfaisante — Der Anschluß erfolgt, sobald die Konzentration als ausreichend beurteilt wird
e Face End — Tête de taille — Strebkopf
f Pipe diameter 180 mm — Tuyau de 180 mm — Rohr von 180 mm Dmr.
g Cavity ≈ 5.0 m × 1.4 m — Chambre ≈ 5,0 m × 1,4 m — Kammer ≈ 5,0 m × 1,4 m
h Direction of Working — Sens de marche de la taille — Abbaurichtung
i Pack — Remblai — Versatz
k Face — Taille — Streb

Fig. 2.49 Pack Cavity in the Waste.

In conventional pack cavity drainage, the cavities are constructed of timber lagging with Padra mesh. For gas emission from the floor, old face conveyor pans or pan sections placed on the floor have been used more recently in France. In order to minimise the inflow of air, and at the same time to give a high capacity, the middle plates of the pans are perforated and the pan lengths are welded together at the top and ends.

1.3.3 Connection to the Drainage Network

Pack cavities are linked to the drainage network by expendable collecting pipes, provided sufficiently high concentrations are obtained. It is recommended that each cavity be connected to its own pipe.

2. Drainage from Old Mine Workings

For a number of years a large percentage of drained quantities of firedamp has originated from old, stopped-off mine workings (Table 2.2). Even though gas emission from relaxed strata falls off rapidly behind a face, there can be no complete cessation of gas emission as long as the strata still contains a certain amount of firedamp. Thus in old workings varying quantities of firedamp are emitted, which collect in the waste and finally emerge into the ventilating airstream causing problems in intake and return airways. To prevent this, gas is drained from stopped-off mine workings. This type of gas drainage is very important when falls in barometric pressure occur, because gas stored in the waste and rock fissures emerges into the roadways. There has been no shortage of methods to combat this awkward form of rapid gas emission, eg by increasing the suction on the stopping when barometric pressure falls. To limit gas emission when air pressure varies, balance chambers have been erected in front of the stopping itself (Figure 2.50).

2.1 Drainage from Stoppings

Following the end of coal production in gassy seams and the salvaging and stopping-off of gateroads, drainage from behind stoppings is frequently carried out to limit the amount of gas entering the ventilating air stream. The construction and monitoring of stoppings is carried out according to the relevant guidelines (Appendix 2.7). Sealed roadways can also be used as bleeder roadways within the terms of Section 1.2.

2.2 Drainage from Disused Mines

The flow of gas in disused mines can continue for extraordinarily long periods. It is important that the pit should remain free of water, that one of the shafts should be prepared for drainage by the installation of the necessary pipe ranges and that the surface openings should be tightly sealed to avoid air inleakage (Figure 2.51). Pipes with inlets at varying depths make firedamp drainage possible, even when the deepest level is filled with water or carbon dioxide.

In order to drain gas economically from a disused mine, the main requirements are:

▷ relatively large gas flows from coal measures,

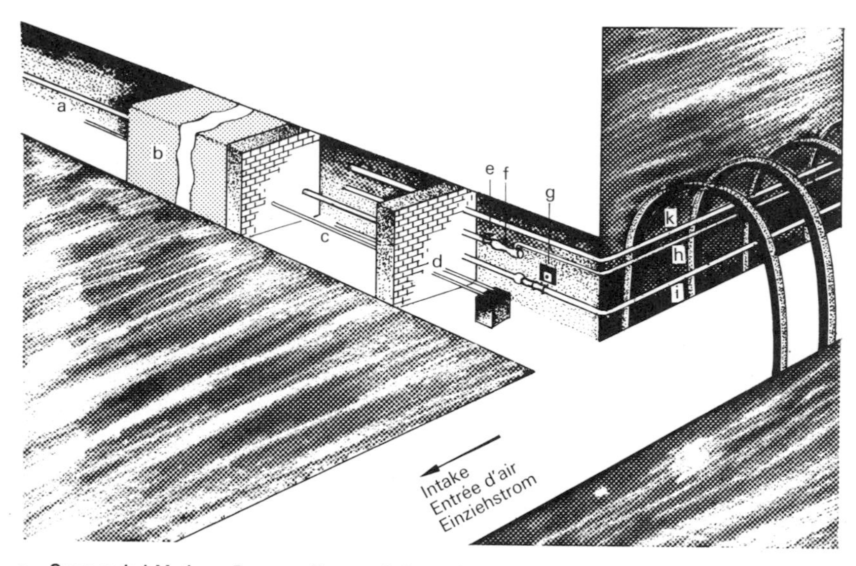

a Open ended Methane Range — Tuyauterie à gaz, à extrémité ouverte — Offene Methan-Absaugleitung
b Main Stopping — Barrage principal — Haupt-Abschlußdamm
c Pressure Chamber — Chambre de surpression — Druckkammer
d Sample Pressure Tube to Inclined Gauge — Tube servant à mesurer la pression, raccordé au manomètre à branches inclinées — Druckmaßleitung zum Schrägrohrmanometer
e Shutter — Obturateur — Schieber
f Venturi — Venturi — Venturi-Düse
g Flowmeter — Débitmètre — Durchfluß-Meßgerät
h Compressed Air or Electricity Power — Air comprimé ou énergie electrique — Druckluft oder Elektrizität
i Methane Range — Tuyauterie de captage — Methan-Absaugleitung
k Pressure Reducing Pipe — Tuyauterie servant à réduire la pression — Druckentlastungsrohr

Fig. 2.50 Pressure Balance Stopping.

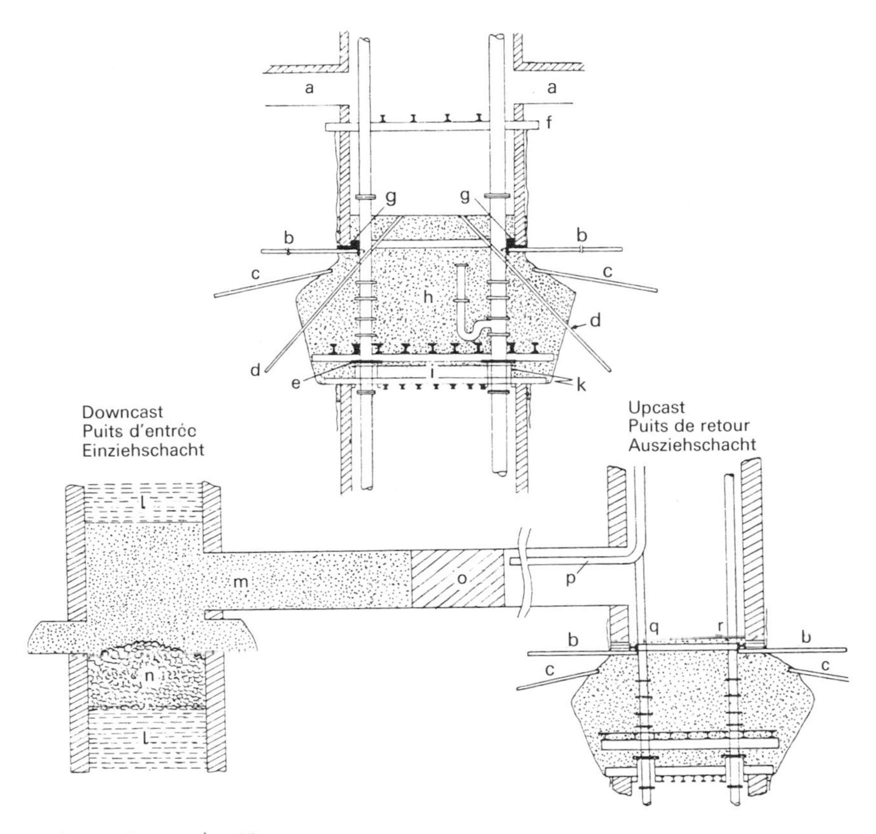

a Inset — Etage — Anschlag
b Strata Bolts — Boulons d'ancrage — Gebirgsanker
c Cantilever Bolts — Boulons avec porte-à-faux — Kraganker
d Pressure Grouting Holes — Trous de cimentage sous pression — Verpreßbohrungen
e Sealing Plates — Plaques de scellement — Abdeckplatte
f Guide Rope Tension Beams — Poutres de mise sous tension des câbles-guides — Spannträger für die Seilführung
g Shaft Wall Support Collar — Collier de support de la paroi du puits — Tragring für den Schachtausbau
h Reinforced Concrete Plug — Bouchon en béton armé — Armierter Betonpfropfen
i Sub Plug — Bouchon secondaire — Unterpfropfen
k Steel Air Duct 24" Diameter — Gaine à air en acier de 24" de diamètre — 24"-Stahllutte
l Tip Material — Remblai — Berge
m Ready mixed Concrete — Béton préparé — Fertigbeton
n Hardcore — Empilage de morceaux de roche — Gesteinshaufwerk
o Stopping — Barrage — Damm
p Auxiliary Ventilation — Ventilation auxiliaire — Sonderbewetterung
q 10" Diameter Column — Colonne de 10" de diamètre — 10"-Leitung
r 13" Diameter Column — Colonne de 13" de diamètre — 13"-Leitung

Fig. 2.51 Sealing Shafts for Firedamp Drainage from Abandoned Mines. Above: Final Plug Arrangements in Upcast Shaft; Avon Colliery. Below: Sealing Arrangements at Inset Level.

▷ previous relaxing and loosening of rock by mining,

▷ strong surrounding strata,

▷ small water inflows,

▷ isolation of the mine from neighbouring collieries and sealing at the surface.

3. Predrainage of Worked Seams

The gas content in a worked seam can be lowered indirectly by over- or underworking. Where firedamp drainage is used this involves methods which have already been described in Section 1.

There are also various ways to reduce gas content directly, the most important being firedamp drainage from the seam prior to working. This so-called predrainage is considered wherever large quantities of firedamp enter the airstream and have to be diluted to permissible concentrations; this is usually the case when all possibilities of increasing the quantities of ventilating air or improving firedamp drainage from roof and floor have been explored.

3.1 Degassing around Roadways and Faces

The creation of underground openings by mining (eg roadways, faces) concentrates strata pressure on to the edges of those openings. As the roadside yields to additional stress, the zone of increased pressure moves further into solid strata at the roadside allowing firedamp to be emitted into the open roadway (Figure 2.52). De-stressed and degassed areas may extend up to 30 m into ribsides over a period of 6 to 12 months. De-stressing may extend as far as the surface above a working and down to 100 m or more in the floor, depending on the area of the excavation.

3.2 Drainage from Undisturbed Seams

Given adequate permeability, a worked seam can be predrained by boreholes drilled at the face, from roadways above or below the worked seam, or from the gate roads.

Predrainage using boreholes which are drilled at the face in the direction of advance has not been successful. In addition it would interfere with coal-getting, and it would be difficult to pipe the drained gas away from the face.

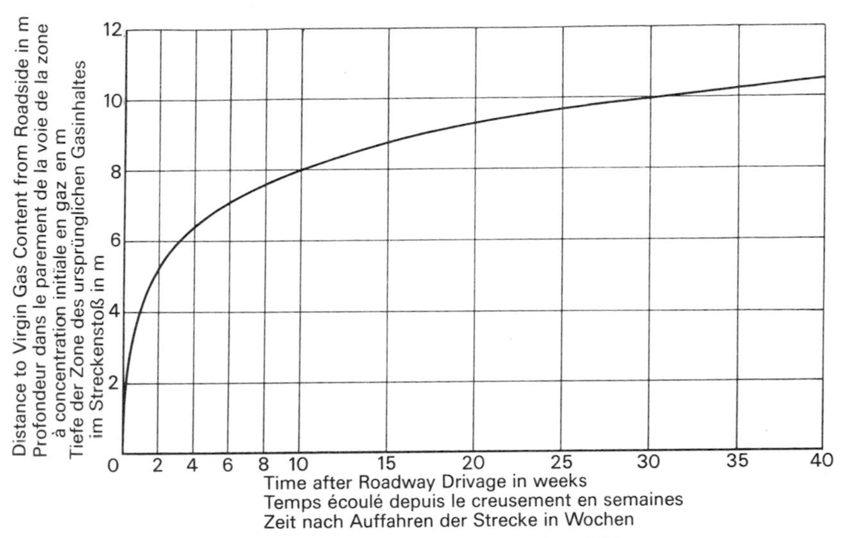

Fig. 2.52 Recession of Virgin Gas Content into the Roadside.

Drainage by boreholes from roadways above or below the worked seam have not succeeded either, because the boreholes intercept the worked seam at a steep angle to the bedding plane and have a limited zone of influence. The distance drilled and/or the low yield make it uneconomic.

On the other hand, predrainage by boreholes drilled from gateroads ahead of the coal face in the worked seam has given satisfactory results. A requirement of this method is that one or both of the gate roads should be driven 6 to 12 months before the face is worked. Because of the low permeability of undisturbed seams, gas flow into boreholes is small, and degassing takes at least 6 months. For a number of seams permeability is so low that degassing is negligible. Typically 43 to 95 mm boreholes are drilled at intervals of 10 to 20 m, usually parallel to the face line, to lengths of between 100 and 150 m. In zones of marked abutment pressure it is advisable to start drilling with a large diameter bit reducing the diameter once this zone is passed. Scrolled drill rods and tungsten carbide bits are used (Figure 2.53). In the UK electro-hydraulic drilling machines and water flushing are employed. Holes are lined for the first 10 to 20 m, sealed and connected to the drainage range. The use of non-metallic* standpipes may have the advantage of causing less inconvenience during subsequent

* Observe national regulations.

Technical Details — Caractéristiques techniques — Technische Daten

Type — Type — Typ		K	L
Total Weight — Poids total — Gesamtgewicht	kg	40	≈ 90
Total Length — Longueur totale — Gesamtlänge	mm	1 800	≈ 2 300
Power — Puissance — Leistung			
Drill Motor — Moteur de forage — Bohrmotor	kW	1,7	5,1
Feed Motor — Moteur d'avancement — Vorschubmotor	kW	1,0	1,0
Rotational Speed — Vitesse angulaise — Drehzahl	rad/s	31.4	39.3, 9.9, 2.6
	r/min	600	750 190 50
Maximum Thrust — Poussée — Andruck	kg	800	800
Handling — Temps d'apprêt — Rüstzeit			
Set up — Mise en place — Aufrüsten	min	20	20
Dismantled — Démontage — Abrüsten	min	10	10
Performance — Rendement — Leistung			
Small boreholes — Petit diamètre — Kleinlochbohrer	mm/s	25	25
	m/min	1,5	1,5
Large boreholes — Gros diamètre — Großlochbohrer	mm/s	6 (to — à — bis)	9
	m/min	0,35 (to — à — bis)	0,50

Fig. 2.53 Rotary Drilling Machine with Scrolled Rods.

working. Use has been made of polyurethane foam* as a sealant in other countries (Appendix 2.4). Suctions of 2 to 10 kPa are normal but are governed by the effectiveness of the borehole seal.

The outcome of predrainage depends on the gas content and permeability of the seam, the applied suction and the duration of drainage. A 10 to 30 % reduction in gas content is achieved when average daily quantities of 100 to 500 l of methane are drained per metre of borehole over a period of 4 to 6 months.

3.3 Drainage during Roadway Drivage

It may be necessary in gassy seams to use firedamp drainage to reduce gas emission into roadways during drivage. This is valid also in undisturbed ground provided that the seam is sufficiently permeable. Boreholes are generally drilled in both sides of the roadway at small angles to its axis, spacing and length being chosen so that they always project beyond the face of the heading. Steel standpipes are used which are sealed with Densotape, cement, gypsum, Hardstop or synthetic resin (Appendix 2.8).

In an example from the Ibbenbüren coalfield (Figure 2.54) boreholes were drilled 65 mm in diameter, 45 m long, at an angle of 16° to the roadway axis and at 25 m spacing. The table in Figure 2.54 shows that around 20 to 40 % of the total gas emission was drained.

In the UK also, it has been necessary in some mechanised in-seam drivages with rates of advance of around 65 m/week, to drain firedamp from the solid coal using the system illustrated in Figure 2.55. Manholes approximately 1 m deep and 2.7 m long are made at intervals of 36 m in each roadside to accommodate a drilling machine. The boreholes may reach up to 27 m or so beyond the face of the heading. These are so arranged that the distance between the end of the last borehole and the next manhole is not more than 2.7 m. Steel pipes 1.5 m long, 51 mm diameter are used to line the boreholes. In the past these were sealed with Hardstop (see Appendix 2.8). Nowadays approved synthetic resin, Bentonite or cement mixtures are used instead. The borehole is then extended at a diameter of 42.5 mm. In very thick seams additional boreholes may be drilled in the roof and

* Observe national regulations.

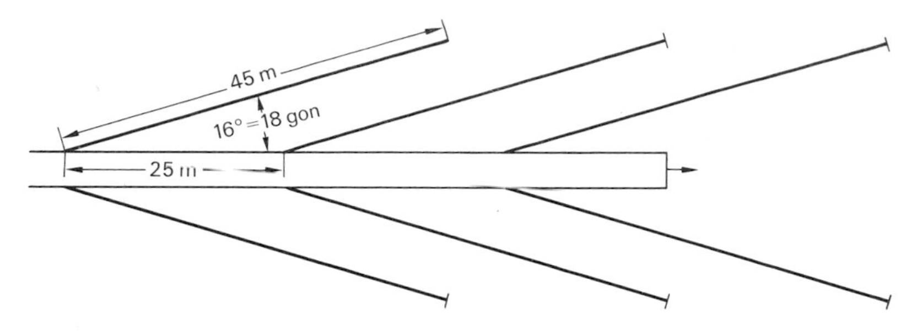

Borehole Diameter — Diamètre de sondage — Bohrlochdurchmesser	65 mm
Roadway Cross-Section — Section de voie — Streckenquerschnitt (Arched — Cintres — Bogen)	10,8 m²
Ventilation at face — Débit d'air à front — Wettermenge vor Ort	450 m³/min

Auxiliary Ventilation: Exhaust — Aérage secondaire: aspirant — Sonderbewetterung: Saugend

Drainage Results	Unit	Ex. 1	Ex. 2	Ex. 3
Methane in Ventilation	l/s	75	83	63
Drained Methane	l/s	33	60	20
Total Methane Emission	l/s	108	143	83
Drained Purity	%	31	42	24
Borehole Gas Flow	l/s	—	0.6	—

Fig. 2.54 Firedamp Drainage from a Coal Heading.

floor. Methane flows of more than 15 l/s have been achieved and gas pressures of more than 14.5 kPa measured. Initial borehole methane flows have ranged from 9 to 12 l/s falling to 2.5 l/s after a few days. The purity of drained gas was initially around 95% methane. The suction applied was approximately 6 kPa and the life of boreholes was about 2 months.

The more common case of predrainage occurs when a roadway drivage enters a de-stressed area, as for example the emission zone of a working or recently closed district. Where local air pressures in the mine are so distributed that the roadway is in a low pressure area, then considerable quantities of firedamp may enter the roadway. Under such conditions it is frequently found that the drivage cannot continue without firedamp drainage. Boreholes are drilled in the seam, in the roof and/or in the floor according to requirements. Occasionally firedamp drainage is also used in stone headings. In the case of a cross-cut drivage in the Saar coalfield (Figure 2.56) the boreholes are drilled from manholes placed at regular intervals on each side of the roadway.

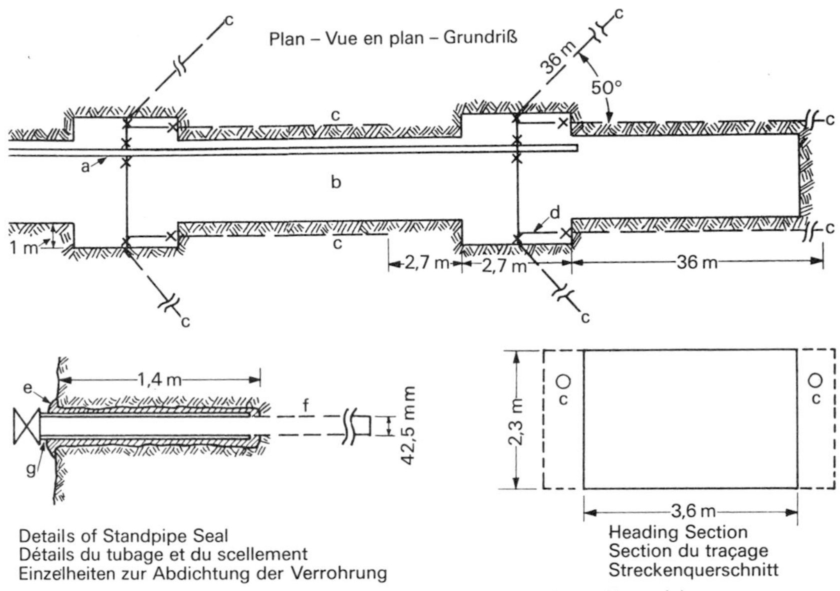

a 150 mm Gas Main — Tuyauterie de captage de 150 mm — 150 mm Absaugleitung

b Coal Heading — Traçage — Flözstrecke

c Borehole — Sondage — Bohrloch

d Borehole Connections — Raccordement des sondages — Bohrlochanschlüsse

e Resin, Cement, Bentonite or Hardstop — Résine, ciment, bentonite ou Hardstop — Kunstharz, Zement, Bentonit oder Hardstop

f Coal — Charbon — Kohle

g 51 mm Steel Pipe — Tuyau en acier de 51 mm — 51 mm-Stahlrohr

Fig. 2.55 Borehole Pattern for Firedamp Drainage in a Coal Heading.

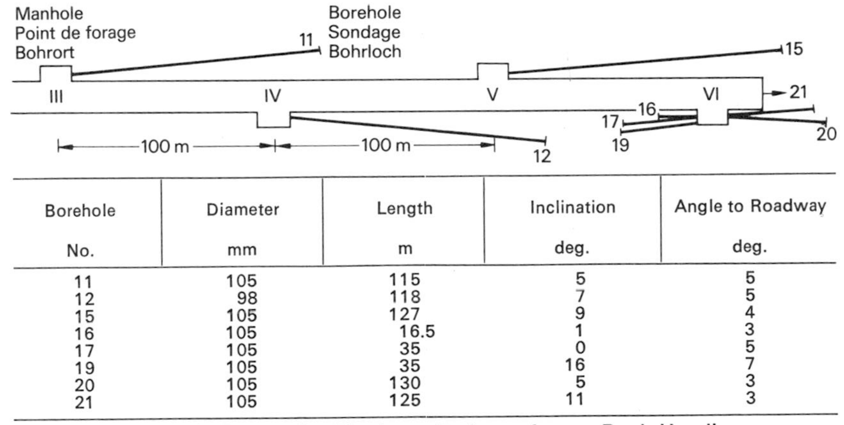

Borehole No.	Diameter mm	Length m	Inclination deg.	Angle to Roadway deg.
11	105	115	5	5
12	98	118	7	5
15	105	127	9	4
16	105	16.5	1	3
17	105	35	0	5
19	105	35	16	7
20	105	130	5	3
21	105	125	11	3

Fig. 2.56 Borehole Pattern for Firedamp Drainage from a Rock Heading.

4. Drainage by Surface Boreholes

4.1 Advantages and Disadvantages

Advantages

Surface boreholes have the advantage that in certain circumstances, drainage can be carried out irrespective of the local mine conditions, ie the firedamp drainage borehole can be drilled where required and does not depend on the availability of a suitable roadway. In addition the borehole penetrates all roof strata and captures quantities of firedamp which probably would not otherwise have found their way into the mine workings. Moreover, due to their large diameter, and their usually favourable position in relation to mining workings, borehole spacings of 250 to 500 m are sufficient. A further advantage is that with each subsequent underworking gas emission may start up again, with the result that, for example in the Saar over a period of several years 21 million m^3 of high purity methane have been drained in this way. Within the zone of influence of a surface borehole, conventional underground boreholes would no longer be necessary.

Disadvantages

One principal disadvantage is that the drilling of deep boreholes is expensive and is not possible in all geological conditions. The choice of site for the borehole may be restricted by surface buildings. Moreover gas piping may be more difficult and costly to install on the surface than it is underground. Difficulties may also be encountered in relation to planning, environment, access and power supply. In faces working to the rise the firedamp yield may be governed by buoyancy effects.

4.2 Layout and Dimensions

The diameter of boreholes depends on the depth and is usually 200 mm. Boreholes have been drilled economically to depths of 600 m (Figures 2.57 and 2.58).

4.3 Drilling and Lining a Borehole

Deep drainage boreholes are drilled using one of the conventional drill rigs, the method depending on the type of overburden. Generally they are positioned ahead of the face. They are lined usually down to the bottom of the borehole, holes having been provided in the standpipe at the position of the gas-producing horizon. Standpipes are necessary to avoid borehole closure when it is underworked.

4.4 Hydrofracture

In the petroleum industry flows of oil and gas from undisturbed strata are increased by hydraulically breaking up the rock. The fissures thus produced are filled with sand etc. In the hydrofracture method, large quantities of water (greater than 80 l/s) are pumped in at pressures up to 100 MPa. Experimental application of hydrofracture to coal

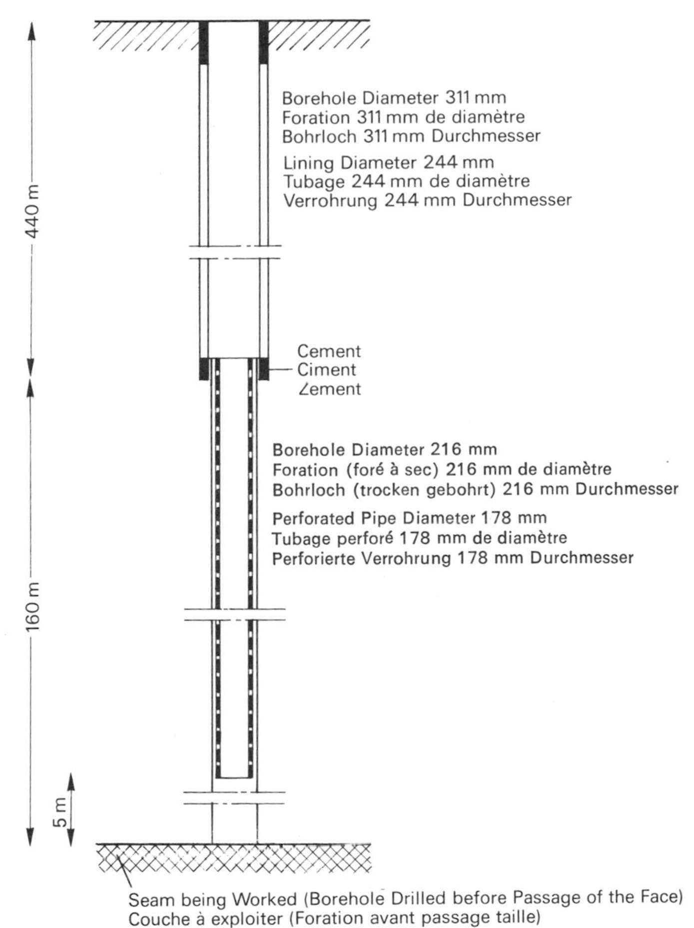

Fig. 2.57 Surface Borehole at Gardanne (Provence).

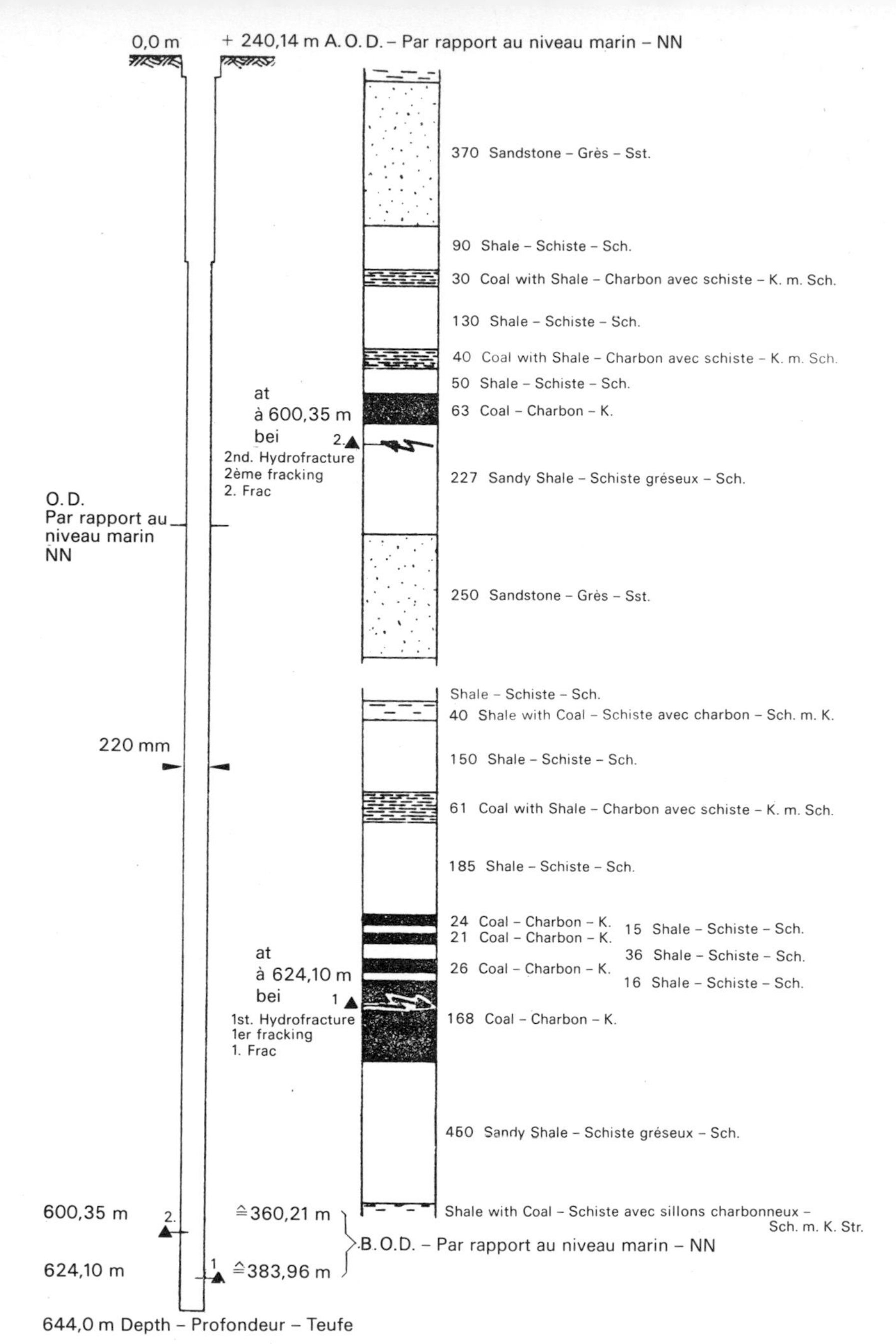

Fig. 2.58 Surface Borehole at Luisenthal. Position of Hydrofracture Horizons (Borehole Klarenthal 5, Saarbergwerke AG).

seams in the Saar (Figure 2.58) did not meet with great success. A fissure was produced in the seam running at a steep angle to the strata, but the quantities of gas obtained from the hydrofractured boreholes remained small until a face passed underneath, when large quantities of gas were produced.

4.5 Water Drainage

Removal of water from deep boreholes is important, because water inhibits firedamp drainage. Holes which penetrate the waste of previous workings do not usually require water drainage facilities. In the case of deep boreholes for the predrainage of firedamp, a submersible pump and a standpipe are vital to keep the holes free from water.

Appendix 2.1

Calculation of the Pressure Difference in Firedamp Drainage Boreholes

The pressure difference (in Pa) in firedamp drainage boreholes (Figures 2.15 to 2.17) can be calculated using a Bergbau-Forschung computer program. The calculations are carried out at standard conditions (p_0 = 101.4 kPa; T = 273 K) and are based on the following assumptions:

▷ methane content of mixture (unless otherwise indicated)	100 %
▷ density of methane	0.716 kg/m^3
▷ borehole length	50 m
▷ angle	45°
▷ roughness of borehole wall	5 mm
▷ roughness of wall of standpipe	1 mm
▷ depth of annular space between the sections of the standpipe assuming constant gap width taken to be	6 mm

The program also takes account of or calculates:

▷ the coefficient of resistance λ,

▷ the pressure absorbed in the standpipe including the loss at the pipe joints,

▷ the pressure loss due to contraction of the flow at the standpipe inlet,

▷ the pressure loss in the non-lined section of the borehole, assuming a linear increase of gas flow between the furthest end of the borehole and the beginning of the lined section,

▷ the buoyancy in the borehole.

A 2.1.1 Calculation of the Basic Parameters

A 2.1.1.1 Coefficient of Resistance λ for a Rough Pipe

$$\lambda = \frac{1}{\left(2 \log \frac{d}{k} + 1.138\right)^2} \qquad \text{[A 2.1.1]}$$

where:

d pipe diameter in mm

k wall roughness in mm.

A 2.1.1.2 Coefficient of Resistance ξ_N for the Standpipe Joints (annular spaces with square cross section)

$$\xi_N = 1.04 \left(1 + \frac{\Delta d}{d_R}\right) \frac{\Delta d}{d_R} n \qquad \text{[A 2.1.2]}$$

where:

Δd depth of slots (6 mm)
n number of joints
d_R diameter of standpipe.

A 2.1.1.3 Loss due to Reduction in Section from Borehole to Standpipe

$$\Delta p_E = \left[1 - \mu_e \left(\frac{d_R}{d_B}\right)^2\right]^2 \frac{\varrho}{2} \overline{w}_R^2 \quad \text{[A 2.1.3]}$$

where:

μ_e reduction factor (typically 0.8)
d_B borehole diameter
d_R standpipe diameter
$\overline{w}_R$ average velocity in the standpipe
ϱ gas density.

A 2.1.1.4 Inflow Factor ψ for Linearly Increasing Flow $Q_{(x)}$ in the Unlined Section of the Borehole

$$\psi = \frac{1}{3} \quad \text{[A 2.1.4]}$$

A 2.1.1.5 Pressure Loss due to Friction on the Standpipe

$$\Delta p = \lambda \frac{l}{d} \frac{\varrho}{2} \overline{w}_R^2 \quad \text{[A 2.1.5]}$$

where:
λ coefficient of resistance of the flow in the pipe
l pipe length
d pipe diameter
$\overline{w}_R$ average velocity in the standpipe
ϱ gas density.

A 2.1.1.6 Buoyancy

$$\Delta p_A = g\, \Delta h\, \Delta \varrho \quad \text{[A 2.1.6]}$$

$$\Delta p_A = g\, l_{total} \sin \alpha\, (\varrho_{air} - \varrho_{gas}) \quad \text{[A 2.1.7]}$$

where:
g acceleration due to gravity (9.81 m/s²)
Δh difference in level
l_{total} total length of borehole
α angle of borehole
ϱ_{air} air density, 1.293 kg/m³ under normal conditions
ϱ_{gas} gas density 0.716 kg/m³ under normal conditions.

A 2.1.2 Pressure Loss due to Gas Flow in the Lined Section of the Borehole

$$\Delta p_R = \left\{ \lambda_R \frac{l_R}{d_R} + \xi_N + \left[1 - \mu_e \left(\frac{d_R}{d_B} \right)^2 \right]^2 \right\} \frac{\varrho_{gas}}{2} \overline{w}_R^2 \quad \text{[A 2.1.8]}$$

A 2.1.3 Pressure Loss in the Unlined Section of the Borehole

$$\Delta p_B = \psi \lambda_B \frac{l_B}{d_B} \frac{\varrho_{gas}}{2} \overline{w}_B^2 \quad \text{[A 2.1.9]}$$

A 2.1.4 Total Pressure Difference in the Borehole (see Figure A 2.1.1)

$$\Delta p_{total} = \Delta p_R + \Delta p_B + \Delta p_A \quad \text{[A 2.1.10]}$$

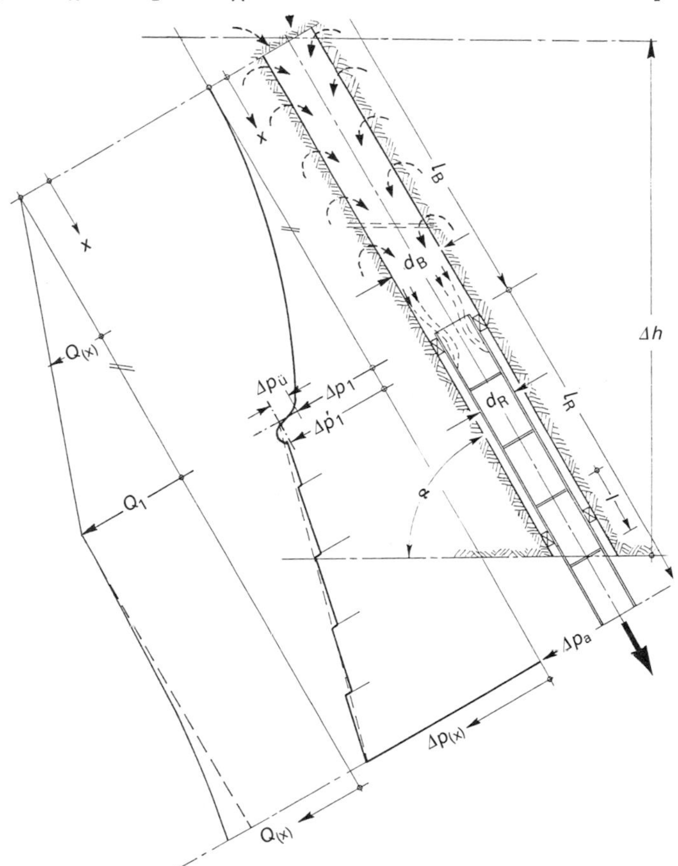

Fig. A 2.1.1 Diagram of Pressure and Gas Flow in a Firedamp Drainage Borehole.

The diagrams (Figures 2.15 to 2.17) for the pressure difference in the borehole were calculated for the state of the gas at normal conditions (p_0 = 101.4 kPa; T = 273 K).

When determining the pressure losses under operating conditions ($\Delta p'_R$ and $\Delta p'_B$) allowance must be made for the actual gas densities:

$$\Delta p'_R = \frac{\Delta p_R}{\varrho} \varrho' \quad \text{and} \quad \Delta p'_B = \frac{\Delta p_B}{\varrho} \varrho' \qquad \text{[A 2.1.11]}$$

The average gas density in the borehole is given by:

$$\varrho' = \frac{p_0 - \Delta p_a - \frac{1}{2} \Delta p'_{total}}{R_{gas} T_{gas}} \qquad \text{[A 2.1.12]}$$

where:

$p_0 - \Delta p_a$ (absolute) pressure at the mouth of the borehole
$\Delta p'_{total}$ total pressure difference in the borehole
R_{gas} gas constant
T_{gas} temperature of the gas mixture in the borehole.

For buoyancy under operating conditions the following value must be used:

$$\Delta p'_A = g\, l_{total} \sin \alpha \,(\varrho'_{air} - \varrho'_{gas}) \qquad \text{[A 2.1.13]}$$

Appendix 2.2

Recommendations for Dry Drilling* of Firedamp Drainage Boreholes in the Ruhr

At one colliery in the Ruhr coalfield firedamp ignitions have occurred during the drilling of firedamp drainage boreholes. A 76 mm diameter roofhole being drilled from a tail gate in the Blücher seam was 24 m long at the time of the ignition. In the period prior to the first ignition the penetration rate was virtually nil. Later, it was discovered that one of the screw connections on the drill rods had been so badly worn that the thread had been stripped, and therefore full torque could not be transmitted to the drill bit. Expansion of the end of the rod had been caused by frictional heating of the metal parts during the application of thrust by the drilling machine.

To study the question of firedamp ignition by overheated rods, an experimental installation was built to simulate the effects of friction in an explosive gas mixture; this was done in collaboration between the Experimental Roadway facility (BVS) at Dortmund-Derne, Bergbau-Forschung GmbH, Essen-Kray and the StBV member collieries concerned. During these tests the ends of the drill rods reached temperatures of 770 to 870 K after a very short time and temperatures were substantially higher after half an hour, leading to firedamp ignitions. It should be pointed out that air flushing was not used in this case.

On the basis of the trial results the StBV, in collaboration with the Dortmund Mines Inspectorate, the BVS, the Mine Ventilation Testing Department and the Federal office for Materials Testing, drew up recommendations for the drilling of firedamp drainage borehole using air flushing.

In some cases it may be considered necessary to drill firedamp drainage boreholes using air flushing and suction to extract the cuttings, instead of water flushing. To reduce the risk of firedamp ignitions in the borehole due to frictional heating during dry drilling, the following safety precautions are proposed:

A 2.2.1 The drill rod diameter and the power of the drilling machine must be compatible. The maximum torques of drilling machines used for firedamp drainage boreholes in coal mines and the appropriate rod diameters are shown in Table A 2.2.1.

Materials and design specifications of the rods shall comply with the requirements of draft standard DIN 20312 «Drill rods up to 100 mm diameter for large diameter boreholes in coal mines», August 1962. Specific reference should be made to this standard when ordering and compliance should be checked on delivery.

A 2.2.2 Great care should be taken to ensure that rods and drill bits used for dry drilling are in perfect condition. It is recommended that the drilling team should be equipped with the appropriate thread gauges. In every case the state of the rods and the accuracy to gauge of the thread must be checked before use. Table A 2.2.2 may be used for reference.

---

* Observe national regulations.

Table A 2.2.1 Drilling Machines and Drill Rods for Drilling Firedamp Drainage Boreholes: Maximum Torques as specified by Manufacturers.

Manufacturer	Drilling Machines		Drill Rods	
	Type	Maximum Torque kNm	Diameter mm	Maximum Torque kNm
Maschinenfabrik	HBM 15/KHy	2.45	68	7.35
Rudolf Hausherr &			80	12.26
Söhne GmbH,	DK 9 UB 160—640	0.40	51	5.49
Sprockhövel			68	7.35
Maschinenfabrik	GBV 15/Z	1.32	52	4.90
Korfmann GmbH,	GBV 15/ZK	1.32	61	8.78
Witten			76	14.12
Stahlhammerwerk Krüner & Co. KG, Sprockhövel	—	—	52	2.45 to 2.94
Turmag	P IV/6 type:		52	≈ 4.90
Turbo-Maschinen-	145/350 min^{-1}	0.29/0.12		
Aktiengesellschaft	220/550 min^{-1}	0.19/0.08		
Nüsse & Gräfer,	85 min^{-1}	0.49		
Sprockhövel	65 min^{-1}	0.65		
	50 min^{-1}	0.84		
	P IV/6K type:		52	≈ 4.90
	150 min^{-1}	0.28		
	200 min^{-1}	0.21		
	50 min^{-1}	0.84		
	40 min^{-1}	1.06		
Maschinen- und	BO	1.23	51	2.94
Bohrgeräte-Fabrik			63.5	4.12
Alfred Wirth & Co. KG,			70	4.12
Erkelenz			73	6.77

A 2.2.3 Prior to drilling the flushing valve should be opened and flushing air regulated to the quantity needed to cool the drill rod and bit. Care should be taken to ensure that suction at the borehole seal is adequate to extract the cuttings into the tank.

A 2.2.4 Before drilling commences the drilling team must be given information on the strata section into which they are to drill and the drill bit should be selected according to rock hardness.

A 2.2.5 In the case of a sudden reduction in penetration rate, the cause (eg hard rock, damage to bit or rod) must be identified immediately. In no circumstances must drilling be allowed to continue without perceptible penetration, otherwise there is a risk that the drill bit or the drill rod will be damaged permanently and overheated beyond permissible limits. For this reason any specific observations should be made known to the official in charge and to the drilling team on the next shift.

Table A 2.2.2 Checks on the Thread Dimensions of Drilling Rods, to be carried out by the Drilling Chargehand, Supervisor or Shift Deputy before starting a Borehole.

Type of check	Tool
1. External Thread a) External diameter must be checked with a caliper gauge. The gauge should *not* be able to slide over the thread.	Caliper gauge
b) The thread profile must be checked with a thread ring. This should *not* be able to turn over the thread.	Thread ring
2. Inside Thread a) The internal diameter must be checked with a cylindrical plug gauge. It should *not* be able to slide into the thread.	Plug gauge
b) The flanks of the thread must be tested with a threaded socket gauge. It should *not* be possible to turn it into the thread.	Socket gauge

All checks must be carried out applying only light pressure and without the use of force.
Drill rods which no longer satisfy these tests must be replaced.
It is recommended that only gauges made to manufacturers' specifications are used.

A 2.2.6 The dust extractor shall be earthed to avoid a build-up of static electricity. Furthermore only rubber hoses approved for dust extractors may be used. Care should be taken to provide adequate ventilation of the extractor site.

Appendix 2.3

Resin Sealing of Firedamp Drainage Boreholes in the United Kingdom

A 2.3.1 Introduction

Trials with resin packs to seal and secure firedamp drainage standpipes in the strata were started in the UK about September 1971, after borehole probing had shown that in some conditions, considerable inleakage was occurring at the top of steel standpipes when mechanical or Densotape seals were used.

A 2.3.2 Method

Each pack has been designed to seal the upper 1.52 m of 76 mm diameter standpipe inserted in a 114 mm diameter hole. It contains 8 litres of material which is sufficient to achieve this. The kit containing all the necessary equipment and sufficient compound for one borehole is provided in a metal canister which may be carried underground by a member of the drilling team.

After the standpipe length has been bored to the required distance, the sealing operation for roofholes is carried out in the following way. First the resin (liquid) and catalyst (powder) are mixed in the metal canister previously used to store and carry the materials. The solid resin piston (Figure 2.32) is inserted at the bottom of the first 1.52 m section of standpipe, the mixed resin is poured into it and the top of the standpipe is then covered with a cap. Next the first section is inserted into the mouth of the borehole, the external solid resin ring is pushed over the bottom of it and the next section coupled on. After sufficient sections have been inserted into the borehole, the bottom section is secured at the mouth of the hole by wooden wedges. Drill rods are then inserted in the standpipe until contact is made with the piston in the top section. Then the piston is pushed slowly up to the top of the upper section forcing the resin into the annular space between standpipe and strata. A modified procedure is used for floorholes.

The mixture of resin and hardener is simply and easily mixed with a stick to form a viscous mass which does not leak easily past the standpipe piston. The setting time of about 45 min at about 298 K is long enough to enable a 10.5 m long, 76 mm diameter standpipe to be inserted into roofholes. Because of differences in the inside diameter of steel sections used, (up to 6.5 mm) and the need to minimise leakage past the piston, it is always advisable to match each piston to a steel section before pouring in the resin.

A 2.3.3 Test Results

The results in the following tables are typical and were obtained during tests made over a period of 20 months.

At one colliery the drilling pattern for roofholes is as follows:

- ▷ angle to horizontal — 60°
- ▷ angle to gate — 90°
- ▷ standpipe diameter — 76 mm
- ▷ standpipe length — 7.5 m
- ▷ total inclined length of borehole — 54 m.

Comparative tests of Densotape and resin seals are given in Table A 2.3.1. Results were obtained by probing two roofholes in the same gate during one shift. Firedamp concentrations were determined using a high concentration methanometer every 1.5 m along each hole. The purity at the bottom of each hole was checked by laboratory analysis.

Comparative results from mechanical and resin seals in roof holes are given in Table A 2.3.2.

Table A 2.3.1 Comparative Sealing Tests in Roofholes: Densotape and Resin Seals.

Distance up hole m	Hole No. 15 27 m from face Densotape Sealed % CH_4	Hole No. 17 13 m from face Resin Sealed % CH_4	Remarks
0.6	17	87	
2.1	18	87	
3.7	18	87	
5.2	18	87	
6.7	22	87	
8.2	75	90	Just above top of standpipe
9.8	80	88	
11.3	90	90	
27.4	90	90	
Pure methane flow l/s	4	28	

Table A 2.3.2 Comparative Sealing Tests in Roofholes: Mechanical and Resin Seals.

Hole No.	Distance from face m	Average % CH_4 Above Standpipe	Average % CH_4 Below Standpipe	Length of Standpipe m	Type of Seal
48	8.5	80	6	7.6	Mechanical
49	4.6	78	67	10.7	Resin

A 2.3.4 Summary and Observations

Numerous probe tests indicate that resin sealed standpipes can improve the purity and effectiveness of firedamp drainage systems at collieries where problems with sealing standpipes may arise. The resin will provide an adequate standpipe seal provided care is taken with the standpipe piston. The use of resin packs in many cases has reduced material costs to 60 % of those of mechanical seals and resulted in more effective firedamp drainage systems.

Appendix 2.4

Sealing Firedamp Drainage Boreholes with Polyurethane Foam* in Germany

In firedamp drainage boreholes air can be drawn in through fissured strata and through the annular space between standpipe and strata. To improve sealing in the latter case, model trials were carried out with a single-constituent polyurethane foam at Bergbau-Forschung in Essen-Kray. The foam is commercially available in 1 kg pressurised containers and is non-toxic and non-flammable. The propellant gas is refrigerant R 12. As a result general Inspectorate permission for use underground was obtained.

In application, a narrow copper tube is inserted in the annulus between standpipe and strata for foam injection. The tube internal diameter is 8 to 10 mm and its

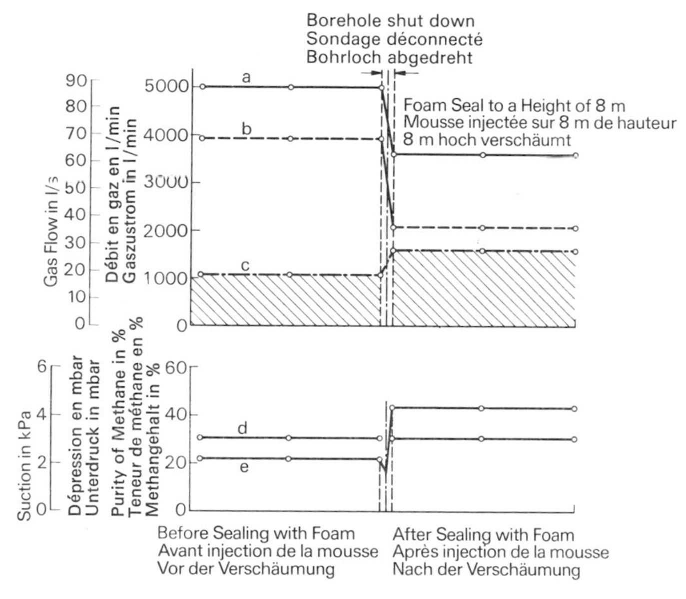

a Mixture — Mélange — Gemisch
b Air — Air — Luft
c Methane — Méthane — Methan
d Suction — Dépression — Unterdruck
e Purity — Teneur — Gehalt

Fig. A 2.4.1 Drainage Results for a Roofhole before and after Sealing with Polyurethane Foam.

* Observe national regulations.

length up to 14 metres. Normally a short rise tube of about 2 m is used to seal the lower part of the hole, and a long tube up to 14 m is employed to seal the upper annular space. By injecting in this manner, a good seal is obtained with minimum consumption of foam. One kilogramme of foam is normally used for the lower section and about 2 kg for the upper section. Where strata is broken so that excess leakages occur with the normal standpipe seal, sealing of the annular space is delayed preferably until a few days after completion of the borehole. If it is not possible to push the (longer) copper tube past the standpipe, a subsequent attempt can be made to push a short tube through the lower sealing material. In some cases an improvement in the drained gas purity has been obtained in this way.

By October 1977, some 26 boreholes had been injected with foam at various Ruhr collieries which, depending on circumstances, has resulted in considerable improvements in methane purity and yield. An example is shown in Figure A 2.4.1 of the changes in methane purity and flow resulting from foam injection. Leakage was reduced by about 50 % and the extracted flow of firedamp/air mixture by approximately 28 %.

Appendix 2.5

The Use of Bentonite for Sealing Firedamp Drainage Roofholes in the United Kingdom

Trials with Bentonite to seal firedamp drainage standpipes effectively into the strata were started in the UK about 1972. Borehole probing had shown that considerable inleakage was occurring above the top of standpipes in weak roof conditions when Densotape seals were used.

A 2.5.1 Material

Bentonite is a fine, buff coloured dry powder which is delivered to collieries in paper bags which hold 28 kg. It is a clay mineral made from calcium montmorillonite, converted to sodium montmorillonite. It is a free flowing, non-irritant and non-corrosive powder. Bentonite is stored in a well ventilated, covered site and above floor level to prevent deterioration of the paper bags. Addition of water makes it swell to many times its dry volume resulting in a jelly-like suspension. When stirred it becomes fluid but reverts to the jelly form if allowed to stand.

A 2.5.2 Methods

Bentonite is introduced into the borehole using a small diaphragm-type water pump, often used for the wet drilling of firedamp drainage boreholes. Half a bag of Bentonite is mixed in about 160 l of clean water in the water circulating tank ie at a concentration of about 8 % Bentonite by weight.

Two alternative methods of mixing have been used:

▷ The Bentonite powder is added very slowly with high pressure water into the mixing tank (205 l capacity).

▷ Bentonite is added slowly to about 160 l of water in the tank. Mixing is achieved by agitating with compressed air through a 25.4 mm diameter steel pipe, which is perforated radially with 3 mm holes over 300 to 460 mm of its length from the blind end. This agitation is continued throughout the whole of the pumping operation.

The length of standpipe used is 9 m (6 × 1.5 m sections) and their diameter is 51 mm. Densotape is wrapped around the coupling nearest the mouth of the 85 mm borehole.

Prior to mixing, the water pump delivery hose is connected to the waterhead of the drilling machine by a suitable adaptor. The agitated mixture is then delivered through the drill rods, and Bentonite commences to fill the spaces above the rubber or wooden ring (Figure 2.31). As pumping continues a back pressure is generated. It has been found that satisfactory results are obtained with back pressures of about 350 kPa. After discontinuing pumping, the rods are removed, a drill bit attached and rods replaced. Wet drilling of the productive length can proceed in the usual way. Any Bentonite remaining in the drum is dispersed in the drilling water.

A 2.5.3 Test Results

Numerous roofholes with suctions up to 6.3 kPa have been successful after the application of Bentonite, and these have shown substantial increases in purity of drained gas and pure methane flow rates.

For example, Bentonite was introduced in a district in which considerable difficulty had been experienced in sealing 6 m standpipes. Prior to the introduction of Bentonite, purities of less than 20 % were obtained even at suctions as low as 0.75 kPa and total district drained flow rate was 20 to 25 l/s of pure methane; difficulties were being experienced with firedamp concentration around the return ripping lip.

Typical values are given in Tables A 2.5.1 and A 2.5.2 of drainage performance before and after the introduction of Bentonite. As a result of the treatment, total yield from roofholes rose to 40 to 45 l/s pure methane, and district percentage capture increased from about 32 to 50 %.

Table A 2.5.1 Before Introduction of Bentonite.

Borehole Ref.	Suction Pa	Purity % CH_4	Yield Pure Methane l/s
A	625	25	3.35
B	225	10	0.85
C	1 438	29	6.40

Table A 2.5.2 After Selective Introduction of Bentonite.

Borehole Ref.	Suction Pa	Purity % CH_4	Yield Pure Methane l/s
D	525	65	7.85
E	6 275	45	24.50

A 2.5.4 Other Advantages and Uses

The method is simple, and requires no special skills. Apart from Bentonite it requires no special material. A mechanical method of agitating the mixture is an advantage. Compared with most other methods little or no time is wasted during the sealing of borehole cavities. The material is non-flammable, non-toxic and has no known health hazards. The method can be used selectively to seal apertures, cracks and bed separation planes in roofholes below the horizons at which productive firedamp sources are encountered. Bentonite has also been used effectively for sealing standpipes in difficult physical conditions where the "drill cuttings" method of sealing has had limited success or been unsuccessful.

Appendix 2.6

The Application of Double Standpipes in Firedamp Drainage Roofholes in the United Kingdom

A 2.6.1 Introduction

Particular problems may be encountered in sealing firedamp drainage standpipes when bed separation planes, gaps or breaks are encountered at heights of about 17 to 25 m above the roof of a roadway. In practice, great difficulty is experienced in sealing the standpipes of such roofholes with the result that, unless special techniques are used, the purity of firedamp in drained gas may be very low (often less than 25 % methane). Since such bed separation planes or breaks tend to continue as coal faces move, effective firedamp drainage may become very difficult or impracticable which may create local firedamp problems. One practical solution, the Bentonite method of sealing, has been described already in Appendix 2.5. This Appendix describes an alternative method of sealing roofholes using double standpipes.

A 2.6.2 Method

A long small-diameter steel standpipe is placed inside the conventional standpipe, as shown in Figure A 2.6.1. The initial (outer) standpipe length is bored at a diameter of 115 mm for a 76 mm bore standpipe or 85 mm for a 51 mm bore standpipe and may be 3 to 15 m long according to local conditions. This standpipe may be sealed by Densotape and cuttings, resin, cement or Bentonite. After securing the standpipe, the productive length of the hole is completed in the usual manner with diameter of 70, 60 or 50 mm. The roofhole is then connected to the firedamp drainage range.

If significant bed separation planes or breaks exist, measurements at a newly completed roofhole would show abnormally low purity and extraction rates of drained methane although the expected flow rates of gas mixture might be achieved. Examination of the district would show that the new roofhole had little effect within the district, so that general body firedamp concentrations at the return end of the face and in the vicinity of the return gate side pack could be higher than usual.

Probing of the roofhole would then be necessary to determine methane concentrations in the borehole at intervals of 3 m while the roofhole was under suction. Using this method, bed separation planes or breaks may be located; high purity gas is invariably found above such bed separation planes or breaks. Such high purity gas could be extracted provided it could be isolated from the bed separation planes or breaks.

Having located the position of bed separation planes or breaks the hole is disconnected from the firedamp drainage range. The drilling machine is then used to push standpipe sections of 25 mm bore and 1.5 m length into the roofhole, one at a time. Adjacent standpipe sections are connected by steel couplings. The first (top) section has its upper end closed and is provided with at least 40 holes of 6 mm diameter, around its periphery. The closed end prevents rock or dirt entering the

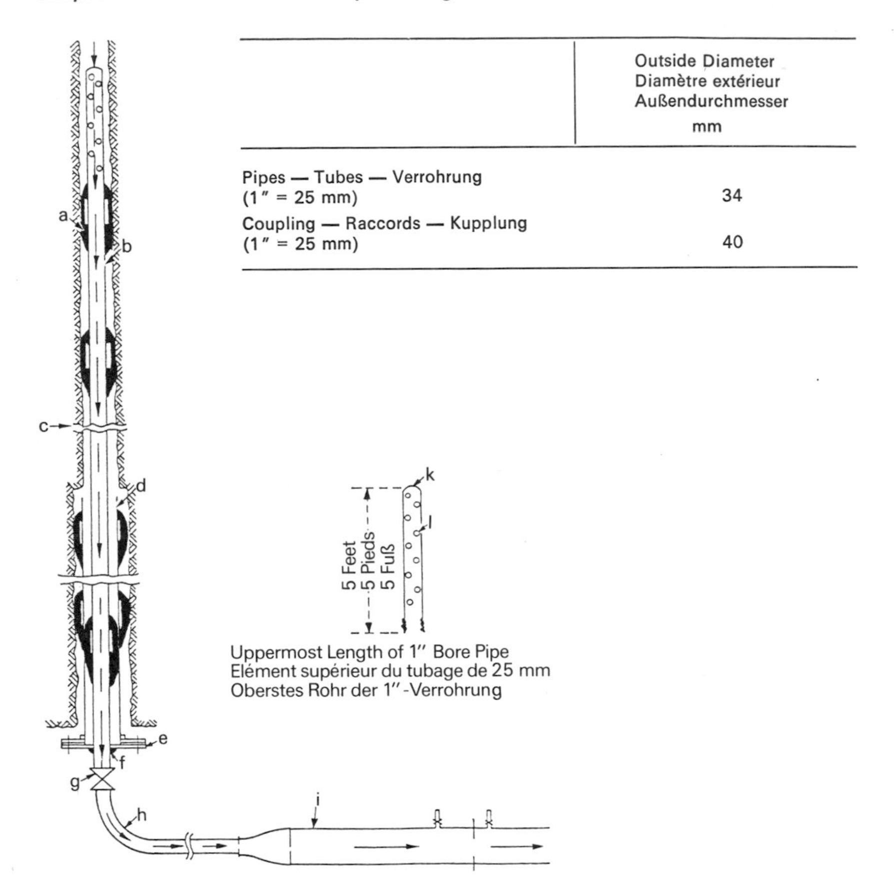

	Outside Diameter Diamètre extérieur Außendurchmesser mm
Pipes — Tubes — Verrohrung (1″ = 25 mm)	34
Coupling — Raccords — Kupplung (1″ = 25 mm)	40

a Densotape — Joint Denso — Densobinde
b 1″ Bore inner Standpipe — Tubage interne 25 mm de diamètre — Innere Verrohrung von 1″ Dmr.
c Strata breaks — Fractures du terrain — Gebirgsrisse
d 2 or 3″ Bore outer Standpipe — Tubage externe 50 ou 75 mm de diamètre — Äußere Vorrohrung von 2 oder 3″ Dmr.
e Flange — Bride — Flansch
f Weld — Soudure — Schweißnaht
g 1″ Valve — Vanne de 25 mm — 1″-Ventil
h 1″ Bore Hose — Flexible de 25 mm interne — 1″-Schlauch
i 2″ Borehole Equipment — Station de mesure du sondage 51 mm de diamètre — 2″-Bohrloch-Meßstrecke
k Closed end — Extrémité fermée — Geschlossenes Ende
l Minimal 20 × 1/4″ Diameter or 60 × 1/8″ Diameter Holes — Au minimum 20 trous à 6 mm de diamètre ou 60 trous à 3 mm de diamètre — Mindestens 20 Löcher von 1/4″ oder 60 Löcher von 1/8″ Dmr.

Fig. A 2.6.1 Method of Applying Double Standpipes to Improve Purity and Flow of Drained Firedamp.

inner standpipe while the peripheral holes allow gas to enter when suction is applied. Densotape is wrapped around the first and second (top) joints of the inner standpipe in the usual manner.

The inner standpipe is built up inside the borehole until the top end is about 3 m above the known bed separation planes or breaks. When nearing this position, the last coupling at the bottom of the inner standpipe is wrapped with Densotape and secured within the original outer standpipe.

A gate valve is fitted at the bottom of the inner standpipe which is then coupled by flexible hose to standard 51 mm or 76 mm borehole equipment. The roofhole is finally reconnected to the firedamp drainage range, valves reopened and purity of drained gas and gas flow rates measured.

Appendix 2.7

Regulations or Directives Relating to the Erection of Stoppings in Roadways

A 2.7.1 France

Rogez, C.: Isolement des quartiers — Barrages en cendres. Doc. Techn. Charb. France 1965 Nr. 3 S 223/27.

Crerin, J.: La techniques des barrages au plâtre.

A 2.7.2 Belgium

Aucune prescription ou réglementation. En pratique, les barrages en voie ont une longueur de 3 m, comprenant deux murs en claveaux de béton cimentés de 0.8 m d'épaisseur chacun; un espace intermédiaire de 1.4 m, rempli de pierres et ensuite de «filler» calcaire injecté sous pression.

A 2.7.3 United Kingdom

Coal and Other Mines (Ventilation) Regulations 1956. SI 1956 No. 1764. Part V, Regulation 21.

A 2.7.4 German Federal Republic

Richtlinien des Landesoberbergamts Nordrhein-Westfalen für Sperrung und Abdämmung von Grubenbauen im Steinkohlenbergbau vom 21. 4. 1971.

Bestimmungen des Oberbergamts Saarbrücken über den Brandschutz unter Tage auf Steinkohlengruben vom 6. 5. 1964.

Appendix 2.8

The Composition and Properties of Hardstem and Hardstop

A 2.8.1 General

Both Hardstem and Hardstop consist mainly of gypsum (calcium sulphate) with chemical additives to control setting times.

Hardstem (setting time 15 min) is used for stemming shotholes where it has advantages of simplicity, greater safety and saving in time and explosives over other methods.

Hardstop is used during the erection of explosion-proof stoppings, pack consolidation, cavity filling, reducing leakage around door frames and aircrossings, roadway coatings, and sometimes now for sealing firedamp drainage boreholes in selected applications. The setting time for Hardstop can be varied during manufacture, two grades being commonly used — the Short Set (30 min) and the Long Set (approximately 90 min).

Both Hardstem and Hardstop are non-combustible, non-toxic compounds and are usually packed in 12 kg, 4 ply paper bags. They do not present any known health hazard and no special precautions are taken by workmen during application.

A 2.8.2 Mixing

Both Hardstem and Hardstop can be hand mixed. Hardstop is usually mixed by machine (when used for stoppings and roadway lining) and is usually applied behind shuttering for stoppings, sealing gateside packs etc. The recommended mixing proportions of both Hardstem and Hardstop are 38 kg of the material to 18 kg of water.

A 2.8.3 Application of Hardstop to Firedamp Drainage Work

Hardstop is now used in firedamp drainage work only to seal the bottom of the standpipe and thereby reduce leakage at the roadway side. It has been used for sealing short standpipes of boreholes drilled in, or from, the sides of coal headings. Formerly it was employed to grout floorholes but this practice has been restricted because standpipes were found not to be adequately anchored on occasions.

Chapter 3

Planning, Calculating and Setting up Gas Drainage Networks and Extractor Stations

1. Planning Gas Drainage Networks

1.1 Estimation of Firedamp Emission Levels

Firedamp drainage forms an essential part of comprehensive ventilation systems in many mines. Planning of such systems is of prime importance so that effective installations and safety, production and economic objectives can be achieved.

The planning of gas drainage networks commences with the estimation of firedamp emission levels in productive districts, headings, old workings or other areas which might contribute to total firedamp extraction values. A number of methods may be used to assess future firedamp levels.

a) Estimates of future firedamp emission rates are often based on information derived from historical and current coal production and relevant firedamp emission data.

b) Results are obtained from data provided continuously from mine environmental monitoring schemes, such as those employing local and remote monitoring systems. These data need to be related to strata sections in those working areas and particularly to coal seam densities (cm of coal per metre of strata) in roof and floor formations. Thicknesses of coal seams, methods of working (advance or retreat mining), methods of strata control (caving or solid stowing, hand packed or machine packed gate side packs), depth of working, rank of coals, type of adjacent strata (massive sandstone, mudstones etc.) are relevant also.

c) Analytical methods are employed for the prediction of specific gas emissions from working districts which require, for example, a knowledge of the firedamp content of seams, the degree of degasification caused by earlier working of adjacent seams and the degasification zones which surround the working. Details of such methods are discussed in Appendix 3.1 as well as the direct and indirect methods of determining the gas content of coals. The influence of working operations and the formation of relaxed zones are of prime importance, as it is within these zones that firedamp from adjacent strata is desorbed and eventually finds its way into the workings.

A predominant consideration is whether coal is to be produced from areas which have, or have not, been already influenced by previous workings. With similar methods of mining at comparable depths, firedamp emission rates from working the same seam in a virgin area will be substantially higher than those obtained from the same seam if affected by previous working. In the estimation of firedamp emission levels, therefore, it is necessary to establish, in relation to local conditions, what seams (if any) have been mined within about 200 m of the worked seam.

In virgin areas, with no prior information of gas characteristics of the coal, firedamp contents of the seam to be worked and those in the adjacent strata are obtained from coal samples provided by borehole cores or cuttings (Appendix 3.1). Assessments necessary include the rates at which firedamp would be emitted from the coal front itself, and the permeabilities of the worked seam. The composition of each coal, its ash and moisture content, the physical composition of the worked seam and the disposition of any dirt bands need to be taken into account. Experience shows that the presence and positions of any geological discontinuities such as faults, folds, rolls, washouts, thinning and thickening of coal seams, and seam splitting and convergence can cause increases and decreases in emission rates. Particular attention should be devoted to floor strata sequences.

In previously worked areas, similar basic information would be sought and applied. In addition, allowance should be made for the gas remaining in seams within the influenced zone, remnant coal pillars, composition of adjacent strata and firedamp emission rates encountered previously.

1.2 Estimation of Firedamp Extraction Levels

Once the levels of firedamp emission have been ascertained, it is necessary to assess the proportion of the total firedamp emission which can be drained. This proportion varies from about 20 to 70 per cent (exceptionally even more) of the total firedamp emission in a working, or in an old district. Factors which influence this proportion include local practices, natural factors (seam densities in roof and floor strata and local geology) and the effectiveness of the drainage system.

Practical considerations would include:

a) Identification and drilling into the sources of firedamp.

b) Effectiveness of drilling patterns.

c) Successful sealing of standpipes.

d) Adequate design of underground gas main systems.

e) Satisfactory suction at boreholes.

f) Close control of the system.

g) Arrangements for removing excess water from gas mains.

It is important to assess firedamp emission rates from the coal front itself since, with certain exceptions, it is not practicable to drain such gas (Chapter 2, Section 3.2). The effectiveness of firedamp drainage systems tends to be less in districts with high coal front gas emission rates than in others. It varies continuously in working districts and a mean or range of values is employed in assessing the quantity of firedamp to be handled by a planned firedamp drainage system (Chapter 1, Section 4.2).

Factors to be considered in estimating firedamp extraction levels are:

a) Probable primary sources of firedamp in roof and floor strata.

b) Composition of the adjacent strata to determine the lengths of borehole and standpipes needed (Chapter 2, Section 1.1.2).

c) Whether roof and floor holes will be needed in one or both gates.

d) The effective sealing of standpipes.

e) Rates of advance.

f) The maximum allowable distance from the front borehole to the face (Chapter 2, Section 1.1.2).

One of the limitations in the methods of estimating firedamp extraction levels is in deciding the amount which can be drained. The importance of timing in drilling boreholes cannot be over emphasised.

Experience shows that is necessary to allow for additional capacity during the planning of firedamp drainage systems.

2. Calculation of Gas Drainage Networks

2.1 Technical Data on Flow

Design methods for gas drainage networks vary according to whether or not drained gas needs to be considered as an incompressible fluid. In most applications it is essential to employ formulae and computer programs which consider drained gas as a compressible fluid. The required basic data include the following items:

a) Details of the physical layout of a proposed scheme, using ultimate distances for each element of the grid.

b) Expected mean and maximum values of pure methane and drained gas (methane/air mixture) flow rates in each limb.

c) The diameter of the pipe ranges in each limb, including the shaft range and the range to the surface extraction plant.

d) Estimated air in-leakage.

e) Required or maximum permitted borehole suction at the most remote positions.

f) Expected number of boreholes and pure methane flow rates from them.

g) Expected purity of drained gas in various parts of the network.

h) Gradient of pipe ranges and differences in level.

i) Position of each orifice set or flow measuring device and losses therein.

j) Position of each valve, bend and water drain, and losses therein.

k) Proposed type, size and number of extractor(s) and their proved characteristic curves and performance limitations.

l) Maximum recommended gas velocities — usually about 15 m/s — in pipe systems.

m) Temperatures of gas in various parts of the network.

It is imperative that the best practical estimates of gas flow rates in each limb are made as this is a prime variable in all calculations.

2.2 Resistances of Pipe Ranges and Fittings

Resistance values of pipe ranges and associated fittings are required for the design of gas drainage networks. Many methods can be employed to calculate the resistances of pipe ranges and fittings, Appendices 3.2 (pipes) and 3.3 (fittings), and losses in standpipes (Chapter 2, Appendix 2.1).

2.3 Computations and Computer Programs

Several simple orthodox calculations and complex computer programs are employed for assessing losses in and the requirements of gas drainage networks as indicated below.

2.3.1 Simple Method using a Desk or Hand Calculator

To calculate the pressure and capacity requirements of gas grid systems, simple methods can be used. The formulae and resistance values given in Appendices 3.2 and 3.3 are employed. Calculations are made using an ordinary slide rule, desk calculator or small electronic hand calculator. Except in the case of low pressure (local) drainage systems, the formulae for compressible flow in pipes are used (Appendix 3.2). Generally a simple tabular method of approach is adopted as shown in Table 3.1.

Table 3.1 shows an existing level underground layout with firedamp drainage being applied in two return gates (B to D and B to C), the total drained quantity of gas mixture being extracted along the gas main B to A to the firedamp extractor at A. In the Table itself, details of the pipe run, pipe diameters, drained gas flow rates, pipe lengths and purity (per cent methane) of drained gas are inserted in the appropriate columns. Values of d^5 and Q^2 for Section A to B are obtained. The calculation is commenced knowing the suction pressure p_2 at the extractor A to be 50 kPa (absolute). The value of $p_2{}^2$ is readily calculated as 2500, and the value of $p_1{}^2$ is obtained using expression (A 3.2.3) in Appendix 3.2. The absolute pressure p_1 at B is obtained from the square root of $p_1{}^2$. The procedure is repeated for pipe run B to C to determine the absolute pressure at C, and for pipe run B to D to ascertain the absolute pressure at D. A friction coefficient λ of 0.0166 has been used throughout. Calculated values can then be compared with direct measurements.

Where it is necessary to determine the vacuum pressure required at the extractor A, a similar procedure is followed commencing with known p_1 at D and C. In another type of problem it may be necessary to determine the optimum pipe diameters for given gas flow rates; in this case the same procedure is carried out using successive approximation calculations until an acceptable solution is obtained (values of p_2 at C and D are known).

The above method has many advantages. It can be employed for most firedamp drainage systems. It can be readily used at collieries using a pocket electronic calculator to assess the effects of proposed changes

Table 3.1 Gas drainage network analysis by desk calculator.

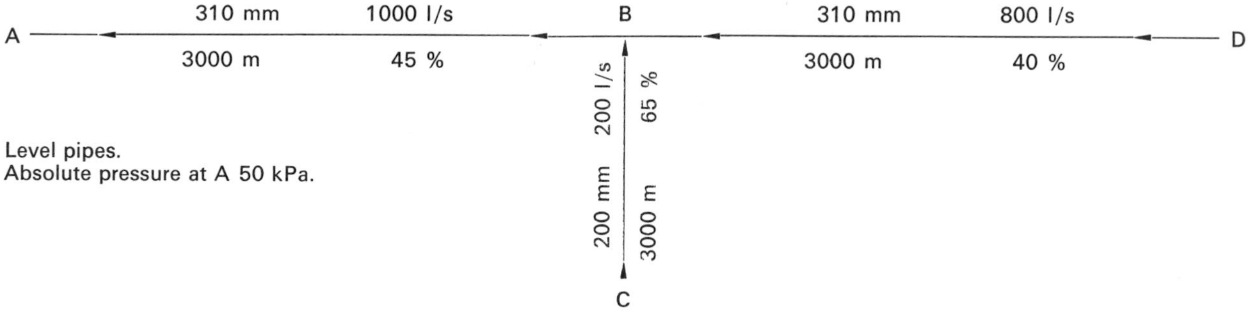

A ← 310 mm, 1000 l/s, 3000 m, 45 % ← B ← 310 mm, 800 l/s, 3000 m, 40 % ← D

B ← 200 mm, 200 l/s, 3000 m, 65 % ← C

Level pipes.
Absolute pressure at A 50 kPa.

Pipe run	d mm	d^5 mm^5	Q l/s	Q^2 (l/s)^2	l m	p_2 kPa	p_2^2 (kPa)^2	p_1^2 (kPa)^2	p_1 kPa
A—B	310	2.863×10^{12}	1000	1.00×10^6	3000	50.0	2500	5270	72.6
B—C	200	0.320×10^{12}	200	0.04×10^6	1500	72.6	5270	5710	75.6
B—D	310	2.863×10^{12}	800	0.64×10^6	3000	72.6	5270	7089	84.2

d Internal diameter of pipe in mm
Q Gas mixture flow in l/s
l Length of pipe in m
% Purity (per cent methane) of drained gas
p_1 Inlet (or upstream) absolute pressure in kPa
p_2 Outlet (or downstream) absolute pressure in kPa
λ 0.0166 for this underground installation

and modifications to systems, and has been of great value when incidents have occurred and quick assessments are required of possible alternative schemes. However, it may become laborious when extensive gas main networks need to be analysed.

2.3.2 Simple Method using Purpose Designed Calculators

Purpose designed calculators are used to carry out calculations on the pressure and capacity requirements of gas drainage networks; examples of these are the NCB/Mears "Methane Drainage Pipe Calculator" shown in Figure 3.1 and described in Appendix 3.4 and the Gaz de France slide rule shown in Figure 3.2 and also described in Appendix 3.4.

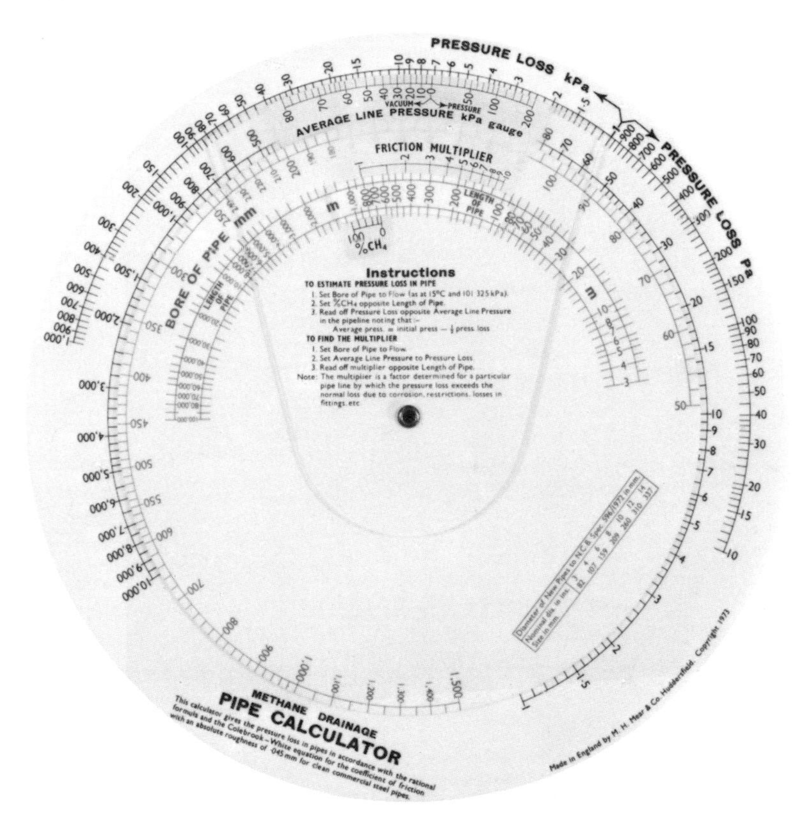

Fig. 3.1 a NCB Methane Drainage Pipe Calculator (Front).

The tabular layout employed with the NCB circular hand calculator is shown in Table 3.2. (A similar layout can be used with the Gaz de France calculator). The same example is used as in Section 2.3.1 and Table 3.1. The appropriate values of d, Q, l and p_2 are inserted for pipe run A to B. The hand calculator is employed to find the value of the difference p_1—p_2, which in this case is 22 kPa. Since p_2 is 50 kPa (absolute), the value of p_1 is 72 kPa (absolute). Similar calculations are carried out for pipe runs B to C and B to D.

The use of special calculators has many advantages. Calculations are quickly carried out (analyses of most underground drainage networks can be completed in about 3 hours). Calculations can readily be made at the collieries themselves, so that the merits and demerits of proposed changes are determined quickly. The calculators are cheap, but they

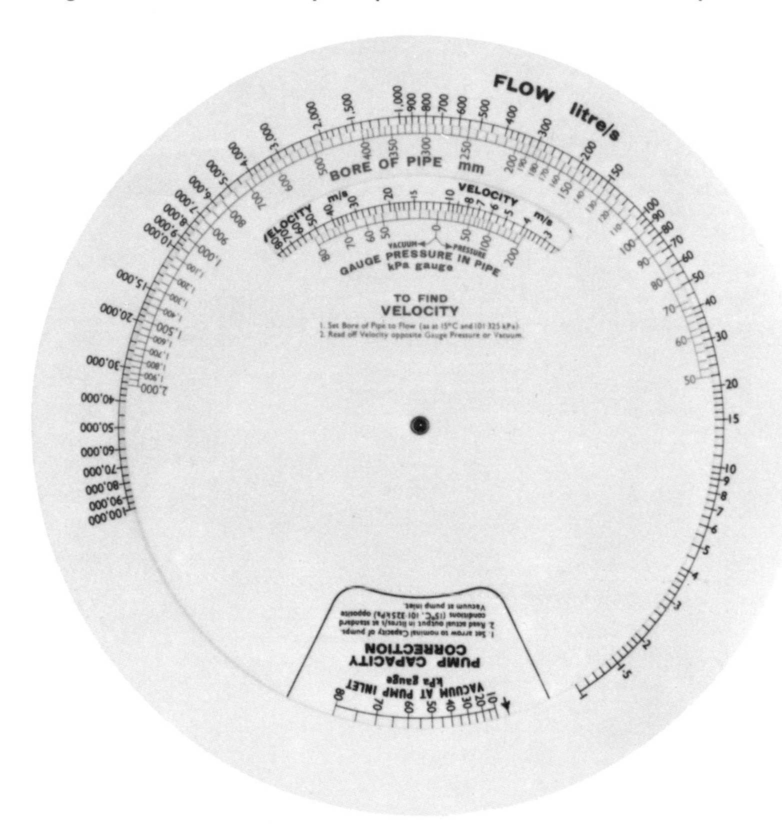

Fig. 3.1 b NCB Methane Drainage Pipe Calculator (Back).

do have the inherent disadvantage of limited accuracy which, in most cases, is not a serious detraction.

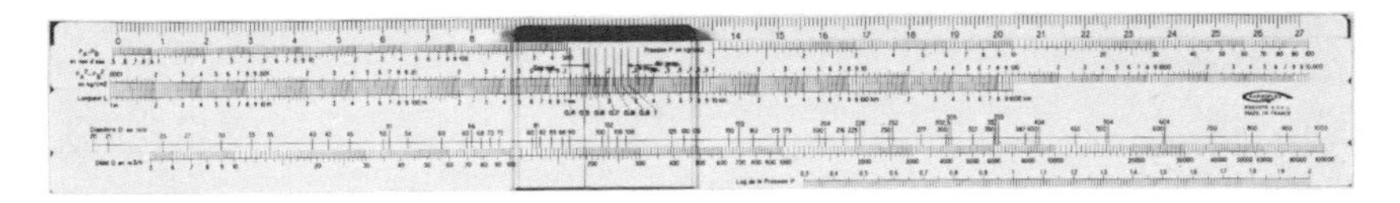

Fig. 3.2 Gaz de France Methane Flow Calculator.

2.3.3 Reglagaz Computer Program (Cerchar)

The program is intended for calculating gas flows in straight cylindrical pipes and simple branched ranges.

It can be used to calculate any one of the five following parameters for one branch, when the remaining four values are known:

▷ the gas pressure upstream,

▷ the gas pressure downstream,

▷ the flow rate in the pipe,

▷ the pipe diameter,

▷ the pipe length.

In addition the density, viscosity and temperature of the gas, and differences in level of the range must be known.

The equations used (Appendix 3.2) are based on the assumptions that the gas is perfectly compressible, the temperature is the mean between the two ends, the pipe is straight, cylindrical and smooth and the Reynolds Number is between 2×10^4 and 2×10^6. A correction factor K is introduced which is fixed by the user; it is greater than unity when some of the assumptions are not met, such as straightness of the pipe and roughness of its inner walls.

The data input is simple, there being only one card per calculation, and an unlimited number of cards may be used following on from each other, which set in motion a number of calculations independently or in chains.

Results are presented in three lines with respective titles Pipe, Gas and Flow (Figure 3.3):

▷ The first line gives the characteristics of pipe: length, diameter, difference in level, temperature (equal to that of gas), correction factor.

Table 3.2 Gas drainage network analysis by special calculator.

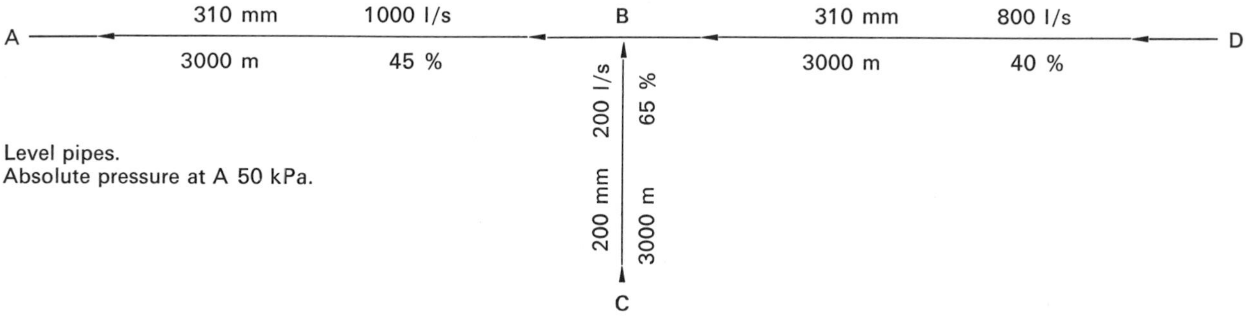

A — 310 mm, 1000 l/s, 3000 m, 45 % — B — 310 mm, 800 l/s, 3000 m, 40 % — D

B — 200 mm, 200 l/s, 3000 m, 65 % — C

Level pipes.
Absolute pressure at A 50 kPa.

Pipe run	d mm	Q l/s	l m	p_2 kPa	$p_1 - p_2$ kPa	p_1 kPa
A—B	310	1000	3000	50	22	72
B—C	200	200	1500	72	4	76
B—D	310	800	3000	72	13	85

d Internal diameter of pipe in mm
Q Gas mixture flow in l/s
l Length of pipe in m
% Purity (per cent methane) of drained gas
p_1 Inlet (or upstream) absolute pressure in kPa
p_2 Outlet (or downstream) absolute pressure in kPa
λ 0.0166 for this underground installation

▷ The second line gives density and viscosity of gas.

▷ The third line gives flow characteristics: upstream and downstream pressures, rate of flow, Reynolds Number and direction of flow.

The value being calculated is underlined. Figures 3.3a and b show the computer output of a worked example.

Benefits:

▷ readily used (a single card per calculation),

▷ can calculate any one of five parameters (flow, length, diameter, upstream pressure, downstream pressure) given the other four, for one section,

▷ can calculate a succession of pressures in one run through the computer, giving rapid results for the entire drainage system,

▷ economical: a very efficient program (non iterative).

Limitations:

▷ not applicable to complex networks or those involving two extractors.

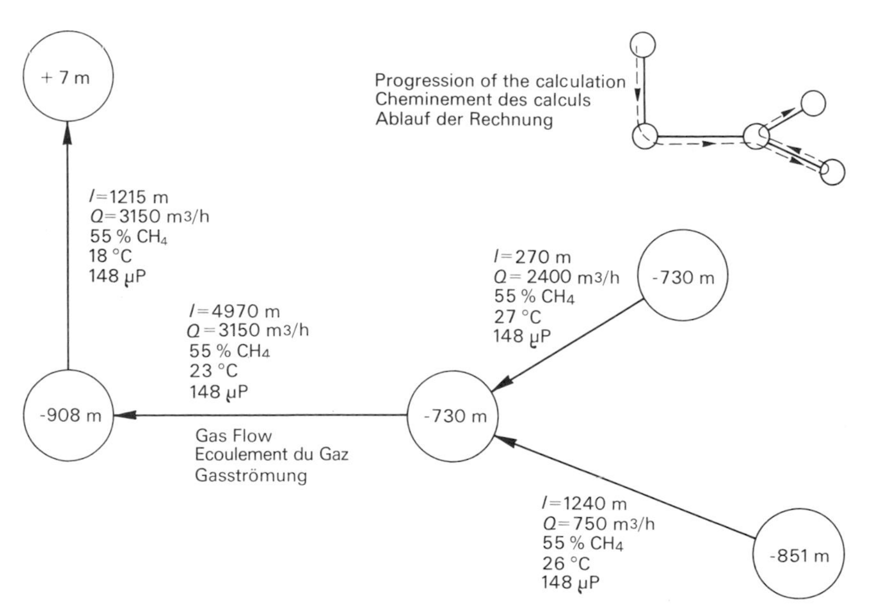

Fig. 3.3 a Reglagaz Computer Program — Example with Print Out Overleaf.

REGLAGAZ

Flow of a perfectly compressible gas in a cylindrical and rectilinear pipe the friction coefficient is equal to 0.17200 * (Reynolds No.) ** — 0.18. Flows are in m³/h at 15 °C and 1 atm.

Ecoulement d'un gaz parfaitement compressible dans une conduite cylindrique et rectiligne le coefficient de perte de charge est egal a 0,17200 * (Nbre. de Reynolds) ** — 0,18. Les dèbits sont exprimes en m³/h rapportes a 15 degres c et 1 atm.

Strömung eines vollkommen kompressiblen Gases in einer zylindrischen und geradlinigen Leitung. Der Reibungsbeiwert ist gleich 0,17200 * (Reynoldszahl ** — 0,18). Die Volumenströme sind angegeben in m³/h bei 15 °C und 1 atm.

```
CONDUITE    L=1215. M      D=400. MM      DZ=  915. M     T=18. DEGRE C     K=1,30

GAZ         DENSITE= .7500                VISCOSITE=148.0 MICROPOISE

ECOULEMENT  PA= 9162. MME  PB= 8250. MME  Q=3150. M3/H    NBRE DE REYNOLDS=   172992.  SENS=DE A VERS B
            -------------


CONDUITE    L=4970. M      D=400. MM      DZ= -178. M     T=23. DEGRE C     K=1,30

GAZ         DENSITE= .7500                VISCOSITE=148.0 MICROPOISE

ECOULEMENT  PA= 9821. MME  PB= 9162. MME  Q=3150. M3/H    NBRE DE REYNOLDS=   172992.  SENS=DE A VERS B
            -------------


CONDUITE    L=1240. M      D=400. MM      DZ=  121. M     T=26. DEGRE C     K=1,30

GAZ         DENSITE= .7500                VISCOSITE=148.0 MICROPOISE

ECOULEMENT  PA= 9938. MME  PB= 9821. MME  Q= 750. M3/H    NBRE DE REYNOLDS=    41189.  SENS=DE A VERS B
            -------------


CONDUITE    L=1240. M      D=400. MM      DZ=  121. M     T=26. DEGRE C     K=1,30

GAZ         DENSITE= .7500                VISCOSITE=148.0 MICROPOISE

ECOULEMENT  PA= 9938. MME  PB= 9821. MME  Q= 750. M3/H    NBRE DE REYNOLDS=    41189.  SENS=DE A VERS B
                           -------------


CONDUITE    L= 270. M      D=400. MM      DZ=    0. M     T=27. DEGRE C     K=1,30

GAZ         DENSITE= .7500                VISCOSITE=148.0 MICROPOISE

ECOULEMENT  PA= 9964. MME  PB= 9938. MME  Q=2400. M3/H    NBRE DE REYNOLDS=   131804.  SENS=DE A VERS B
            -------------
```

Fig. 3.3b Reglagaz Computer Program — Print Out.

2.3.4 Resogaz Computer Program (Cerchar)

The Resogaz program is used to calculate the unknown pressures at junctions and the rates of flow in the branches of a complete drainage network. The network may be branched or looped. It is an iterative calculation. The characteristic curve of the extractor(s) and the flow/pressure characteristics of the sections must be given with the input data.

There are three types of branches used for the network: "passive", "exhauster" and "district" branches. In passive branches it is assumed that the gas is perfectly compressible, flow is isothermal and the pipe is straight, cylindrical and smooth. This part of the calculation is similar to the Reglagaz Program (Section 2.3.3).

The exhauster with its bypass is represented by a single branch with the following characteristics:

▷ The gas can only circulate in one direction.

▷ The discharge pressure is constant and normally close to atmospheric pressure.

▷ The rate of flow of the branch is equal to the volume flow of the exhauster minus that of the bypass.

The program offers the alternatives of calculation for the point of operation of the exhauster if the characteristic of the branch is known, or calculation for a given point of operation if the characteristic of the branch is not known. In practice although the characteristic of the exhauster is known, with the bypass open it is not, hence the first type of calculation can only be done with the bypass closed. The second type of calculation is more common, since it checks on the suitability of the network for a given flow rate and suction.

Districts are sources of methane and the program localises these sources at the upstream end of the sections. The gas is drained and emitted in the network at a pressure that is generally less than the local atmospheric pressure, and the flow of the source varies as a function of this negative pressure. As methane concentration is important, a double characteristic must be established for flow of pure gas and mixture against suction. In practice these characteristics are not usually known, so that is necessary to specify a flow and purity, independent of pressure drop, in which case the negative pressure available at the districts can be calculated.

The unknowns in the calculation are the pressures at junctions. The network is solved by successive approximation, examining junctions one by one. At a given node the algebraic sum of the flows which reach this node is a function of the pressure assumed to prevail there, the pressures of the adjacent nodes being given and the flows through each split being determined by the type of branch specified. The calculation stops when either the junctions are balanced (convergence) or if the specified number of iterations has been reached (non-convergence).

The formulae, which are given in Appendix 3.2, presuppose straight smooth pipes, conditions which are not usually met. A correction factor (K in Figure 3.4) is introduced into the formulae to allow for roughness (or corrosion) and is normally about 1.4.

In its present form, which is written in Fortran, the program can deal with a maximum of 100 junctions, 20 exhausters and 20 districts, with normally a maximum of 6 branches to the same junction. The number of branches to a junction can be raised to 12 by changing the presentation of the data.

The computer printout of a worked example is given in Figure 3.4 a, b and c. It can be seen that full details of the network are given. In the example (Figure 3.4 a), it can be seen that all the nodes are numbered, and these are used to define the branches. The depth (m) of each node is specified, and the pipe length, diameter, temperature and correction factor are specified for each branch. The rectangular blocks (eg 9) represent the districts with boreholes and show the total flow and purity.

Benefits:

▷ calculates pressures at the nodes and flows in the branches,

▷ deals with complex pipe networks.

Limitations:

▷ the maximum size of network which can be handled is:

100 nodes, 20 extractors, 20 districts, 6 branches at the same node.

2.3.5 RAG Drainage Network Program (Ruhrkohle AG)

The program is used to calculate meshed pipe networks, in which compressible media are flowing. It is immaterial for the purposes of this program whether the flowing medium is above atmospheric pressure (compressed air networks) or below (firedamp drainage networks). In addition to the compressibility of the gas, the program also takes into account the difference in the altitude at the network junctions.

The program is based on the assumption that, in the whole network, it has:

▷ the same temperature,

▷ the same composition of gas and

▷ the same roughness on the walls of the range.

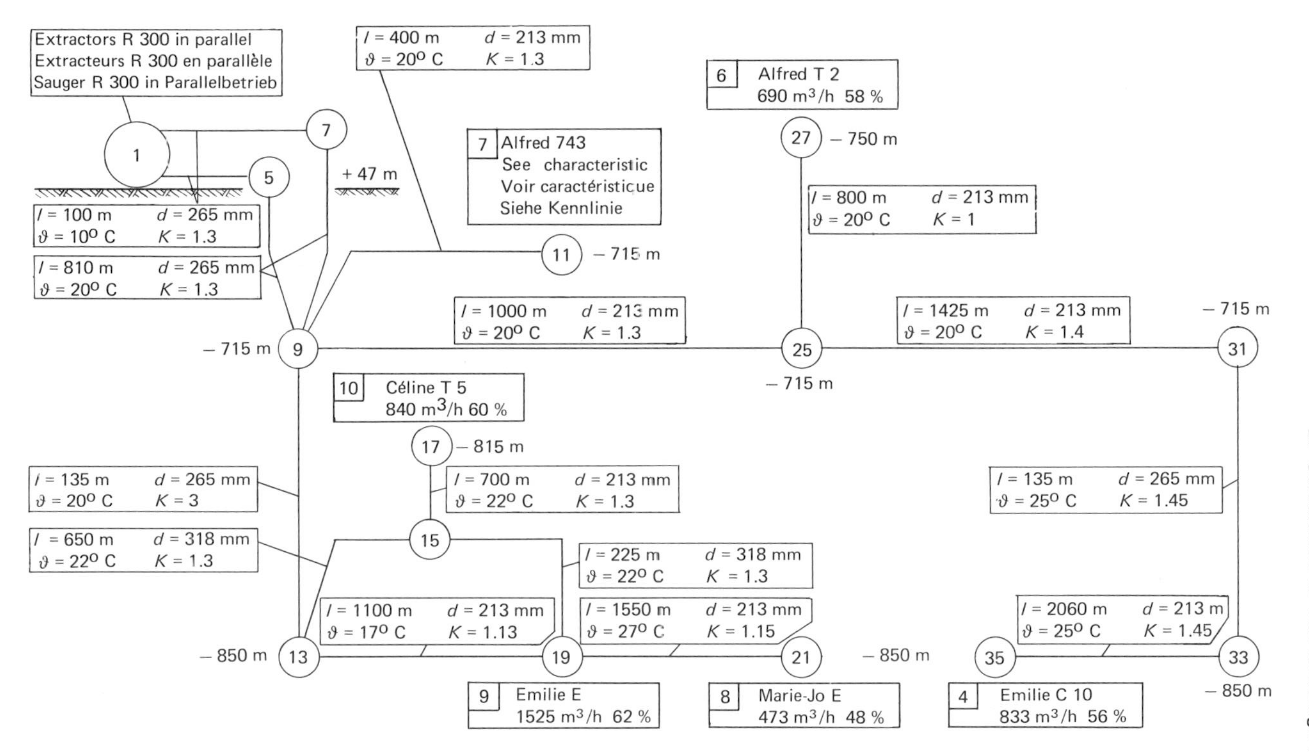

Fig. 3.4 a Resogaz Drainage Program — Example Showing Input Information.

```
RESOGAZ/DONNEES/
                              CALCUL D'UN RESEAU DE CAPTAGE

                                        EXEMPLE
CARACTERISTIQUES DES EXTRACTEURS
--------------------------------
(EXHAUSTER  CHARACTERISTICS)
                              EXTRACTEUR  2. 3 R300 EN PARALLELE

DEBIT BRUT  7860.      0.      0.      0.      0.      0.      0.      0.      0.      0.
DEPRESSION     0.  10138.  10500.  11000.  12000.  13000.  14000.  15000.  16000.  17000.
PRESS.JOUR 10138.

CARACTERISTIQUES DES QUARTIERS
------------------------------
(DISTRICT  CHARACTERISTICS)
                              QUARTIER  4 . EMILIE C10

DEBIT BRUT   833.    833.    833.    833.    833.    833.    833.    833.    833.    833.
DEBIT NET    466.    466.    466.    466.    466.    466.    466.    466.    466.    466.
DEPRESSION     0.  20000.  21000.  22000.  23000.  24000.  25000.  26000.  27000.  28000.
PRESS.FOND 11500.

                              QUARTIER  6 . ALFRED T2

DEBIT BRUT   690.    690.    690.    690.    690.    690.    690.    690.    690.    690.
DEBIT NET    400.    400.    400.    400.    400.    400.    400.    400.    400.    400.
DEPRESSION     0.  20000.  21000.  22000.  23000.  24000.  25000.  26000.  27000.  28000.
PRESS.FOND 11295.

                              QUARTIER  7 . ALFRED 7+3

DEBIT BRUT     0.    180.    350.    510.    660.    800.    930.   1050.   1160.   1260.
DEBIT NET      0.    140.    260.    360.    440.    500.    540.    560.    590.    594.
DEPRESSION     0.    400.    800.   1200.   1600.   2000.   2400.   2800.   3200.   3600.
PRESS.FOND 11295.

                              QUARTIER  8 . MARIE.JO E

DEBIT BRUT   473.    473.    473.    473.    473.    473.    473.    473.    473.    473.
DEBIT NET    227.    227.    227.    227.    227.    227.    227.    227.    227.    227.
DEPRESSION     0.  20000.  21000.  22000.  23000.  24000.  25000.  26000.  27000.  28000.
PRESS.FOND 11540.

                              QUARTIER  9 . EMILIE E

DEBIT BRUT  1525.   1525.   1525.   1525.   1525.   1525.   1525.   1525.   1525.   1525.
DEBIT NET    946.    946.    946.    946.    946.    946.    946.    946.    946.    946.
DEPRESSION     0.  20000.  21000.  22000.  23000.  24000.  25000.  26000.  27000.  28000.
PRESS.FOND 11546.

                              QUARTIER 10 .CELINE T5

DEBIT BRUT   840.    840.    840.    840.    840.    840.    840.    840.    840.    840.
DEBIT NET    504.    504.    504.    504.    504.    504.    504.    504.    504.    504.
DEPRESSION     0.  20000.  21000.  22000.  23000.  24000.  25000.  26000.  27000.  28000.
PRESS.FOND 11376.
```

```
CONSTITUTION DU RESEAU
----------------------
(NETWORK  DETAILS)
BRANCHE  21- 19                L=1550. M   D=213. MM   DZ=    0. M   T=27. DEGRE C   K=1.15
BRANCHE  21-208  QUARTIER  8
BRANCHE  19- 13                L=1100. M   D=213. MM   DZ=    0. M   T=17. DEGRE C   K=1.13
BRANCHE  19-209  QUARTIER  9
BRANCHE  19- 15                L= 225. M   D=318. MM   DZ=    0. M   T=22. DEGRE C   K=1.30
BRANCHE  15- 13                L= 650. M   D=318. MM   DZ=    0. M   T=22. DEGRE C   K=1.30
BRANCHE  15- 17                L= 700. M   D=213. MM   DZ=   40. M   T=22. DEGRE C   K=1.30
BRANCHE  17-210  QUARTIER 10
BRANCHE  13-  9                L= 135. M   D=265. MM   DZ=  135. M   T=20. DEGRE C   K=3.00
BRANCHE  35-204  QUARTIER  4
BRANCHE  35- 33                L=2060. M   D=213. MM   DZ=    0. M   T=25. DEGRE C   K=1.45
BRANCHE  33- 31                L= 135. M   D=265. MM   DZ=  135. M   T=25. DEGRE C   K=1.45
BRANCHE  31- 25                L=1425. M   D=213. MM   DZ=    0. M   T=20. DEGRE C   K=1.40
BRANCHE  27- 25                L= 800. M   D=213. MM   DZ=   35. M   T=20. DEGRE C   K=1.50
BRANCHE  27-206  QUARTIER  6
BRANCHE  25-  9                L=1000. M   D=213. MM   DZ=    0. M   T=20. DEGRE C   K=1.30
BRANCHE  11-  9                L= 400. M   D=213. MM   DZ=    0. M   T=20. DEGRE C   K=1.30
BRANCHE  11-207  QUARTIER  7
BRANCHE   9-  5                L= 810. M   D=265. MM   DZ=  762. M   T=20. DEGRE C   K=1.30
BRANCHE   5-  1                L= 100. M   D=265. MM   DZ=    0. M   T=10. DEGRE C   K=1.20
BRANCHE   9-  7                L= 810. M   D=265. MM   DZ=  762. M   T=20. DEGRE C   K=1.20
BRANCHE   7-  1                L= 100. M   D=265. MM   DZ=    0. M   T=10. DEGRE C   K=1.30
BRANCHE   1-102  EXTRACT.  2

DONNEES COMPLEMENTAIRES
-----------------------
(ASSUMED  VALUES)
CRITERE DE CONVERGENCE=   .10                                    (Convergence Criterion)
FACTEUR DE RELAXATION=1.60                                       (Relaxation Factor)
COEFFICIENT DE PERTE DE CHARGE=   .17200*(NB.DE REYNOLDS)**- .18 (Friction Coefficient)

CONVENTIONS
-----------

DANS LA BRANCHE A-B  DZ=COTE DU POINT B -COTE DU POINT A         (In Branch AB  DZ = Level B - Level A)
AU NOEUD A   LES DEBITS QUI ARRIVENT EN A SONT POSITIFS          (At Node A - Flow into A is positive
             LES DEBITS QUI PARTENT DE A SONT NEGATIFS                        Flow out of A is negative)
LES PRESSIONS SONT EXPRIMEES EN MMCE(KG/M2)                      (Pressures in mm.wg. ie kg/m2)
LES DEBITS SONT EXPRIMES EN M3/H RAPPORTES A 15 DEGRES C ET 1 ATM (Flows in m3/h at STP)
```

VEREINBARUNGEN

Im Zweig AB ist DZ = Niveau B — Niveau A.

Im Knoten A ist der Zustrom positiv, der Abstrom negativ. Die Drücke werden in mm WS (kg/m²) angegeben.

Die Volumenströme werden in m³/h bezogen auf 15 °C und 1 atm angegeben.

Fig. 3.4 b Example of Resogaz Computer Program Print Out — Network Description.

NOEUD	PRESSION	BRANCHE	DEBIT	TENEUR	DEPRESSION	
		1- 5	2688.	.58		
1	6934.	1- 7	2688.	.58		
		EXTRACT. 2	-5376.	.58	3204.	-.08470
		5- 9	2688.	.58		
5	7048.	5- 1	-2688.	.58		-.09686
		7- 9	2688.	.58		
7	7043.	7- 1	-2688.	.58		-.09686
		9- 13	2838.	.59		
		9- 25	1523.	.57		
9	8424.	9- 11	1014.	.55		
		9- 5	-2688.	.58		
		9- 7	-2688.	.58		-.08472
		11- 9	-1014.	.55		
11	8615.	QUARTIER 7	1014.	.55	2680.	-.07811
		13- 19	661.	.59		
13	8849.	13- 15	2177.	.59		
		13- 9	-2838.	.59		-.07424
		15- 19	1337.	.59		
15	9018.	15- 13	-2177.	.59		
		15- 17	840.	.60		-.05878
		17- 15	-840.	.60		
17	9204.	QUARTIER10	840.	.60	2172.	-.05340
		19- 21	473.	.48		
		19- 13	-661.	.59		
19	9042.	QUARTIER 9	1525.	.62	2504.	
		19- 15	-1337.	.59		-.07669
		21- 19	-473.	.48		
21	9204.	QUARTIER 8	473.	.48	2336.	-.05028
		25- 31	833.	.56		
25	9370.	25- 27	690.	.58		
		25- 9	-1523.	.57		-.07481
		27- 25	-690.	.58		
27	9528.	QUARTIER 6	690.	.58	1767.	-.09960
		31- 33	833.	.56		
31	9822.	31- 25	-833.	.56		-.04521
		33- 35	833.	.56		
33	9952.	33- 31	-833.	.56		-.09873
		QUARTIER 4	833.	.56	906.	
35	10594.	35- 33	-833.	.56		-.08445
NODE	PRESSURE	BRANCH	FLOW	PURITY	SUCTION	

RESIDU MAXIMUM .09950

Fig. 3.4c Example of Resogaz Computer Program Print Out — Results Showing Depressions, Flows and Purities.

These parameters therefore only need to be entered once, at the start of the calculation. The program calculates independently the dynamic viscosity and the density of the flowing medium as well as the coefficient of friction for the separate sections of the range. This last parameter is automatically uprated in the course of the calculation.

The network may consist of a maximum of 320 branches. Any number of these can be treated as fixed quantity sections or as pressure generators.

Apart from the values mentioned above, which apply to the network as a whole, the following values must be entered for each branch separately:

▷ Initial and final junctions with respective altitude, diameter, length and where necessary additional resistance (eg to take account of bends and fittings) for normal pipe-range sections.

▷ Initial and final junctions with respective altitude and volume flow for fixed quantity sections.

▷ Initial and final junctions with respective altitude and pressure difference between these two junctions for pressure generators.

For the normal sections of the range, the volume flow and the pressure difference are calculated, for fixed quantity sections only the pressure difference, and for pressure generators only the volume flow is calculated.

The program can be used for the extension of existing networks, the setting-up of new networks and the connecting of existing networks. It can be used to resolve the following questions which occur frequently:

▷ Is an existing network adequate to cope with a new panel being developed?

▷ Is it better, if the network is not adequate, to enlarge the cross-section of the existing network or to increase the suction?

▷ How large should the pipe cross-sections be for the new panel?

Although the program does not calculate the optimum gas-range diameter, combinations of drainage networks can be calculated, and up to 12 such combinations can be selected in one run-through. Hence an important range can be entered as having different diameters and combined with various exhausters. The points at which gas enters the drainage network from the strata are defined as fixed quantity sections or pressure generators. In the former case a fixed volume flow is entered into the program, which may be the result, for

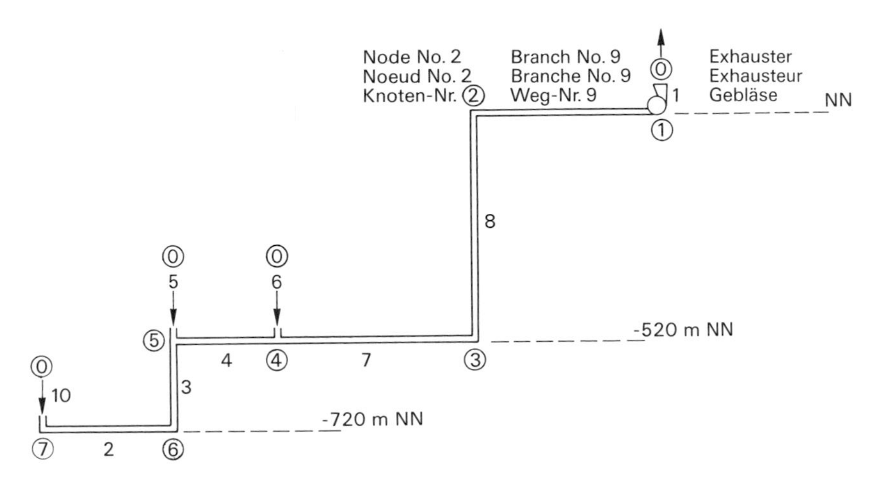

Fig. 3.5a RAG Program — Example of a Drainage Network (Layout).

Eingabedaten

WICHTE 0.0 ,ZAEHIGKEIT 0.0 ,K 0.2,TEMP 45.0 LUFTDR.KNOTEN 0 755.

GAS	ANTEIL %	DYN.ZAEHIGKEIT KPS/M2	WICHTE KP/M3 BEI 0 GRAD 760 TORR
LUFT	50.00	0.17407E-05	1.293
CH4	50.00	0.10401E-05	0.717
GEMISCH		0.14114E-05	1.005

		Knoten von	Knoten nach	Menge m^3/h	Ø mm	L m	zusätzl. Widerstand ξ	Höhe NN Anfangs-Knoten	Höhe NN End-Knoten	Druck-erzeugung / bedarf at
Weg-Nr. 1	GEBLAESE	1	0	0.	0	0	0	0	0	0.4000
" 2		7	6	0.	495	1000	5	-720	-720	0.0
" 3		6	5	0.	352	200	5	-720	-520	0.0
" 4		5	4	0.	352	550	5	-520	-520	0.0
" 5		0	5	1232.	0	0	0	0	-520	0.0
" 6		0	4	1232.	0	0	0	0	-520	0.0
" 7		4	3	0.	352	2850	5	-520	-520	0.0
" 8		3	2	0.	495	520	2	-520	0	0.0
" 9		2	1	0.	352	175	2	0	0	0.0
" 10		0	7	0.	0	0	0	0	-720	-0.1000

KNOTEN	0 MIT ZWEIGEN	5	6	10	1
KNOTEN	1 MIT ZWEIGEN	1	9		
KNOTEN	2 MIT ZWEIGEN	9	8		
KNOTEN	3 MIT ZWEIGEN	8	7		
KNOTEN	4 MIT ZWEIGEN	7	4	6	
KNOTEN	5 MIT ZWEIGEN	4	3	5	
KNOTEN	6 MIT ZWEIGEN	3	2		
KNOTEN	7 MIT ZWEIGEN	2	10		

Fig. 3.5b Example of Input Data for the RAG Network Program.

Errechnete Werte in den Wegen

WICHTE GAS (NORM) 1.0050 (KP/M3) , DYNAMISCHE ZAEHIGKEIT 0.141136E-05 (KPS/M2)
WANDRAUHIGKEIT 0.2(MM) , TEMPERATUR 45.0 (OC) 10 WEGE 8 KNOTEN

KNOTENNR. von	nach	HOEHE(M NN) ANFANG	ENDE	MENGE (M3/H) NORM	BETRIEB	DRUCK (ATA) ANFANG	ENDE	DRUCKDIFFERENZ GESAMT	ROHRREIB.	DURCHM. (M)	LAENGE (M)	ZUS. WID.	W (M/S)	REYNOLD-ZAHL	REIBUNGS-BEIWERT
1	0	0	0	5191.	7560.	0.6263	1.0263	0.4000	DRUCKERZEUGER						
7	6	-720	-720	2727.	3260.	1.0088	1.0047	-0.0041	-0.0041	0.495	1000	5	4.7	141477.	0.019
6	5	-720	-520	2727.	3304.	1.0047	0.9818	-0.0229	-0.0059	0.352	200	5	9.4	196952.	0.019
5	4	-520	-520	3959.	4923.	0.9818	0.9536	-0.0282	-0.0282	0.352	550	5	14.1	288838.	0.019
0	5	0	-520	1232.	1477.	1.0263	0.9818	-0.0444	FESTE MENGE						
0	4	0	-520	1232.	1498.	1.0263	0.9536	-0.0727	FESTE MENGE						
4	3	-520	-520	5191.	7600.	0.9536	0.6902	-0.2634	-0.2616	0.352	2850	5	21.7	378723.	0.019
3	2	-520	0	5191.	9319.	0.6902	0.6505	-0.0397	-0.0108	0.495	520	2	13.5	269314.	0.018
2	1	0	0	5191.	9785.	0.6505	0.6263	-0.0243	-0.0243	0.352	175	2	27.9	378723.	0.019
0	7	0	-720	2727.	3225.	1.0263	1.0088	-0.0175	DRUCKBEDARF						

Errechnete Werte an den Knoten

KNOTEN NR.	DRUCK ATA	WICHTE KP/M3	LUFTDRUCK TORR	DRUCK ATUE	HOEHE NN M
0	1.0263	0.8571	755.	0.0000	0
1	0.6263	0.5230	755.	-0.4000	0
2	0.6505	0.5433	755.	-0.3757	0
3	0.6902	0.5764	798.	-0.3950	-520
4	0.9536	0.7964	798.	-0.1316	-520
5	0.9818	0.8199	798.	-0.1034	-520
6	1.0047	0.8390	816.	-0.1041	-720
7	1.0088	0.8425	816.	-0.1000	-720

Fig. 3.5c Example of Output Data for the RAG Network Program.

instance, of a gas emission prediction. In the latter case, a requirement is established that there must be a predetermined level of suction in this branch. The quantities which are then calculated are not the actual volume flows but the volume flows which are possible given the capacity of the network.

A simple example of the calculation of a drainage network is shown in Figure 3.5 a and b.

The characteristic curves of the extractors are not taken into account by the program.

2.3.6 Drainage Network Program TU Clausthal

The TU Clausthal program is principally an optimisation program and hence is different from any of the previous programs.

The theoretical capacity and geometry of gas drainage networks are subject to changes which occur in stages as a result of changes in the layout, seams and faces worked at the mine. The necessary adaption of the drainage network involves various technical measures such as

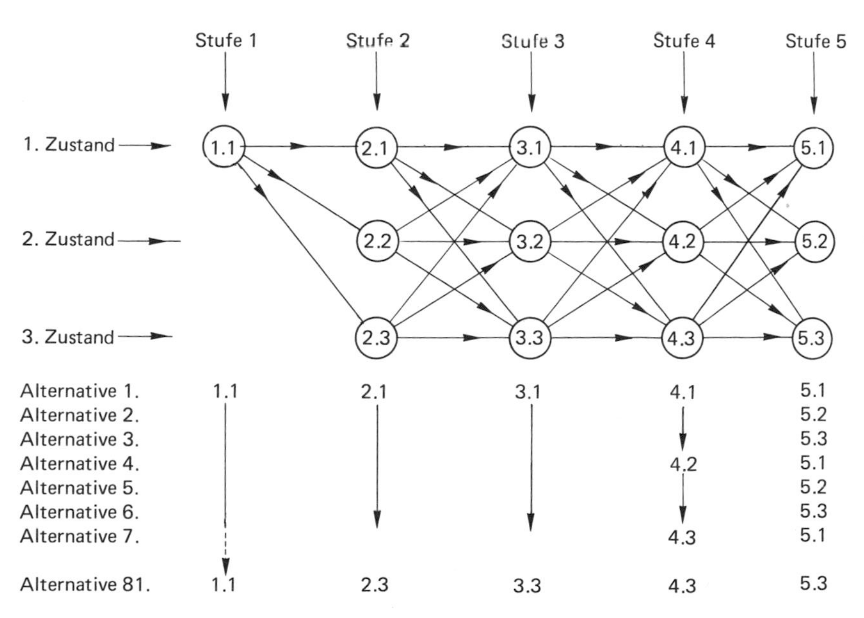

Fig. 3.6 a TU Clausthal Computer Program. Critical Path Analysis Shown in Graphic Form.

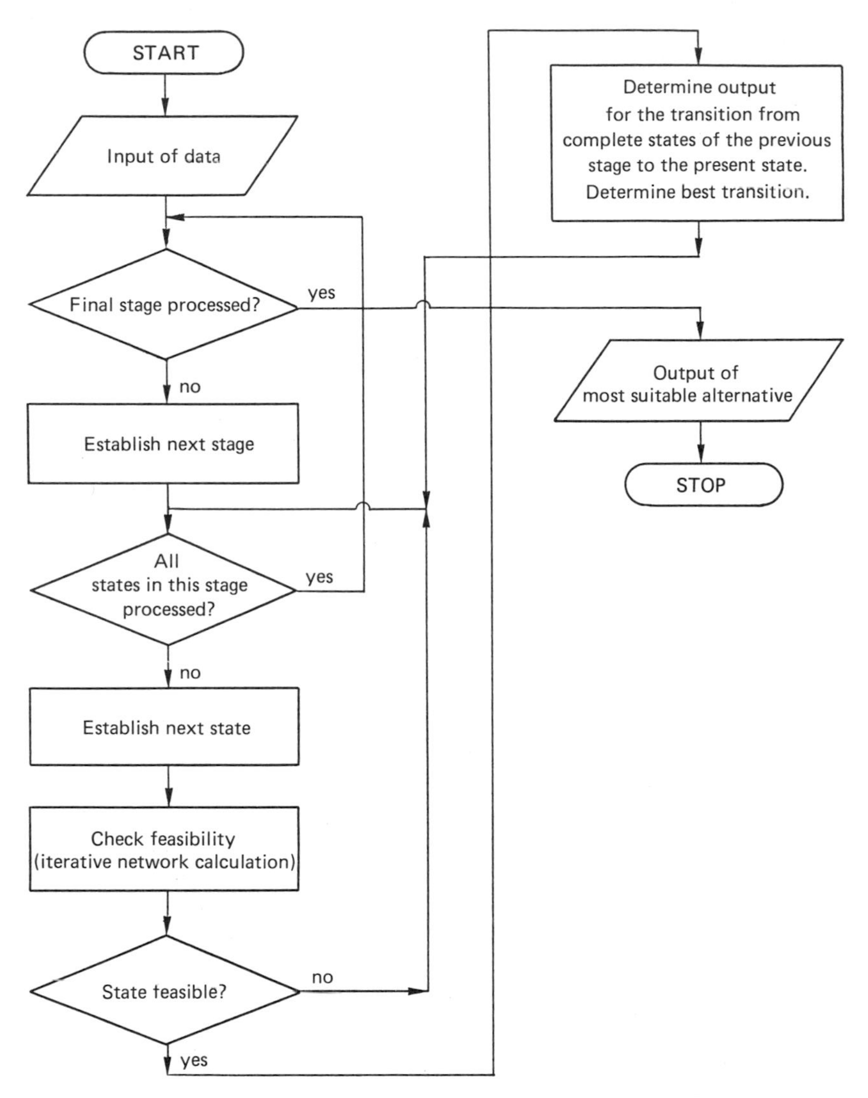

Fig. 3.6b TU Clausthal Computer Program. Flow Diagram of the Program.

increasing exhauster capacity or changing range sizes or installing new ranges. In order that a network may be planned for changes which may become necessary in the future, a so called optimisation plan has to be carried out. The problem is solved by critical path analysis, the program selecting the optimum alternative from a predefined number of alternatives with the aid of dynamic programming, using the need to minimise operational costs as the criterion and making due allowance for the financial return on the drained gas.

Figure 3.6 a shows an example of critical path analysis in graphic form; Figure 3.6 b shows a flow diagram of the program.

2.3.7 Comparison of RAG and TU Clausthal Programs

RAG

The program prints out the network description for every combination calculated as well as a list of the parameters in all branches of the network. It is necessary to input all details of the network for all sections in addition to the parameters of gas temperature and composition and wall roughness which are considered the same for all sections. It is not an optimisation program, but up to 12 combinations can be put through in one run. Only information on technical possibilities is given. Economic results can be obtained using firedamp drainage costs.

TU Clausthal

In addition to the information required for the RAG program, all technically possible changes must be entered. Financial aspects are examined and hence relevant prices are required. The program then gives the network which is the optimum from both economic and technical standpoints. The program is currently being modified to cope with slight changes to an existing permanently stored basic program. The TU Clausthal program offers greater ease of calculation than the RAG program. In terms of practical use, certain modifications still appear necessary.

2.3.8 Choice of Calculation Method for Drainage Networks

As can be seen from the preceding sections there are a number of ways of carrying out these calculations, covering the whole range of problems from a single pipe to a complex network. Practical guidance as to the best method to use for the various types of calculation encountered is given in Table 3.3.

Table 3.3 Application of the Various Firedamp Drainage Calculation Methods.

Type of problem	Desk or Hand Calculator (sect 2.3.1)	Purpose designed Calculator (sect 2.3.2)	Computer Programs			
			Reglagaz (sect 2.3.3)	Resogaz (sect 2.3.4)	RAG (sect 2.3.5)	TU Clausthal (sect 2.3.6)
Single horizontal pipe	X	X				
Several successive pipe lengths (horizontal)	X	X	X			
Several successive pipe lengths (inclined)			X			
Several successive lengths studying different variables (eg optimum diameter)			X			
Determination of "natural buoyancy" of vertical boreholes			X			
Study of branched ranges			X	X	X	X
Study of complex pipe networks				X	X	X
Optimisation of plant and network						X

3. Construction of Gas Drainage Networks[1]

3.1 Collecting Mains

3.1.1 Diameter and Number

Collecting gas mains are made of steel pipes of 150 to 350 mm diameter with wall thicknesses varying from 4.5 to 9.5 mm in the UK, 4 to 5.6 mm in Germany, 4 to 8 mm in Belgium and 2.5 to 6 mm in France.

Steel pipes may be purchased in lengths of 5 to 6 m. Collecting mains in gate roadways usually have internal diameters of 150, 200, 250, 300 or 350 mm but duplicate mains, each of 250 mm nominal diameter, may be used. They may be installed in intake and return gates of individual districts and sometimes in headings.

3.1.2 Materials

Tubes are made of steel as outlined in Table 3.4. Reference should be made to national regulations and specifications.

3.1.3 Fittings and Measuring Devices

Joints

A suitable joint is one that does not leak under a negative pressure (suction). Bolted loose flange, screwed fixed flange, welded fixed flange and flexible joints are employed, as shown in Table 3.5.

Valves and Flow Measuring Facilities

Valves are widely used in firedamp drainage networks. They are usually of the flanged, bolted type and made of cast iron or steel. Gate or fullway valves are almost invariably employed to minimise pressure losses (Table 3.6). Automatic valves are also used (Table 3.7). Isolating valves and flow measuring facilities are fitted into each collecting main.

3.2 Main Gas Pipe Ranges

3.2.1 Diameter

The main gas pipe is one into which a number of collecting gas mains are fed. Main gas pipe diameters are usually from 150 to 500 mm

---

[1] Measuring instruments are described in Chapter 4.

Table 3.4 Details of Pipe Materials and their Protection for Firedamp Drainage.

Item	Belgium	France	Germany	United Kingdom
Material	Steel welded pipe (St 37 or St 33 for small diameters)	Steel pipe welded on "generator" or in a spiral	Steel welded pipe (St 33 or St 37)	Steel hot finished seamless, in accordance with BS 3601.
Internal treatment	Galvanised	Hot galvanised	Galvanised	Cleaned to remove all scale, rust, grease, oil, and other foreign material. Then given phosphate coating and later coated with red lead paint.
External treatment	Galvanised	Hot galvanised	Galvanised	Smooth continuous coating of bituminous preparation to BS 534 after all scale, rust, grease, oil, and other foreign matter removed.
Test pressure	5000 or 6000 kPa (50 or 60 bar)	500 kPa (5 bar)	5000 kPa (50 bar)	Hydraulically tested to withstand test pressure of not less than 5000 kPa (50 bar) or such pressure as may be specified.
Identification	Yellow band at each end (marking not uniform)		50 mm wide, yellow ring at each pipe end	Yellow band near ends of tube not less than 75 mm wide approximately 300 mm from each end.
Specifications		ST/13-200b M 82-245 (Lorraine) SH 111C (Nord)	DIN 20001 DIN 20002	BS 3601; BS 534 NCB Spec. No. 596/1972.

Table 3.5 Main Types of Pipe Joint.

Joint	Description
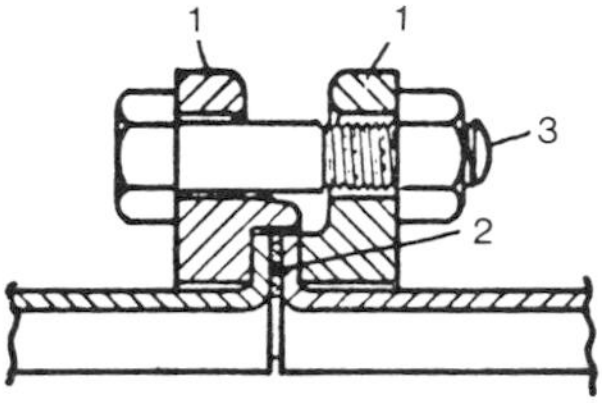	**Loose flange bolted joint** Formed by bolting together two loose flanges (1), one at the end of each pipe. A joint ring (2) is inserted to ensure air tightness and is made of rubber or approved material. Bolts (3) are spaced equidistantly around the flanges. Standard sizes are made up to 310 mm bore. Joints are suitable for pressures up to 1050 kPa. Special joints are available for higher pressures. Steel or cast iron flanges are used for pipes up to 310 mm bore. Joint with limited flexibility: used in shafts.
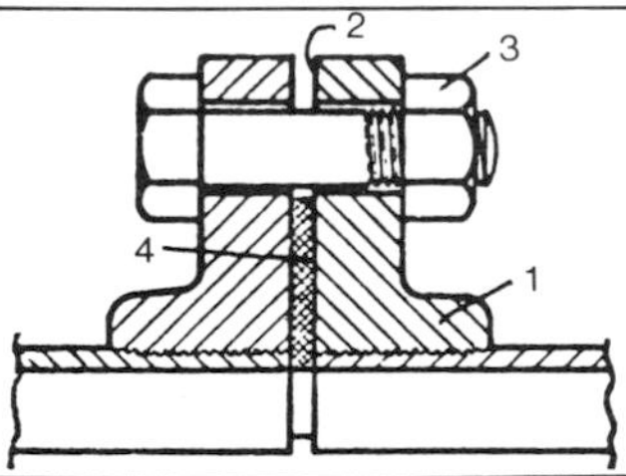	**Screwed fixed flange joint** Screwed on flanges (1) are employed, especially on smaller pipe sizes, where pipes are sufficiently thick to permit of a satisfactory screwed joint. Flanges are faced plain (2) and bolted (3) according to appropriate national standards. Rubber or other appropriate jointing material (4) inserted between flanges. Joint has limited flexibility. May be used in gate roadways.
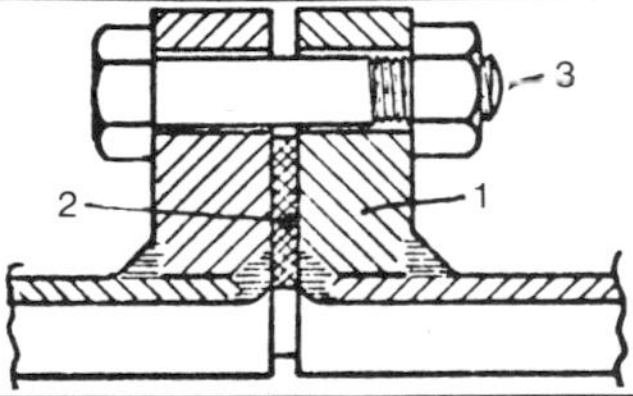	**Welded fixed flange joint** Steel pipes may be provided with welded on joints either of the flat ring type (1) or male and female type. Flanges are made of steel with rubber or other acceptable jointing material (2). Flanges (1) are bolted (3) according to appropriate national standards. Joint has limited flexibility; may be used in shafts.
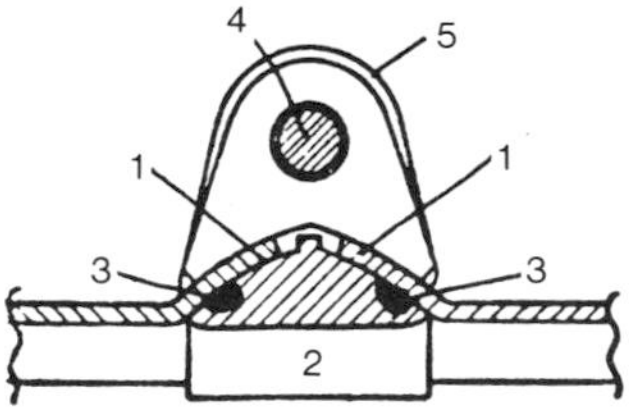	**Carlton flexible joint** The ends of each steel pipe length are enlarged to form special 'Bell' ends (1). A ferrule (2) is made of cast iron and is provided with two rubber rings (3). The ferrule is inserted between two adjacent bell ends, and the joint is completed by bolting (4) together the two half steel housings (5). This joint has the advantages that it forms a positive seal under suction and pressure. It permits angular adjustment during or after laying of from 8° to 6° on larger sizes. Used almost exclusively in the United Kingdom for all underground applications.
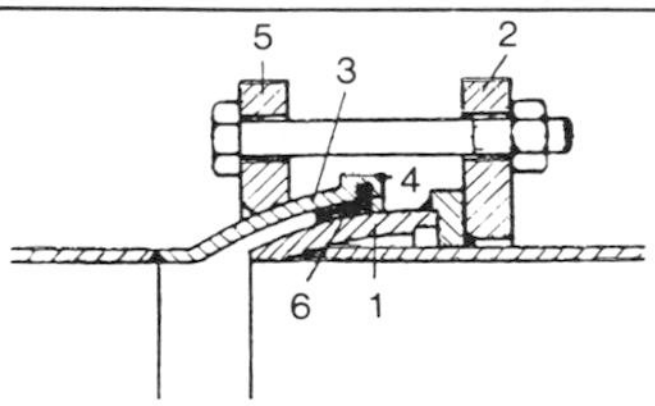	**Spherical flange connection** The pipes terminate at one end in a forged, surface-machined hollow sphere (1), behind which there is a loose flange (2). At the other end there is a forged socket (3) with machined groove (4) and similar loose companion flange (5). A sealing ring (6) is inserted in the groove. This connection is made for 3 and 5 m long pipes of 150 to 300 mm nominal diameter. It has the advantage that the pipes can be deflected up to 8°.

Table 3.6 Details of Manual Valve Types.

Valve	Description
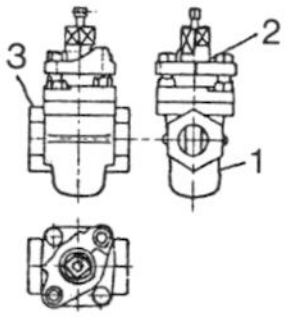	**Lubricated taper plug valve** Robust, plug type valve which offers little resistance to gas and water flow. Quick acting, self sealing, easily operated by wrench and simple in design. Body (1) usually made in cast iron with carbon steel bolts (2) with drilled flanged or screwed ends (3).
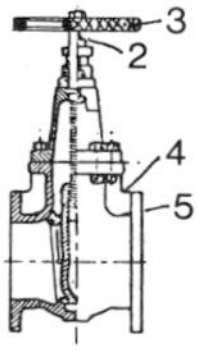	**Full way gate valve** Fullway gate valve with parallel or wedge type gate (1) usually of the non rising stem type (2). Offers very little resistance to flow, easily operated by hand-wheel (3). Robust with body (4) usually made of cast iron with threaded ends (smaller sizes made of bronze), or with flanged ends (5) for larger cast iron valves.
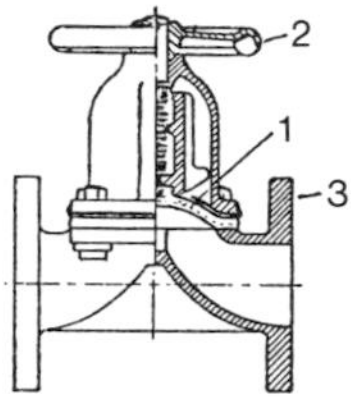	**Full flow diaphragm valve** Flow through this valve is streamlined. Provided with flexible, reinforced, resilient diaphragm (1) supported in all positions, offers little resistance to gas and water flow. Provided with non rising stem handwheel (2) and lubricated working parts are isolated from gas or water. No glands, robust with cast iron body (3), diaphragm material specially selected for drained gas.
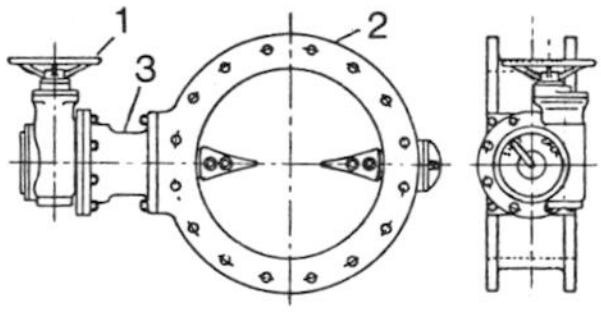	**Butterfly valve** Full flow through butterfly valve with hand wrench or worm wheel (1) operation. Slim, compact, easy to instal, flanged bolted design (2). No pockets, self-cleaning. Usually about one-quarter turn to fully open or close-tight shut off. Body (2, 3) made of cast iron.
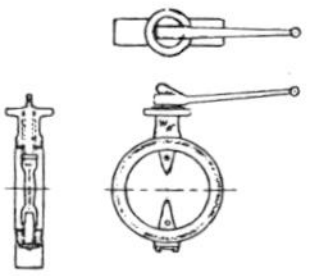	**Circular damper** Housing with vulcanised joint. Streamlined damper. Operating lever with setting stops and O-ring seals. Installed without flange. Very compact construction.

Table 3.7 Details of Automatic Valve Types.

Valve	Description
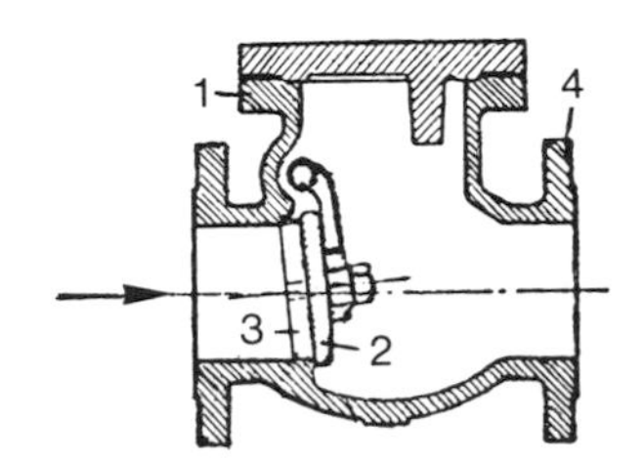	**Non Return Valve** Self acting, non return valve with body (1) made of cast steel or cast iron, with solid flap (2), seat ring (3) and leather faced flap. Flanged (4) and bolted, with flanges drilled to appropriate national standards. Used on suction of water seal extractors and in pipe lines. Can be fitted with counter balance weight and dashpot for quick action and damping in pulsating flow.
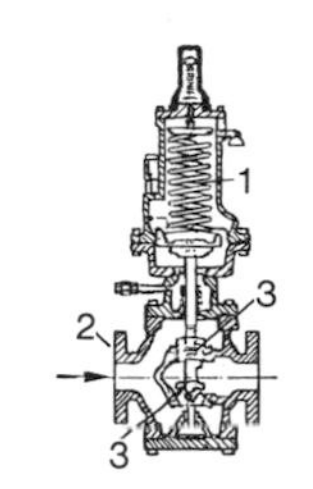	**Diaphragm Pressure Regulator** Self acting spring regulator (1) used to relieve excess gas pressure from discharge side of surface extraction plant. Begins to open when preset gas pressure reached below which pressure valve remains closed. Valve wide open when pressure about 7 kPa above pre set pressure. Made of high grade cast iron (2) with all internal trim of rustless materials. Guided double ported, balanced valves with Nitrile or Viton rubber inserts and reinforced synthetic rubber diaphragm. Often fitted with micro switch.
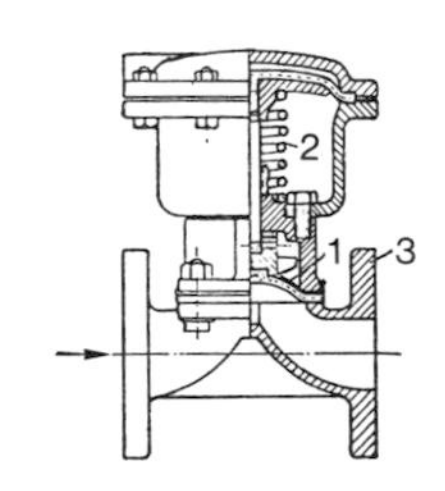	**Diaphragm Operated Valve** Valve with flexible diaphragm (1) operated by compressed air, water, or other acceptable fluid against spring (2). High pressure opening or closing as in diagram. Robust with cast iron body (3). Suitable for remote operation and control to shut off or admit compressed air or other fluid to machinery. Can be fitted with microswitch.
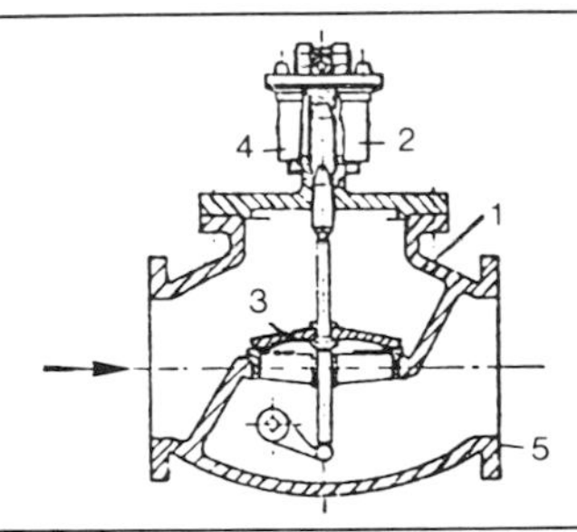	**Hand Opening Electro Magnetic Valve** 'Globe type' valve made of cast iron (1), operated manually by external handle and maintained in open position by d. c. energised magnetic coil (4) installed in flameproof enclosure (2). Commonly made in sizes from 12 to 250 mm. Larger sizes provided with flanges (5). Valve and seat (3) made of gun metal, used on suction and delivery sides of surface firedamp extraction plants to provide automatic cut off of gas flow in certain conditions eg. low purity of drained gas, mains power failure etc.

(continued overleaf).

Table 3.7 (continued).

Valve	Description
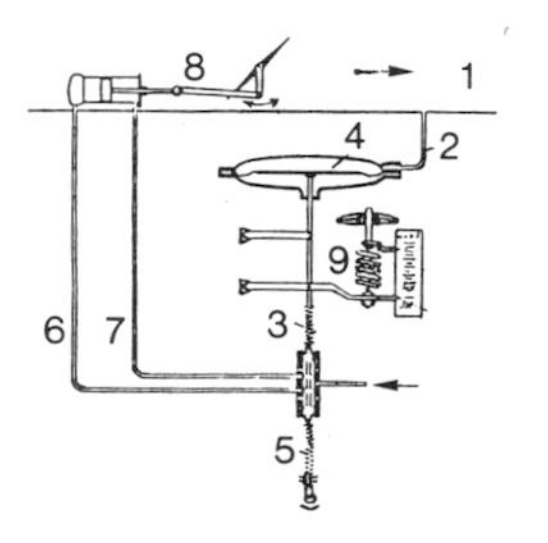	**Low Pressure Regulator** The pressure which is to be kept constant at (1), by means of the impulse duct (2) acts upon the membrane (4) which is tensioned by a spring (3). The movements of the membrane are transmitted to an elastically suspended valve (5) controlling the hydraulic oil. The hydraulic oil injected into control tube (6) or (7) actuates a control mechanism (8). By means of an adjustment (9) the desired pressure can be set. Control is by a butterfly or gate type valve.
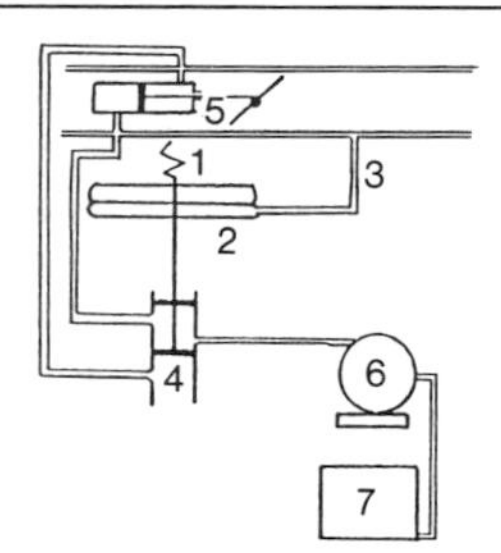	**Hydraulic Membrane Pressure Regulator** A membrane (2) held under tension by spring (1) is acted upon by the pressure in the sensing tube (3). A valve (4) connected to the membrane controls the feed of hydraulic oil by which the control mechanism (5) (butterfly or gate type) is actuated. A pump draws oil from reservoir (7).

nominal size, supplied in random pipe lengths of 5 to 6 m. Duplicated 250 or 300 mm pipe ranges are used in some cases.

3.2.2 Materials

Pipe ranges are usually made of steel to the same specification as given in Table 3.4.

3.2.3 Fittings and Measuring Devices

Joint and Valves

The joints and valves employed are as described in Section 3.1.3 above. Some valves may be controlled remotely (Table 3.7).

Flow, Pressure and Purity Measuring Devices

Tappings are required at regular intervals along the length of steel mains so that pressures and purities of drained gas in the system can be measured, for example to detect air inleakage.

3.3 Shaft Gas Pipes

3.3.1 Diameter

Shaft gas pipes usually have nominal diameters of 150 to 600 mm depending on gas extraction rates and depths of shafts. Duplicated 250 or 300 mm pipe ranges are used in some cases. Fixed lengths of steel piping are employed, usually about 5 m long. Pipes of similar sizes are used in staple shafts. It is recommended that methane drainage pipes are installed in upcast shafts. In the UK, pipe ranges cannot be installed (by law) in any "shaft or outlet" through which air enters the mine.

3.3.2 Materials

Pipe ranges are made of steel to the specification mentioned in Table 3.4.

3.3.3 Fittings and Measuring Devices

Joints and Valves

Bolted, welded, flanged joints are used (Table 3.5). Telescopic joints are usually provided in shaft mains (Figure 3.7) to allow for movement in shafts. The telescopic joint consists of two main castings, one sliding within the other and provided with end flanges for bolting to

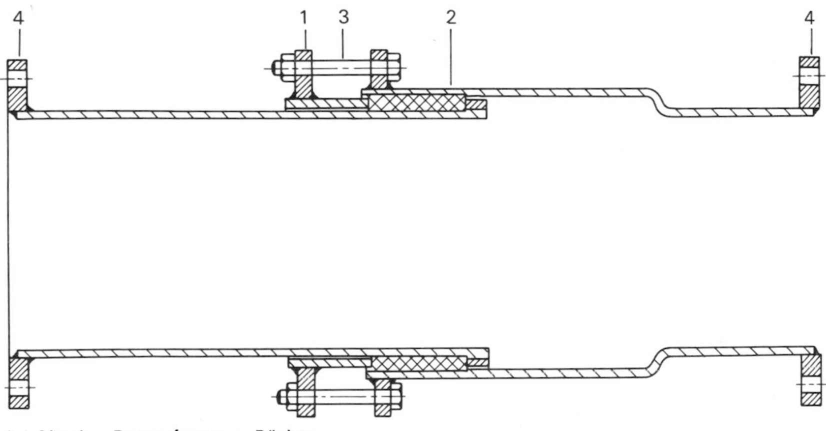

1 Gland — Presse étoupe — Büchse
2 Packing — Garniture — Dichtung
3 Packing Gland Bolts — Boulons du presse-étoupe — Dichtungsschrauben
4 End Flanges — Brides d'extrémité — Endflansche

Fig. 3.7 Shaft Pipe Telescopic Joint.

the shaft pipes in the required position. A gland (1) and stuffing box arrangement is used, the gland being secured by a number of bolts (3) around its periphery, which also serve to compress the packing (2). Fullway isolating valves are inserted at the bottom and top of the shaft range.

3.4 Surface Gas Pipes

At the surface, pipes should be laid in safe positions and provided with isolating valves. They should be protected against frost and installed according to national specifications. As an anti-frost measure, steel pipes may be lagged with heat insulating material to reduce the effects of temperature changes and condensation. Alternatively thermal, electric powered, wrapping may be applied to reduce condensation and freezing in the colder winter months.

3.4.1 Inlet Side to Gas Extractor Plant

3.4.1.1 Diameter

Surface gas pipes have diameters of 150 to 600 mm depending on gas extraction rates, distances involved, and local considerations. Duplicated 250 or 300 mm pipe ranges are used in some cases.

3.4.1.2 Materials

Pipe ranges are made of steel to the specification mentioned in Table 3.4.

3.4.1.3 Measuring Devices

Such equipment must conform with national and local regulations and directives. National documents in some countries show the positions and specify equipment such as methanometers, valves, gauges, protective devices, discharge chimney and flame traps and describe the layout, building requirements, and protective circuits needed. Specifications are given of the layout, fittings, measuring devices and approved equipment. Basic details are given in Appendix 3.5.

3.5 Installation of Gas Ranges

Firedamp drainage pipes should be laid so that they are protected from mechanical damage. Although local conditions will govern the type of installation, in general gas mains should be supported from roadway supports, usually at a height of 2 m or more above floor level. This method has advantages of easier checking, reduced external corrosion and maintenance, better protection and easier accommodation for strata movement compared with laying pipes on the floor of roadways. Flexible joints, such as Carlton or spherical flange type, have a number of advantages when used below ground, particularly where strata movement is encountered. It is necessary to support gas pipes at regular intervals. Pipe supports (chain or steel wire rope) should provide facilities for adjusting pipe positions in event of strata movement. Before fitting and making each pipe joint, the end of each pipe should be examined; any indentations or damage should be corrected so that an effective seal can be obtained when the joint is made. All bolts should be inserted in each joint. Firedamp drainage pipes should be earthed. They should not be installed in trolley locomotive roadways.

Gas ranges should be installed so that, as far as natural conditions will allow, uniform gradients are achieved. To enable water to be removed and drained off periodically or continuously, it is essential that positive "low points" are formed in the gas range for water to accumulate. Full size ("equal") tee pieces should be inserted at such low points and a water trap incorporated. Manual water traps may be installed though automatic water traps are preferred. All such traps should be installed so that air leakage into the gas main is minimised. Water traps should be capable of operating under negative and positive pressures.

A fullway isolating valve should be installed in each branch of the gas main so that the branch can be isolated immediately in emergency, for maintenance, extension and testing of gas mains and for other purposes; valves must be capable of being effectively maintained without their removal from the gas mains.

Before commissioning a gas range, joints and pipes should be tested for leakage using compressed air if available. Alternatively, extractor suction may be used initially to find and identify positions of inleakage before commissioning the length of pipe. For this and other purposes, sampling and measuring points should be installed at regular intervals along the gas main. With such facilities, positions of inleakage of air can be identified by making methane concentration surveys along the length of the pipe. During installation, flow measuring equipment may be installed in each branch, at the outbye end of each gate, at the shaft bottom and shaft top and elsewhere where necessary. Provision should be made by the installation of convenient isolating valves for the gas main in gate roadways to be extended regularly and for new boreholes to be connected into the pipe system in a minimum of time.

After installation, checks for leakage should be carried out systematically by taking measurements of the purity of drained gas at sampling points along the pipe using hand held methanometers.

Shaft pipes should be of the fixed flange, bolted type (Table 3.5) and be securely fastened to buntons and installed in a safe position. Where necessary, telescopic joints (Figure 3.7) should be inserted in shaft ranges at intervals of about 100 m. Normally such pipes should be laid in upcast shafts, but reference should be made to local regulations. Gravity type water traps should be inserted at the bottom of each shaft column (Figure 3.8).

All gas mains should be painted with a readily distinguishable colour. Reference to local regulations should be made in the selection of colour, the type of distinguishing mark needed, and their position.

Pipes should be installed to a planned design and be shown on mine plans. On completion of the installation, such plans should be checked

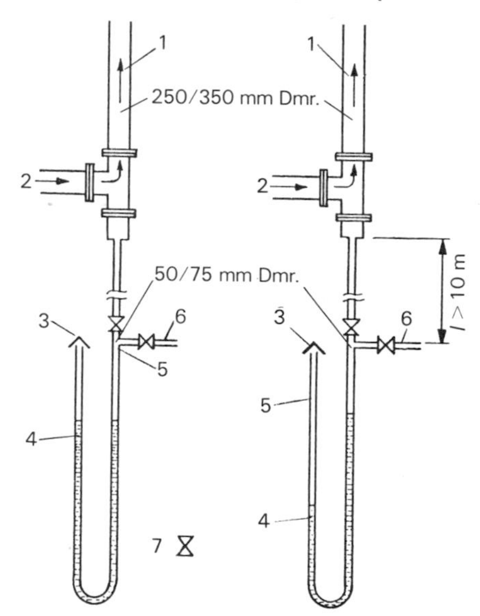

1 Upcast Shaft Range — Collecteur de puits — Leitung im Ausziehschacht
2 Drained Firedamp — Gaz capté — Abgesaugtes Grubengas
3 Protective Cap — Chapeau de Protection — Schutzkappe
4 Water — Eau — Wasser
5 Steel Water Tube — Tube en U ou acier — Wasserrohr aus Stahl
6 Water Connection — Raccordement eau — Wasseranschluß
7 Stop Valve — Vanne d'arrêt — Absperrventil

Fig. 3.8 Shaft Pipe U Type Water Trap.

to ensure that all relevant details are inserted including gas pipe diameters and lengths, the position of all low points, water drains, sampling points, valves, measuring positions, as well as stoppings, current productive districts and boreholes and any other places from which firedamp is drained. Such plans should be kept up to date. Each measuring station and borehole should be numbered for ready identification.

3.6 Drainage of Water from Collecting Mains

3.6.1 Sources

Water found in gas mains originates partly from the strata. Therefore, water often comes off with the firedamp and accumulates in the gas main, even when strata appear to be dry. Floorholes frequently contain more water than do roofholes. An additional amount of water is extracted with the gas immediately after connecting new boreholes to the gas main when wet drilling is practised. Another source of water is the saturated drained gas in the pipe, from which water is condensed when the gas main is exposed to significant temperature falls as, for example, when gas mains are taken from a return to an intake roadway, or a gas main emerges from a warm upcast shaft and airlock to a colder environment at the surface of a mine. Additional amounts of water may be found in pipes on the discharge side of water seal extractors.

3.6.2 Water Traps and Separators

Water traps and separators in gas mains are essential and are installed at each low point. When water traps are removed connections to the gas main should be sealed. A number of water traps have been described in Chapter 2, Section 1.1.4.6.

In addition, the two chamber, automatic, compressed-air driven water trap and separator (1) (Figure 3.9) complete with compressed air water pump (2), is designed for draining water from underground gas mains in situations where, because of the large water flow, automatic water dumping is necessary. Automatic removal of water is obtained by an air valve (3), which is controlled by a float in the separator. This in turn operates a control valve (4), which admits compressed air to the inlet of the water pump air motor (2). The water levels at which the water pump starts and stops can be varied by adjusting the float arm of the air valve (3). The total capacity of the reservoir is about 0.4 m^3 and the unit can be operated over a 125 mm water level differential ie between automatic pump starting and stop-

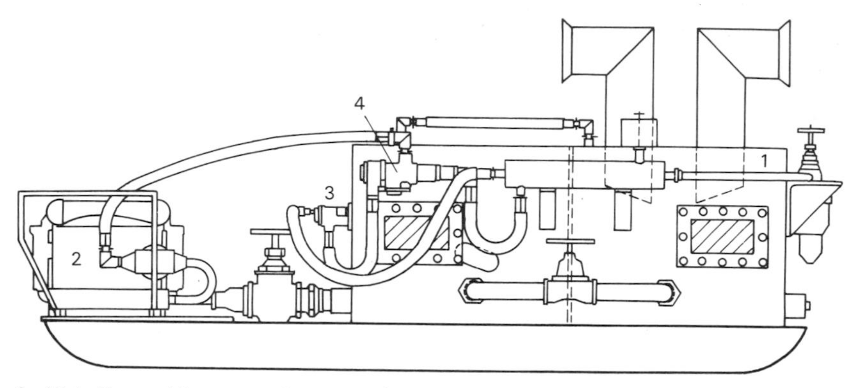

1 Water Trap and Separator — Purgeur et séparateur — Wasserabscheider
2 Compressed Air Water Pump — Pompe à eau à air comprimé — Druckluftgetriebene Wasserpumpe
3 Compressed Air/Water Float Valve — Vanne à flotteur — Schwimmergesteuertes Druckluftventil
4 Control Valve — Vanne de commande — Steuerventil

Fig. 3.9 Automatic Two Chamber Water Trap and Separator.

ping. The pump capacity is 1 l/s. Positive action of the valve is required to prevent hunting between high and low water levels.

A special U type water trap is inserted at the bottom of shafts (usually upcast shafts), as shown in Figure 3.8. Water separates out from the saturated drained gas flowing into, and in, the shaft main and falls by gravity into the U type water trap. Such water traps need to have one limb (connected to the shaft range) sufficiently long so that the water level in that limb is always well below the water connection shown in Figure 3.8. Dirt, scale, and other foreign material enters the water trap so that periodically it is necessary to flush out this material by applying water under high pressure through the water connection, after having first isolated the U water tube from the shaft gas main.

A tangential water separator is used at the outlet of a base-mounted surface water-seal extractor (1) (Figure 3.10). Water is removed by ensuring that the gas leaving the extractor is forced to follow a tangential direction (2). A ball float valve located in the float chamber (3), at the base of the separator maintains a water seal and prevents the release of gas with the dumping of the water removed from the gas main through outlet (4).

In tank mounted units, a small horizontal type water separator, 10 in Figure 3.18, is used, in which water is separated automatically from the gas by a baffle plate and by reducing gas velocity. The water removed from the gas flows back into the water tank beneath the extractor.

3.7 Flame Traps and Extinguishers

Flame traps are employed as safety devices to arrest the travel, and prevent the spread, of flame in firedamp extraction systems in the event of the firedamp/air mixture becoming ignited. There are mechanical flame traps and flame extinguishers.

3.7.1 Mechanical Flame Traps

Mechanical flame traps are designed to offer a large surface area to the flame and this is achieved by providing a large number of narrow passages in parallel. In this manner heat is removed progressively

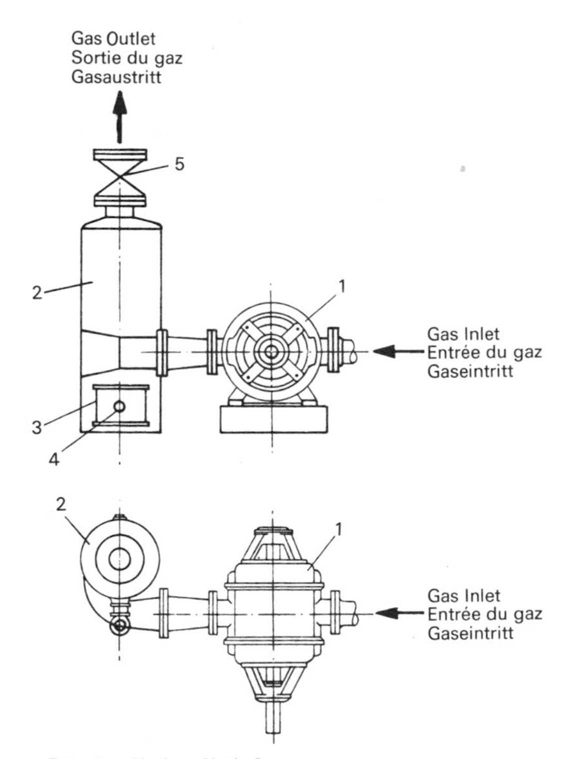

1 Nash Extractor — Extracteur Nash — Nash-Sauger
2 Tangential Water Separator — Séparateur tangentiel — Tangential-Wasserabscheider
3 Float Chamber and Ball Float Valve — Chambre à flotteur et vanne à flotteur — Schwimmerkammer und schwimmerbetätigtes Kugelventil
4 Water Outlet — Sortie d'eau — Wasseraustritt
5 Delivery Stop Valve — Vanne d'arrêt de refoulement — Druckseitiges Absperrventil

Fig. 3.10 Tangential Water Separator.

until the flame is extinguished and flame propagation is no longer possible. Care must be taken, in the design stage, to minimise pressure losses across the flame trap. Mechanical flame traps may lose their effectiveness if they are exposed to flames for a long period of time. They may, therefore, be supplemented by automatic extinguishing devices.

For firedamp drainage applications four types of mechanical flame trap are used. They are:

▷ Gauze type flame traps (particularly in the UK);

▷ Ribbon type flame traps;

▷ Plate type flame traps (Belgium and France);

▷ Glass sphere type flame traps (Germany).

In each case the flame arresting element is installed in a cast iron or steel plate conical housing, to minimise pressure losses. The housing has flanged ends for connection to the gas mains. The diameter of the pipes being protected ranges between 150 and 600 mm, with housing diameters up to 1400 mm.

3.7.1.1 Gauze Type Flame Traps

This type consists of a housing in which several small discs (usually five) are mounted side by side with their surfaces covered by metal (copper or stainless steel) gauze or crimped metal strip, and are widely used in the UK.

3.7.1.2 Ribbon Type Flame Traps (Figure 3.11 a)

In this type of flame trap the arrestor element consists of sheets arranged in parallel made from alternate layers of smooth and corrugated metal ribbon. Ribbon traps have the same explosion and flow properties as the glass spheres described later.

3.7.1.3 Plate Type Flame Traps

These flame traps consist of closely-spaced rectangular metal plates which resemble the arresting elements used on diesel engines.

3.7.1.4 Glass Sphere Type Flame Traps (Figure 3.11 b)

These consist of a conical steel housing (up to 1400 mm in diameter) at the widest point of which is located a tray with metal gauzes. This tray is packed with a layer of glass balls and is 90 mm thick for 6 mm diameter balls. In Germany some 80 % of firedamp drainage systems are equipped with glass sphere flame traps.

3.7.1.5 Maintenance and Supervision

Pressure losses across mechanical flame traps may be considerable due to build-up of foreign material and can be monitored by a pressure gauge preferably in a fixed position. To avoid accumulations of dust,

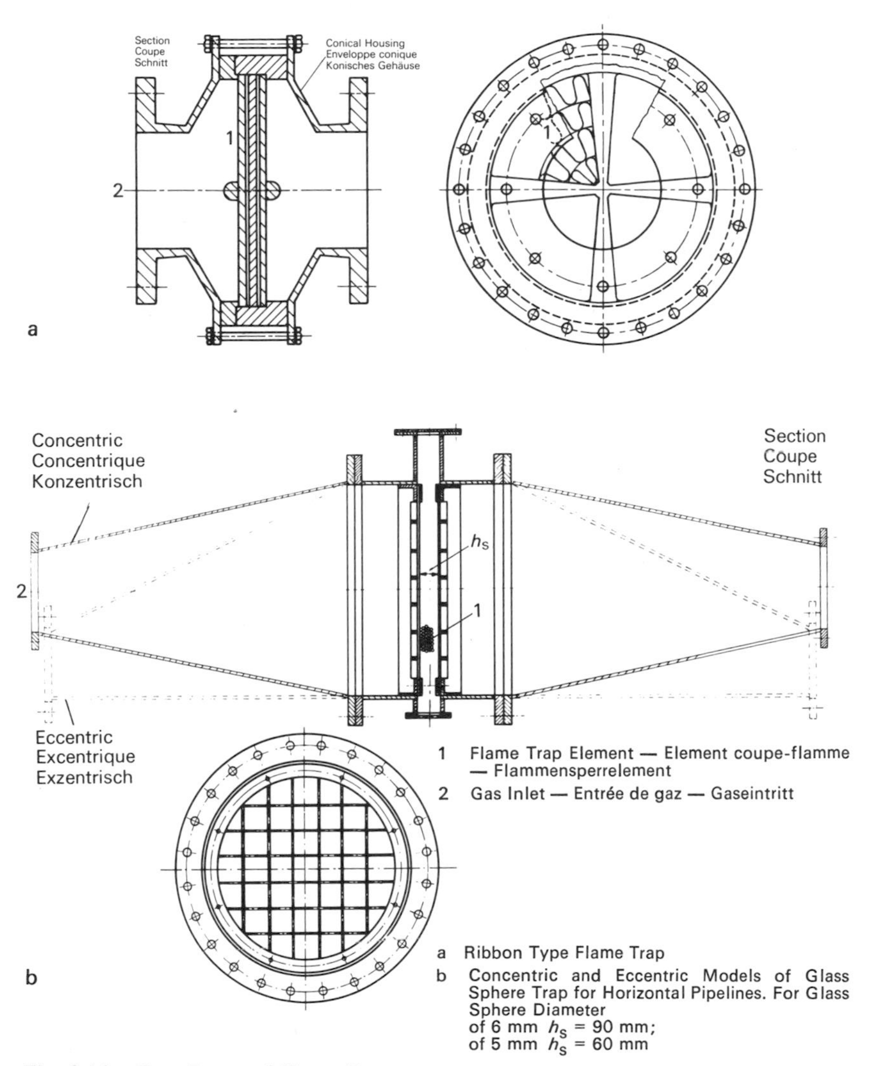

Fig. 3.11 Two Types of Flame Trap.

rust and deposits of carbon and extinguishing powder after ignitions, regular cleaning of the elements is necessary to ensure that the flame trap is maintained in good working order and pressure losses minimised. It is essential therefore that the elements are readily accessible for inspection, cleaning or replacement. In the UK maintenance of flame traps forms part of plant preventative maintenance schemes. Two flame traps are often arranged in parallel so that one can be cleaned while the other is in operation. In some countries, arrestor elements are always removed for inspection and maintenance after an ignition of firedamp has occurred.

Provision is made for regular examination of the flame trap and its extinguishing equipment, and also in cases where drained gas has been ignited.

3.7.2 Flame Extinguishers

In some countries flame extinguishers are used and are triggered electrically by a heat sensor. The extinguishing medium which is stored in pressurised flasks is blown into the firedamp range to prevent further propagation of the flame. Flame extinguishers have the advantages that they do not cause pressure losses and are not easily blocked by dirt. Extinguishers are equipped with stand-by cylinders which are actuated by the heat sensor if, after the extinction of one flame, a further ignition occurs. Downstream equipment may require cleaning after injection of extinguishing powder.

4. Vacuum Generators

4.1 Machine Types

4.1.1 Venturi Extractors

Compressed air or closed circuit water powered venturis and airmovers are occasionally used when small local, often temporary, firedamp extraction schemes are required. They must be earthed when in use. Wet venturi extractors are used in the United Kingdom. (Reference needs to be made to national regulations.)

The main disadvantages of venturi extractors for firedamp drainage are that they are relatively inefficient, and are capable of producing only limited suction. They are, however, small, cheap and easily installed. Figure 3.12 shows the general arrangement and typical performance

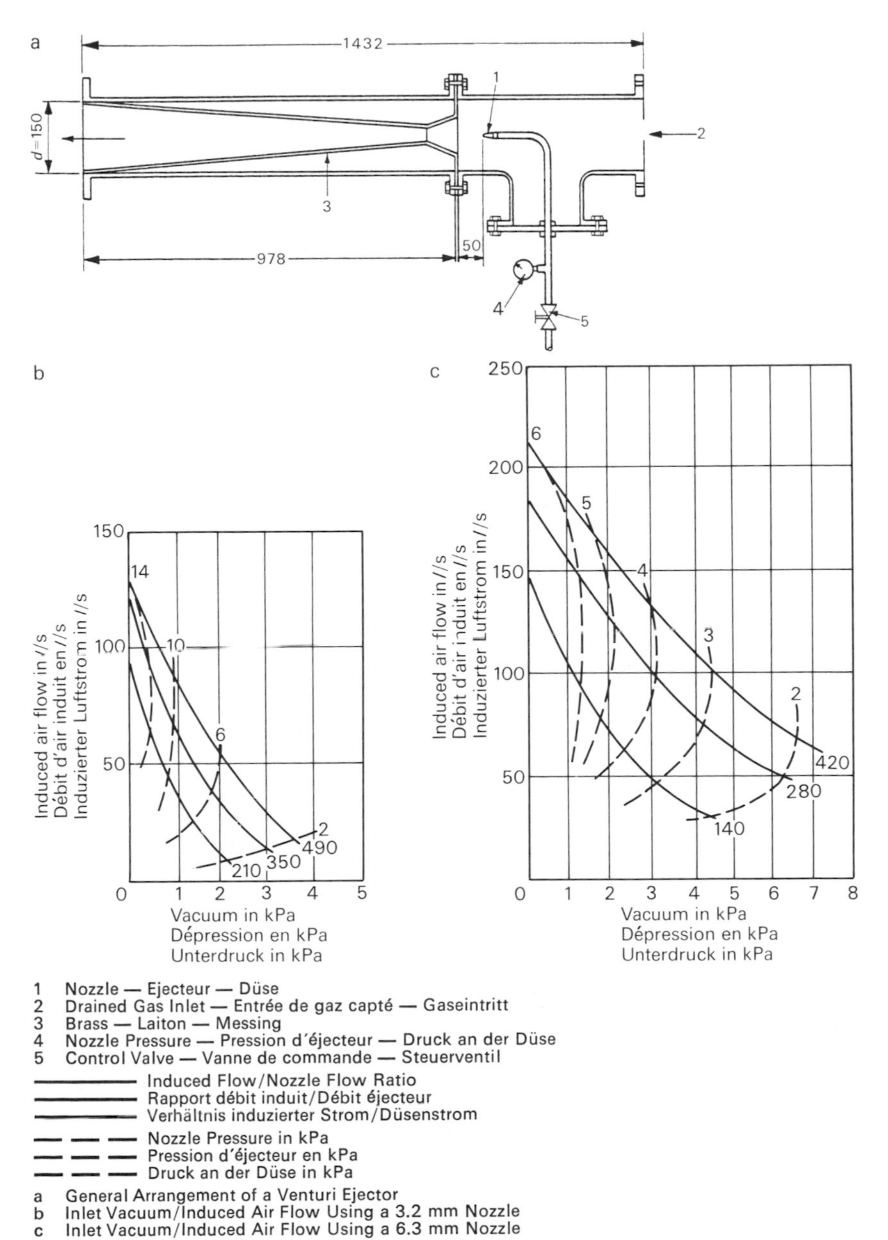

Fig. 3.12 Compressed Air Venturi Ejector with Characteristic Curves.

curves of venturi extractors employing 3.2 and 6.3 mm diameter nozzles. The water flow circuits of, and the prime mover for, a water powered venturi installation are shown in Figure 3.13. Water is pressurised to about 7000 kPa using an electrically driven ram pump (9). This water is fed to a 3.2 mm diameter jet (11), which is carefully centralised near the entrance to the venturi extractor. When water is passed through the jet, a firedamp/air mixture is extracted through the pipe (1), and discharged from the venturi extractor with the jet water. The water and drained gas are separated in the separator (7), the water falling into the tank (8). Drained firedamp is discharged from the water separator (7), into a discharge cage, similar to that shown in Figure 3.22.

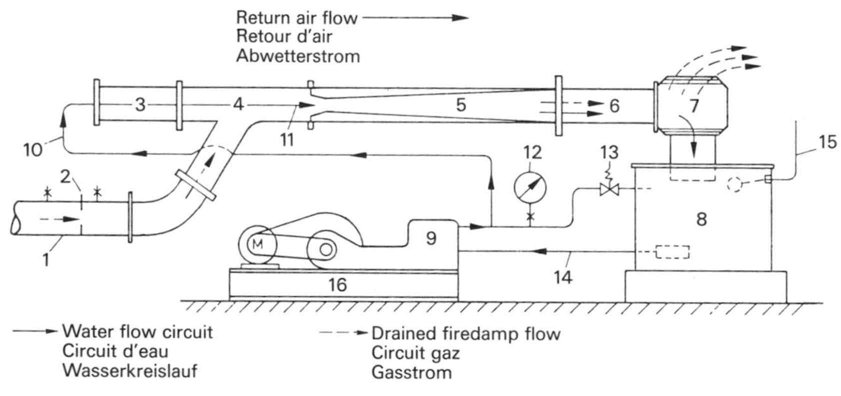

—— Water flow circuit
Circuit d'eau
Wasserkreislauf

– – – Drained firedamp flow
Circuit gaz
Gasstrom

1 Firedamp Drainage Pipe — Conduite de captage — Absaugleitung
2 Orifice Plate — Diaphragme — Meßblende
3 Aligment Unit — Element de centrage — Begradigungsstück
4 Y Piece — Té Y — Y-Abzweig
5 Water Venturi Extractor — Extracteur à venturi — Nasser Venturi-Ejektor
6 Steel Matching up Pipe — Conduit de raccordement acier — Paßrohr aus Stahl
7 Water/Gas Separator — Séparateur eau-gaz — Wasserabscheider
8 Water Tank — Réservoir d'eau — Wassertank
9 Electrically Driven Water (Pressure) Pump — Pompe électrique pour eau sous pression — Elektrisch angetriebene Druckwasserpumpe
10 Pressure Hose from Water Pump to Water Jet — Flexible éjection — Druckschlauch von der Wasserpumpe zur Wasserdüse
11 Water Jet — Jet d'eau — Wasserdüse
12 Water Pressure Gauge — Indicateur de pression d'eau — Manometer für Wasserdruck
13 Adjustable Water Pressure Relief Valve — Vanne de détente réglable — Regulierbares Wasserdruck-Entlastungsventil
14 Suction Hose from Water Tank to Pump — Flexible aspiration — Saugschlauch vom Wassertank zur Pumpe
15 Make up Water Supply — Eau d'appoint — Wassereinspeisung
16 Base plate — Socle — Grundplatte

Fig. 3.13 Underground Water Powered Venturi Installation for Firedamp Drainage.

4.1.2 Water Seal Extractors

4.1.2.1 Types

In the water seal vacuum extractor, a rotating water seal is used to generate vacuum (and delivery) pressures and to displace gas. Reference should be made to national regulations for conditions of use.

Two types of water seal extractor may be used (Figure 3.14), that in which (a) the rotor is mounted centrally within an elliptical casing and (b) the rotor is arranged eccentrically within a circular casing. Both types operate on the same principle.

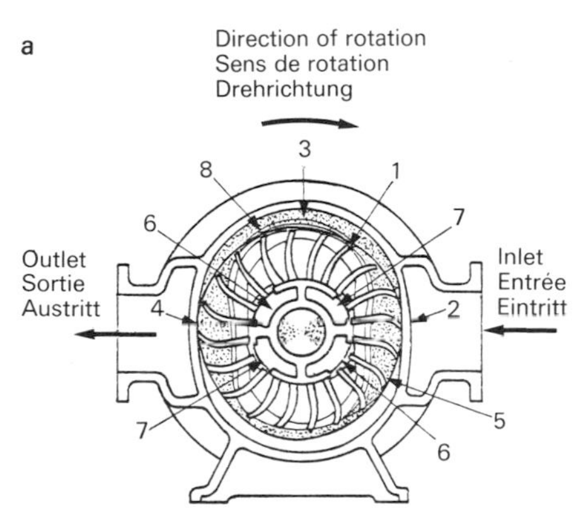

a With Rotor Mounted Contrally in Elliptical Casing

1 Rotor — Rotor — Rotor
2 Elliptical Casing — Corps elliptique — Elliptisches Gehäuse
3 Major Axis — Grand axe — Große Achse
4 Minor Axis — Petit axe — Kleine Achse
6 Inlet Port — Orifice d'entrée — Eintrittsöffnung
7 Discharge Port — Orifice de sortie — Austrittsöffnung
8 Water Seal — Anneau liquide — Wasserring

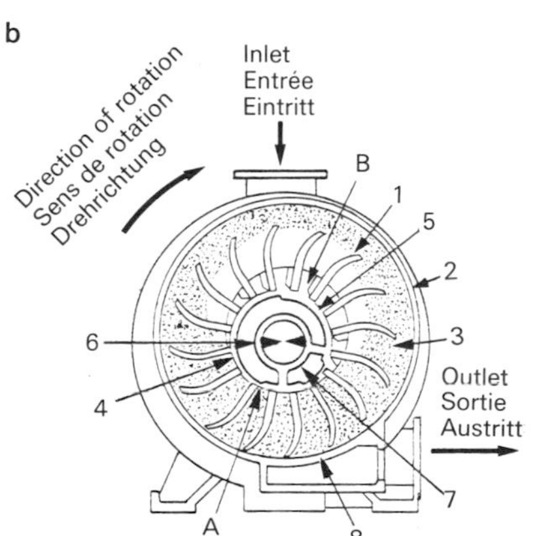

b With Rotor Mounted Eccentrically Circular Casing

1 Rotor — Rotor — Rotor
2 Circular Casing — Enveloppe circulaire — Gehäuse
3 Inner Contour of the Casing — Intérieur de l'enveloppe — Innenkontur des Gehäuses
5 Internal Conical Casing — Orifice d'entrée d'intérieur de l'enveloppe — Eintrittsöffnung des konischen Innengehäuses
6 Internal Inlet Port — Orifice intérieur d'entrée — Innere Eintrittsöffnung
7 Internal Discharge Port — Orifice intérieur de sortie — Innere Austrittsöffnung
8 Unloader — Délestage — Entleerer

Fig. 3.14 Principle of Water Seal Extractors.

4.1.2.1.1 Extractors with Elliptical Casings (Figure 3.14 a)

In the first type, a centrally located rotor (1), revolves freely without contact in an elliptical casing (2), containing water. The rotor comprises a number of forward inclined blades with end rings to form pockets or chambers. Two inlet and two outlet gas ports are provided in the elliptical casing, as shown in the illustration. As the rotor revolves, water within the extractor is forced to follow paths dictated by the

Table 3.8 Performance of water seal extractors. Part A: Nash.

Type	Speed rad/s	Suction kPa	Volume Flow l/s	Shaft Power kW	Circulating Water Flow l/s	Motor Power kW
L5	76.4	35	84.5	9.0	0.53	18.7
	76.4	67.2	38.4	10.8	0.76	18.7
L5	100.5	35	104	13.4	0.53	22.4
	100.5	67.2	47	15.7	0.76	22.4
L6	76.4	35	160	28.0	1.02	44.8
	76.4	67.2	75.5	30.0 [a]	1.59	44.8
L6	100.5	35	230	47.4	1.02	56.0
	100.5	67.2	101	52.2	1.59	56.0
H7	76.4	35	185	26.4	0.49	56.0
	76.4	67.2	80	29.5 [a]	2.20	56.0
H7	100.5	35	248	48.5	0.49	74.6
	100.5	67.2	106	48.5	2.20	74.6
H8	59.7	35	302	37.3	0.91	45.0
	59.7	67.2	154	37.3	1.89	45.0
H8	76.4	35	401	74.6	0.91	89.5
	76.4	67.2	165	74.6	1.89	89.5
H9	41.9	35	483	61.1	0.95	74.6
	41.9	67.2	239.2	61.1	1.89	74.6
H9	52.4	35	708	120	0.95	150
	52.4	67.2	330	120	1.89	150
H10	34.6	35	708	130.5	3.18	150
	34.6	67.2	236	130.5	4.05	150
H10	39.8	35	877	149.2	3.18	186
	39.8	67.2	283	149.2	4.05	186

[a] Estimated.

Based on reference conditions with air at p = 100.75 kPa, relative humidity of 50 per cent, water seal temperatures of 333 K and 50 kPa back pressure.

Table 3.8 Performance of water seal extractors. Part B: Wedag.

Type	Speed rad/s	Differential Pressure kPa	Volume Flow l/s	Shaft Power kW	Circulating Water Flow l/s	Motor Power kW
L119	76.4	34.6 87.8	390 72.8	49 55	1.67	63
L129	60.7	34.6 87.8	503 92.0	58 61	1.89	72
L129	76.4	34.6 87.8	632 111	92 93	2.33	108
L132	60.7	34.6 87.8	559 105	70 75	2.22	85
L132	76.4	34.6 87.8	728 135	109 108	2.44	125
L133	45.5	34.6 87.8	910 166	96 110	3.67	125
L133	52.4	34.6 87.8	1055 194	132 125	4.17	150
L134	45.5	34.6 87.8	1110 199	122 130	5.00	150
L134	52.4	34.6 87.8	1254 237	156 155	5.00	180
L134	60.7	34.6 87.8	1518 288	205 215	5.56	250

Maximum suction 90 kPa; maximum delivery pressure 90 kPa. Reference conditions p = 101.3 kPa, T = 273 K, ϱ = 1.2 kg/m^3. This data refers to air being blown to atmosphere. Hence for this condition the differential pressure figures in Column 3 can be in fact read as suction.

elliptical casing. Thus, seal water is forced outwards at the major axis (3) of the elliptical casing and into the blades at the minor axis (4). As a result, when the rotor chambers are passing towards the major axis as at (5), gas is drawn into the extractor inlet, through the cone inlet ports and into the rotor by means of ports in the inner end of the rotor chambers. Later, when the seal water is forced back into the rotor by the converging part (minor axis) of the casing, gas is discharged through ports at the bottom of the rotor chambers and cone, into the pump outlet, and delivery gas pipe. This occurs twice per revolution to produce a continuous "piston-in-cylinder" effect. Extractor speeds can range from 35 to 152 rad/s. Typical performance details are given in Table 3.8.

The performance curves of one water seal extractor are shown in Figure 3.15 on which is shown an operating point A (suction of 45 kPa for 750 l/s, when the back pressure is 50 kPa). Flexibility in operation is achieved by arranging extractors in parallel. With such an arrangement, capacity can be increased or decreased quickly by the addition of, or stopping, one or more extractors.

In the UK all extractor pumps must be of an approved type and all are performance tested. They are made in cast iron, are required to have a bronze fitted construction (rotor and cones) and a carbon steel shaft. Such units may be mounted on a base plate or on a water tank containing the seal water. Shaft sealing is by grease seal lantern ring stuffing box.

Table 3.8 Performance of water seal extractors. Part C: Neypric and Hibon.

Type	Speed rad/s	Differential Pressure kPa	Volume Flow l/s	Shaft Power kW	Circulating Water Flow l/s	Motor Power kW
N 7 b	77 77	33 66	105 52	8.7 11	0.33	15
N 10	51 51	33 66	176 85	14.5 17.8	0.55	25
N 11 b	51 51	33 66	340 165	26.5 34	0.97	45
N 13 b	36 36	33 66	475 242	38.3 48.5	1.18	65
N 15 b	28 28	33 66	838 421	66 87.5	2.22	115
AL 07	151 151	34.6 61.3	101 78	11.7 12.7	0.5	15
AL 20	101 101	34.6 61.3	269 207	30 32.4	0.83	37
AL 40	77 77	34.6 61.3	481 383	49.5 54	1.39	75
AL 70	52 52	34.6 61.3	900 700	87 93	2.77	

Reference conditions $p = 101.3$ kPa, $T = 273$ K, $\varrho = 1.2$ kg/m^3. This data refers to air being blown to atmosphere. Hence for this condition the differential pressure figures in Column 3 can be in fact read as suction.

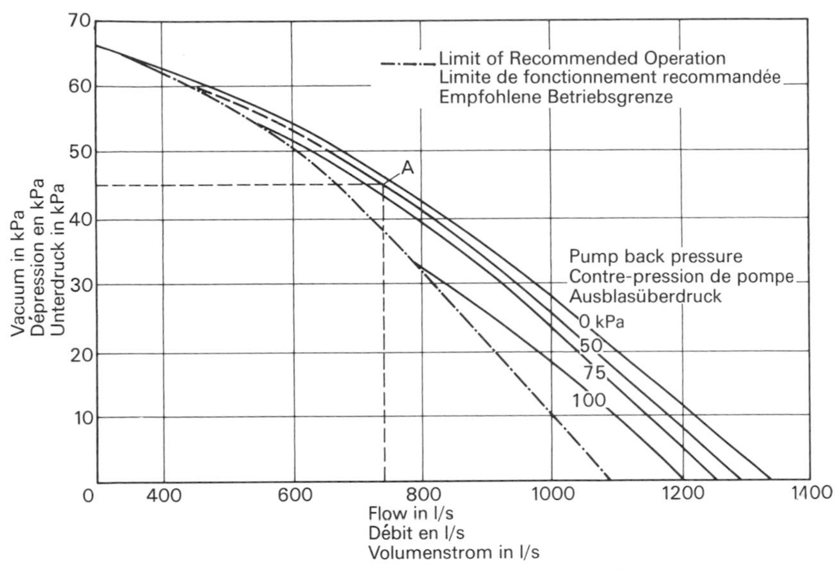

Fig. 3.15 Performance Curves of an Elliptical Casing Type Extractor/Compressor. Nash Extractor (39.8 rad/s).

4.1.2.1.2 Extractors with Circular Casings (Figure 3.14 b)

In the second type of water seal extractor, the rotor (1) is mounted eccentrically within a circular casing (2), without having any metallic contact with it. The water seal (3) is constrained within the casing. As in the elliptical casing type the rotor (1) comprises a number of forward inclined blades so constructed with end rings to form pockets or chambers. The water ring is driven by the rotor and forced by centrifugal action to follow the inner contour of the casing. Thus, at A at the bottom of Figure 3.14 b the water completely fills the rotor chambers whereas at B, at the top of the illustration, the rotor chambers are empty of water. With further rotation, the seal water is again forced back into the rotor by the inner contour of the casing until it is filled completely at A. This cycle takes place once per revolution. As the water begins to leave the rotor at (4), it is replaced by a firedamp/air mixture entering through the inlet ports in the inner conical casing (5) connected to the inlet of the pump. Later as the rotor revolves towards A, the seal water is forced back into the rotor until at A, the firedamp/air mixture is forced out of the rotor chambers into the inner discharge ports of the internal conical casing (5), and the pump outlet.

Typical performance curves of the Nash CL 1002 pump with circular casing are shown in Figure 3.16.

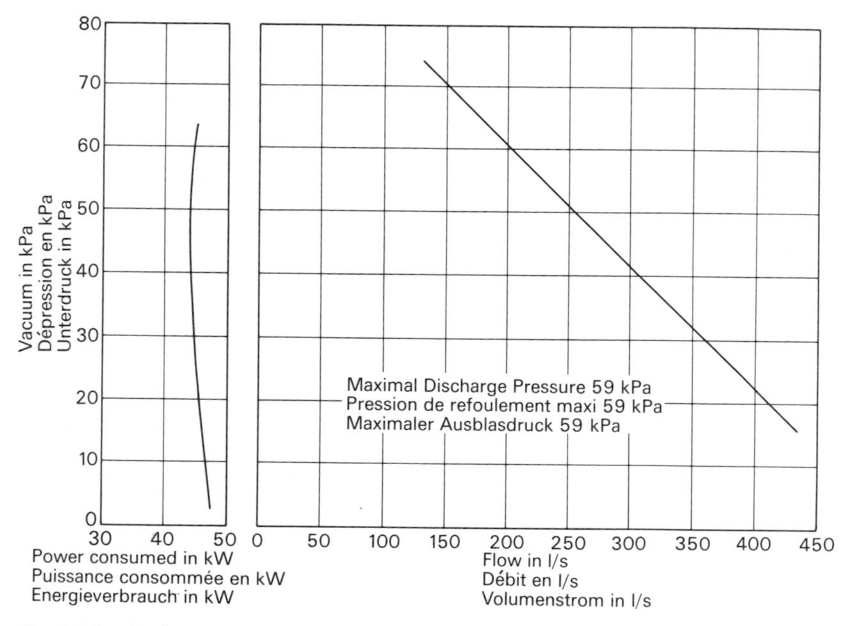

Fig. 3.16 Performance Curves of a Nash CL 1002 Circular Casing Type Methane Extractor at 288 K and 92.1 rad/s.

4.1.2.2 Extractor Drive Arrangements

At the surface of the mine, baseplate-mounted extractor/compressor units are employed (Figure 3.17). In such cases, the water seal extractor (1), and motor (2), are mounted on a fabricated baseplate (3). They are directly coupled to one another in the case of smaller units, but a vee belt (4), or gearbox drive, is used for larger extractors. The gas mixture enters the exhauster from the inlet gas main via inlet stop and check valves, passes through the exhauster, and is discharged through a vertical, tangential, water separator (5), into the delivery gas main. Seal water for the extractors/compressors is stored externally in an open concrete water sump.

For underground and temporary surface use, tank mounted units (Figure 3.18) are used which are suitable for low delivery pressures. In this case, the water seal extractor (1), and its electric motor drive (2), are direct coupled and mounted on a galvanised mild steel tank (3) containing the seal water. This mild steel tank is filled with water to

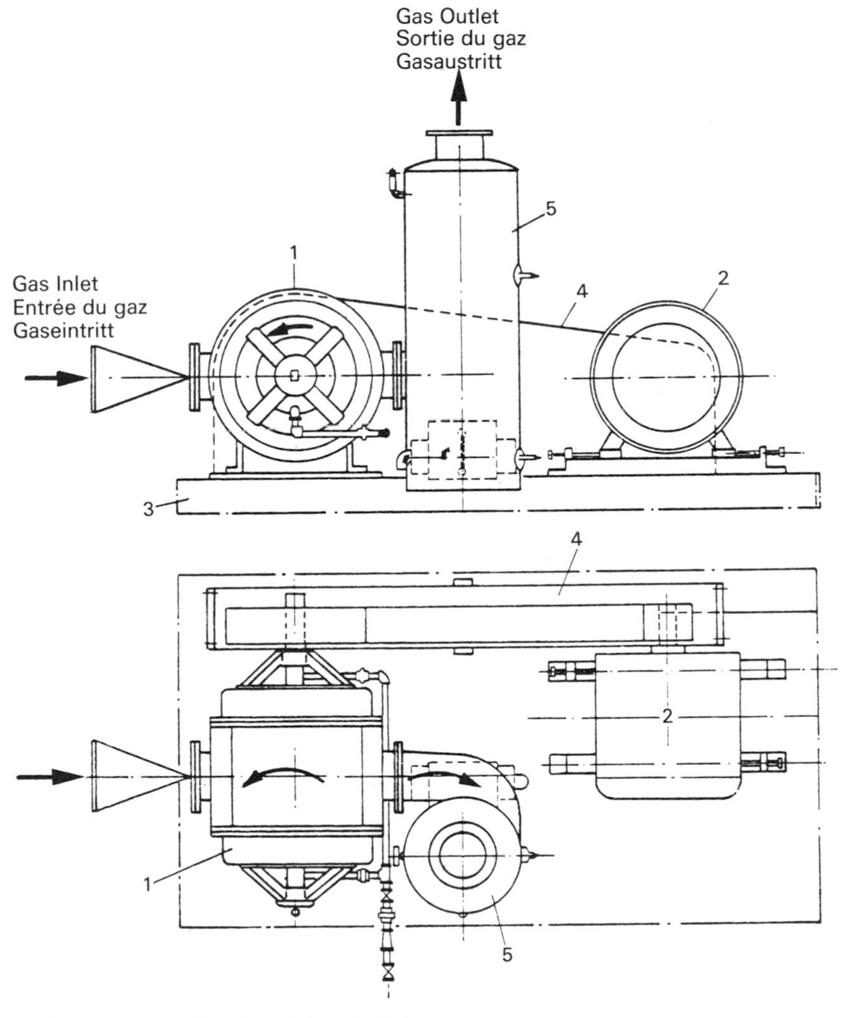

1 Nash Extractor — Extracteur Nash — Nash-Sauger
2 Electric Motor — Moteur électrique — Elektromotor
3 Fabricated Base Plate — Socle — Fabrikgefertigte Grundplatte
4 Veebelt Drive — Courroie trapézoïdale — Keilriementrieb
5 Tangential Water Separator — Séparateur à eau tangentiel — Tangential-Wasserabscheider

Fig. 3.17 Base Mounted Water Seal Extractor.

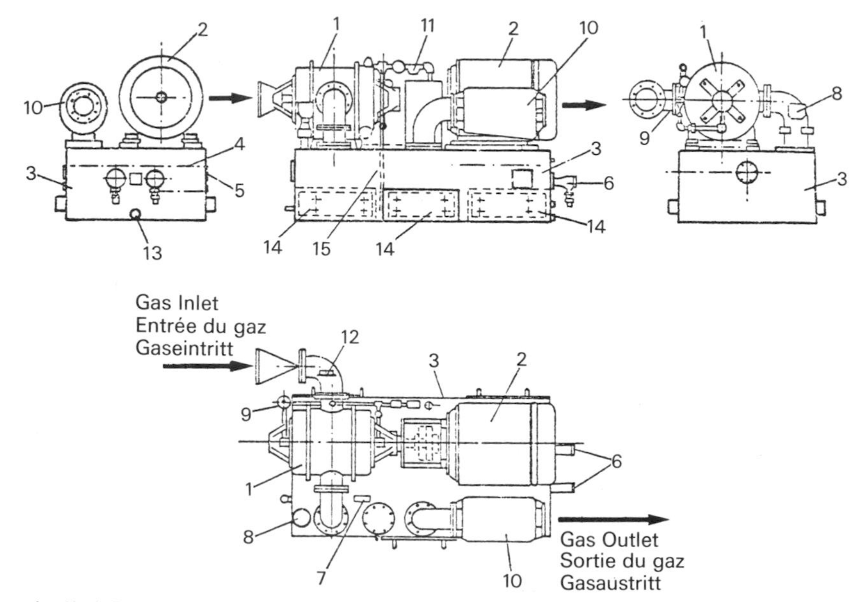

1 Nash Extractor — Extracteur Nash — Nash-Sauger
2 Electric Motor — Moteur électrique — Elektromotor
3 Water Tank — Réservoir d'eau — Wassertank
4 Upper Water Level — Niveau supérieur de l'eau — Oberes Wasserniveau
5 Water Level Indicator — Indicateur de niveau d'eau — Wasserstandsanzeiger
6 Water Level Switch — Contacteur de niveau d'eau — Wasserstandsschalter
7 Water Temperature Indicator — Indicateur de température de l'eau — Wasserthermometer
8 Tank Water Topping up Funnel — Entonnoir de remplissage — Fülltrichter für den Wassertank
9 Extractor Priming Funnel — Entonnoir d'amorçage — Anfahrtrichter für den Sauger
10 Eductor — Ejecteur — Wasserabscheider
11 Seal Water Flow Indicator and Switch — Indicateur de débit de l'anneau liquide et contacteur — Strömungsanzeiger und -schalter für das Ringwasser
12 Vacuum Gauge — Indicateur de vide — Unterdruck-Manometer
13 Tank Drain Plug — Bouchon de vidange — Tankentleerungsstutzen
14 Sludge Doors — Trappes de nettoyage — Schlammabzugsbecken
15 Water Seal Piping — Alimentation de l'anneau liquide — Wasserringrohr

Fig. 3.18 Tank Mounted Water Seal Extractor (for Low Delivery Pressures).

about three quarter level (4), and is provided with water level and water temperature indicators and switches (5, 6, 7), water filling/tank drainage facilities (8, 9, 13) and sludge doors (14). Seal water for the extractor is drawn through piping (15) and later discharged with the gas mixture into the tank (3). The seal water flow indicator is shown at (11). Drained gas is drawn into the extractor through a non-return and an isolating valve. After passing through the extractor, gas and water are discharged into the water tank. The gas then passes over the water therein and out through a water separator (10) into the delivery pipe system and a discharge cage. Such units operate at 76.5, 100.5 or 154 rad/s and displace about 100 to 1200 l/s gas mixture. Extractor vacuum is indicated by a gauge (12). In this arrangement, delivery pressures are limited to about 7 kPa.

An arrangement of a water seal tank mounted extractor for higher delivery pressures is shown in Figure 3.19. The extractor (1), and direct coupled electric motor (2), are mounted on a split skid mounted underframe. This tank mounted unit is equipped with water level switch and indicator, combined water flow indicator and switch,

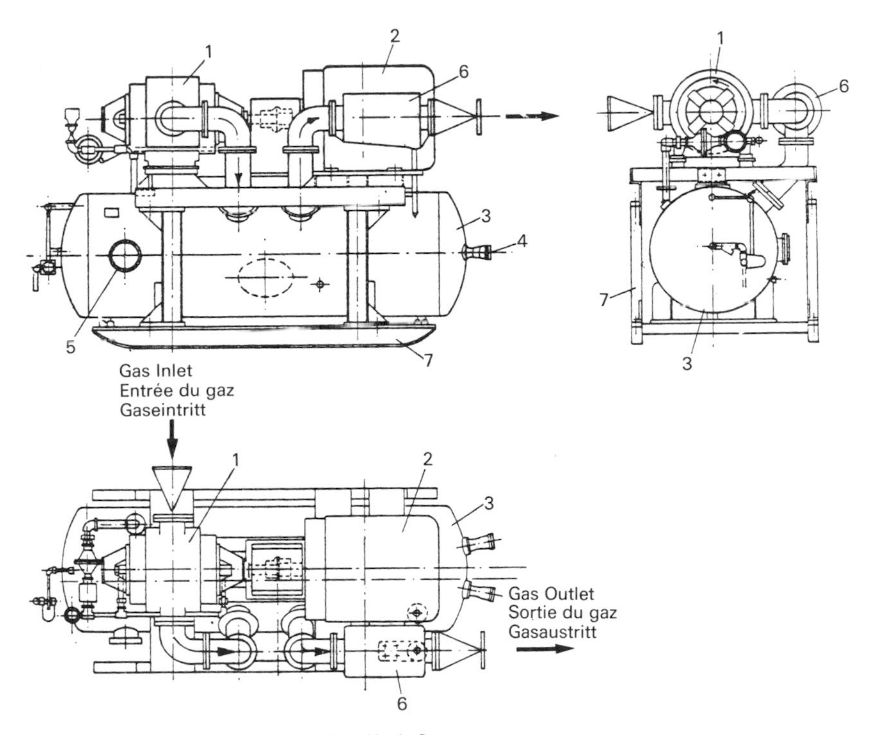

1 Nash Extractor — Extracteur Nash — Nash-Sauger
2 Electric Motor — Moteur électrique — Elektromotor
3 Water Tank — Réservoir d'eau — Wassertank
4 Water Level Switch — Contacteur — Wasserstandsschalter
5 Water Level Indicator — Indicateur de niveau d'eau — Wasserstandsanzeiger
6 Water Separator — Ejecteur — Wasserabscheider
7 Skid Mounted Split Supporting Frame — Chassis démontable sur patin — Geteilter Tragrahmen auf Kufen

Fig. 3.19 Tank Mounted Water Seal Extractor (for Higher Delivery Pressures).

water temperature indicator, priming and topping up funnels, inspection covers and sludge doors. This water tank is suitable for working pressures of about 200 kPa. The unit is employed below ground where long lengths of delivery piping are involved.

4.1.2.3 Advantages and Disadvantages of Water Seal Extractors

A water seal extractor has many advantages:

a) There is no contact between rotating and stationary parts.

b) A bronze fitted construction is used to minimise ignition risks.

c) A water seal is used partly for the same purpose, and for its flame arresting action.

d) Temperature rises across extractors are small — usually of the order of 5 to 7 K.

e) Working temperatures are low, usually less than 320 K.

f) The unit is simple.

g) There are no pistons, valves or need for internal lubrication.

h) Maintenance is low.

i) It is robust.

j) It is easily primed (when necessary).

k) It is easily operated.

l) It is suitable for continuous operation.

m) Few problems arise in practice, and many extractors are operated automatically.

n) Tank mounted units are easily transportable.

o) Increased capacity can be obtained quickly by connecting a number of such units in parallel.

The water seal extractor has some disadvantages:

a) It is relatively inefficient.

b) It may have a rising power characteristic and therefore care needs to be taken in selecting electric motor power.

c) It has a relatively low overall pressure development (at high suction it can only develop a small discharge pressure).

d) It is liable to cause some water to be carried over into the delivery gas main.

e) Periodically it requires dismantling and cleaning (to restore it to design performance after the build-up of scale on the impeller, casing and ports).

f) It is capable of generating only small delivery pressures when used as an extractor/compressor (up to about 150 kPa).

4.1.3 Dry Extractors

4.1.3.1 Types

Dry extractors (Figure 3.20) consist of two symmetrical axially parallel rotary pistons with a lemniscate cross-section, which rotate evenly against each other. The gas mixture flows into the extractor casing in which the two rotary pistons are mounted and is forced into

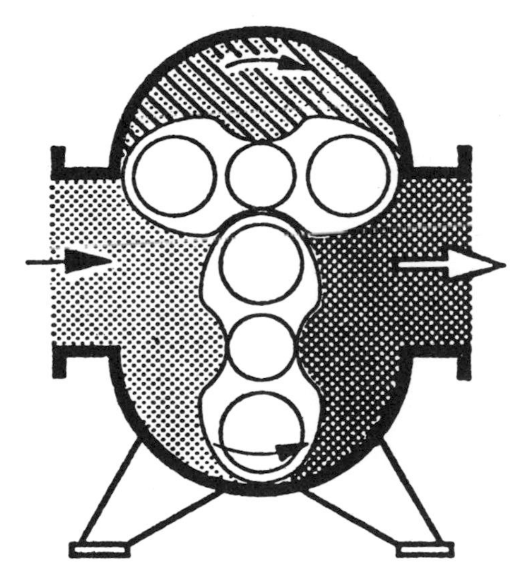

Fig. 3.20 Section of a Dry Extractor.

the pressure side of the chambers formed by the piston and the casing. At the moment when a piston head brushes past the edge of the pressure outlet port the volume of gas is squeezed out of the pressure valve by a return flow effect. Final compression is a function of the resistance of the pipe range and fittings. Typical performance curves of one dry extractor are given in Figure 3.21.

Rotary compressors are usually driven by vee belts. The volume extracted is practically independent of back pressure and it is not

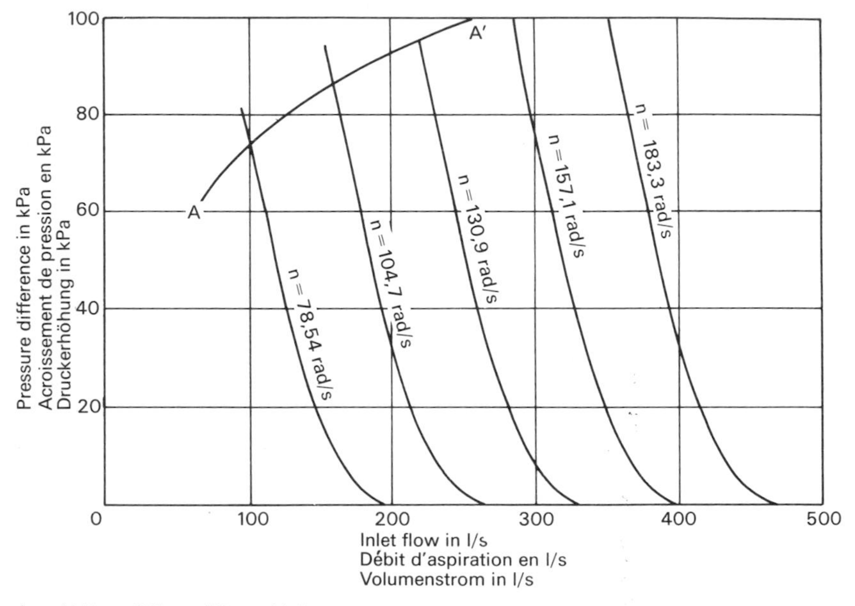

A — A' Normal Thermal Stress Limit
A — A' Limite thermique normale
A — A' Grenze für normale thermische Beanspruchung

Fig. 3.21 Performance Curves of a GL b 14.8 Dry Extractor.

possible to regulate the extractor by throttling. The quantity extracted is regulated in stages by changing the speed. A finer adjustment of vacuum and quantity extracted can be obtained by using a bypass. The gas which is bypassed must be cooled otherwise the machine overheats.

The noise generated by the dry extractor may require suppression measures.

To eliminate the risk of ignitions from frictional sparking it is stipulated that the rotary pistons must be made of a material which will not cause ignition if they rub against the wall of the casing. For this reason, rotors are normally made of gunmetal.

Rotary compressors can generate vacuum down to 50 kPa and delivery pressures up to 100 kPa (Table 3.9). In practice 10 to 20 kPa is usually sufficient to compensate for pressure loss on the exhaust side.

Dry extractors can be operated in parallel.

Table 3.9 Performance of dry extractors.

Make	Type	Speed rad/s	Differential Pressure kPa	Volume Flow[1] l/s	Shaft Power kW	Motor Power kW
Aerzener [2, 3]	GL a 13.6	96.9	58.9	66.1	7.8	10
		151.8	88.3	122.2	17.4	21
		230.4	98.1	216.7	29.9	36
	GL b 14.8	74.4	68.7	93.6	13.5	17
		99.5	78.5	150.8	20.6	25
		151.8	98.1	271.7	39.0	47
		199.0	98.1	391.7	51.2	62
	GL b 15.10	74.4	78.5	223.4	30.2	37
		99.5	88.3	338.4	45.1	55
		151.8	98.1	586.7	75.7	84
	GL b 16.12	75.4	88.3	475.0	65.6	73
		99.5	98.1	693.4	95.8	106
		125.7	98.1	945.1	121.0	134
	GL b 17.14	76.4	98.1	1163.4	164.0	181
		101.6	98.1	1683.5	219.0	241
Roots-Hibon	L10	151.8	9.8	211.8		7.6
			24.5	198.5		
	L20	115.2	9.8	331.9		11.5
			24.5	313.6		
	DV 6	151	10	137	1.69	10
			50	110	8.46	
	DV 6	230	10	218	2.58	15
			50	192	12.90	
	DV 6	301	10	292	3.38	19
			50	266	16.90	
	DV 15	100	10	202	2.47	14
			50	155	12.36	
	DV 15	151	10	324	3.80	21
			50	277	19.00	
	DV 15	230	10	512	5.88	33
			50	465	29.45	

[1] Reference conditions p = 101.3 kPa, T = 288 K, ϱ = 1.23 kg/m^3 except for Aerzener where p = 98.1 kPa.

[2] Maximum suction 50 kPa, maximum pressure 100 kPa.

[3] The data refers to air being sucked in from the atmosphere, consequently the pressures in Column 4 are positive.

Table 3.9 (continued).

Make	Type	Speed rad/s	Differential Pressure kPa	Volume Flow[1] l/s	Shaft Power kW	Motor Power kW
Roots-Hibon	DV 25	100	10 50	367 320	4.20 21.00	24
		151	10 50	574 527	6.40 32.00	35
		209	10 50	806 760	8.82 44.10	49
	DV 50	75	10 50	533 454	6.25 31.60	35
		100	10 50	732 653	8.10 40.50	45
		151	10 50	1147 1059	12.80 64.00	70
	DV 110	62	10 50	981 835	11.80 59.10	65
		79	10 50	1275 1128	14.70 73.50	80
		100	10 50	1641 1495	18.60 93.00	102
	DV 200 g	62	10 50	1800 1545	30 126	138
		76	10 50	2233 1977	35 153	168
		99	10 50	2950 2717	46 200	220
Sulzer SLM	R 60		29.4	259.9		33
	RP 150	75.9 102.6 157.1 209.4	29.4	165.4 316.9 539.3 764.5		36.8 51.5 73.5 101.5
	RP 300	99.5 102.6 151.8	29.4	884.0 884.0 1448.4		
Winterthur S SLM	RZ 60	47.1	49.1	71.2		17

[1] Reference conditions p = 101.3 kPa, T = 288 K, ϱ = 1.23 kg/m^3.

4.1.3.2 Advantages and Disadvantages of Dry Extractors

A dry extractor has many advantages:

a) No seal water is required and cooling water is not needed to achieve operational safety.

b) It needs little maintenance.

c) It is compact.

d) It operates well when used in parallel with other dry extractors, thereby providing greater flexibility.

e) It has a steep characteristic curve so that its gas flow rate (at suction conditions) is virtually independent of pressure difference across the extractor.

The dry extractor has some disadvantages:

a) It can only generate small vacua, up to 50 kPa.

b) It can only generate small delivery pressures, up to 100 kPa, but it is possible to increase this by operating two extractors in series.

c) It heats the gas substantially, so that temperature measuring and tripping devices are essential.

d) It is very noisy so that silencing is nearly always necessary, and sometimes even soundproofing of the extractor house is required.

e) It is sensitive to foreign matter.

f) It is liable to wear.

4.2 Factors Governing Choice of Extractor

Legal as well as technical, safety and environmental factors must be taken into account when ordering extractors and reference should be made to national regulations and specifications.

4.3 Locations of Extractors

Surface Locations

Surface extraction plants (Appendix 3.5) are normally erected near to a shaft and often within easy access of a local surface utilisation plant, such as colliery gas fired boilers. The site for the extractor must be chosen so that sufficient time delay can be obtained for effective monitoring and control of drained gas before it enters the extraction and utilisation plants. Reference needs to be made to national regulations.

Underground Locations

Extractors may be installed underground where drained quantities of firedamp are relatively low and usually limited distances are involved. Underground installations are simple and usually consist of a venturi or tank mounted water seal extractor, a bypass, a discharge cage, and the necessary valve arrangements (Figures 3.13 and 3.22). Underground extractors may be installed in connecting slits between intake and return airways, in main airways sometimes many kilometres from a shaft, or near the bottom of upcast shafts. In the installation shown in Figure 3.22 an extractor is located on the intake side of separation doors between intake and return airways. Extractor E, and electric motor M, are mounted on a water tank from which the seal water supply is obtained. A bypass is provided which is used when the extractor stops. Drained gas is delivered into the discharge cage D, where the gas concentration is diluted to an acceptable figure. A large number of underground extractors are used in the UK, as shown in Table 3.10.

The choice of extractor site depends largely on local factors, including the quantity of drained firedamp relative to the roadway air quantity and existing firedamp concentrations into which the drained gas is discharged. The quantity of firedamp discharged must be such that resultant general body firedamp concentrations in the return airway are below practical and statutory levels. The selection of extractor site may be governed also by the position of a ventilation connection between intake and return airways, to enable the extractor and motor to be located in intake air. The extractor may be located in proximity to a manned position, so that routine inspection visits can be dovetailed into other duties, or output signals from static monitors can be fed easily to a local manned station. Installations may be continuously monitored employing local and remote outstations connected to a local or to an underground to surface data transmission system. In general, the discharge pipe should be kept as short as practicable and the extractor installed in stable ground. Siting of extractors may be governed by noise considerations. Such systems are used because they are most effective from ventilation, safety and production standpoints, simple and cheap, require little maintenance, can be installed and extended quickly, and are continuously monitored without difficulty. About 30 % of total drained methane quantities in the UK is discharged underground.

The numbers of extractors currently employed in different countries are given in Table 3.10.

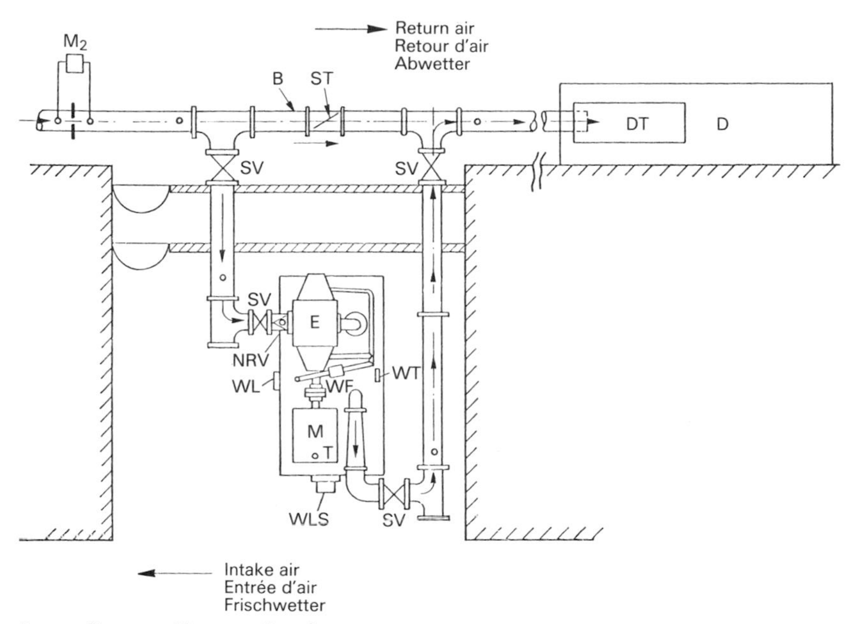

B Bypass — Bipasse — Bypaß
D Discharge Cage — Cage de décharge — Verdünnungskorb
DT Diffusion Tube — Diffuseur — Ausblasrohr
E Extractor — Extracteur — Sauger
M Electric Motor — Moteur électrique — Elektromotor
M_2 Vacuum Gauge, High Concentration Manometer and Orifice Plate — Dépression, grisoumètre hautes teneurs et diaphragme — Unterdruck, Methanometer für hohen CH_4-Gehalt und Meßblende
NRV Non Return Valve — Clapet de non-retour — Rückschlagventil
ST Stop Valve and/or Butterfly Valve — Vanne d'arrêt et/ou vannepapillon — Absperr- und/oder Drosselklappenventil
SV Stop Valve — Vanne d'arrêt — Absperrventil
T Temperature — Température — Temperatur
WF Water Flow Indicator and Switch — Indicateur de débit et contacteur — Wasserströmungsanzeiger und -schalter
WL Water Level Indicator — Indicateur de niveau d'eau — Wasserstandsanzeiger
WLS Water Level Switch — Contacteur de niveau d'eau — Wasserstandsschalter
WT Water Temperature — Température de l'eau — Wassertemperatur

Fig. 3.22 Underground Firedamp Drainage Extractor Site.

4.3.1 Advantages and Disadvantages of Surface and Underground Installations

Surface Installation

Surface installations have a number of advantages:

a) They can be operated continuously in conditions which are not affected by the underground mine environment.

Table 3.10 Number of surface and underground extractors and types in 1975.

Item	Belgium (Campine)	Germany	France	UK
Total number of surface extractor plants	4	39	19	63
Total number of surface extractors in use	4	110	46	147
Total number of surface extractors on standby (installed)	6	113	15	72
Total number of surface extractors	10	223	61	219
Total number of surface water seal extractors	nil	18	34	219
Total number of surface dry extractors	10	205	27	nil
Total number of underground plants	nil	9	nil	87
Total number of underground extractors in use (water seal, dry + venturis)	nil	12	nil	128
Total number of underground extractors on standby	nil	13	nil	17
Total number of underground extractors (water seal, dry + venturis)	nil	25	nil	145
Total number of underground venturi extractors	nil	17	nil	15
Total number of underground water seal extractors	nil	nil	nil	130
Total number of underground dry extractors	nil	8	nil	nil
Total number of extractors and venturis in use	4	122	46	275

b) They are flexible in that installations can be designed to accommodate standby or additional plant.

c) The most advanced equipment can be used to protect them.

d) They provide a drained gas supply to surface utilisation plants, such as gas grids and dual fuel engines.

e) They can deal with large firedamp flow rates.

f) They are readily accessible so that operating problems can be rapidly identified and corrected with minimum loss of time.

g) They can be continuously monitored without manpower.

Surface installations are more expensive than underground installations but in many cases are essential for the safe working of mines. Because of the increased distances involved, power demands are usually higher than those of underground installations for given gas flow rates.

Underground Installations

Underground installations have many advantages in appropriate applications:

a) Within certain limits, they provide the necessary suction and capacity with a high degree of flexibility.

b) They are easily and quickly installed, and are simple.

c) Their capacity can be quickly increased by installing parallel units.

d) Maintenance is low.

e) Extractors can be quickly adapted to changing situations underground and be installed in intake air or connecting slits between intake and return airways so that electric drives can be operated independently of firedamp concentrations in return airways.

f) The plant can be designed for fail safe automatic operation with continuous monitoring locally and remotely.

g) They are relatively cheap to install.

h) Power requirements are relatively low.

When drained firedamp quantities increase, it may become necessary to move underground extractors further outbye into larger ventilation quantities. A position may be reached when drained quantities of firedamp might exceed the value which can be safely discharged and diluted in underground ventilation flows, at which point a surface extraction plant becomes necessary. Underground installations have the disadvantage that they do not provide drained firedamp for utilisation.

Appendix 3.1

Experimental Methods of Predicting Gas Emission

A 3.1.1 Introduction

The planning of mine workings necessitates that modern techniques of mining are compatible with requirements of economy whilst retaining given safety levels. Although the actual levels vary from one country to another, a most important standard is the maximum concentration of methane allowed in the general body of ventilating air. The problem of gas emission into the workings is tackled in two ways: adequate ventilation is provided to dilute gas reaching the airways to an acceptable concentration level, and secondly firedamp drainage may be used to reduce the flow of gas into the airways. From all considerations it is essential that those planning ventilation and firedamp drainage have as accurate a value as possible of the expected gas emission into the workings.

A 3.1.2 Methods of Prediction of Gas Emission

In addition to methods of estimation based on practical experience in similar mining situations, there are several experimental methods of calculation in use in various countries based on simplified models of the physical process of gas emission into a working district. These are the treatments of:

Gunther, subsequently Jeger	(France)
Flügge	(Germany)
Schulz	(Germany)
Winter	(Germany)
Lidin	(Russia)
Airey	(United Kingdom)

A further method developed in the Netherlands by Stuffken, is similar to that of Winter and is not presented here. For details of all methods, the reader is referred to the Bibliography at the end of this Appendix. All prodecures enable a calculation to be made of the quantity known as 'specific gas emission' or 'gas make' which is the quantity of gas (m^3) released into the working from all sources, per tonne of mined saleable coal.

Airey's method has the distinction of being based on a coherent physical theory in which increased stresses in the strata caused by mining are considered to induce an intensifying crack structure in the coal seams, which are consequently thought to be composed of discrete small blocks or lumps. The rate of emission of gas from these lumps depends upon their size and reaches a maximum at the position of maximum stress. The maximum intensity of this stress in an adjacent seam decreases with its distance from the worked seam. The rate of emission of gas is expressed in terms of this distance, the rate of advance of the face and the time constant of emission for the smallest coal lumps induced in the worked seam, which can be measured in the laboratory. The concept of time, which is unique to Airey's theory and which enables emission to be expressed as a function of advance rate, also with the aid of a computer provides a means of predicting detailed changes in emission level with time as advance rate changes, eg from shift to shift, but this is too complex to present here. However, it can be simplfied to a form comparable with the other methods by using the following elements common to them all:

1. The Gas Content of the coal seams contributing to emission.
2. The Zones in roof and floor strata from which gas is considered totally or partially to degas.
3. The Degree of Gas Emission of each contributing seam or gas bearing stratum.

A 3.1.3 The Gas Content of Seams contributing to Emission

There are two different methods used for the measurement of the gas content of coal seams, ie the 'Direct Method' and the 'Indirect Method'. In the direct method coal samples are sealed shortly after retrieval from a borehole and gas is extracted and measured in the laboratory; in the French (Cerchar) version 10 g of drillings of above 2 mm size are sufficient, whereas in the UK (MRDE) version a portion of core of some 30 g mass is taken. In the indirect (StBV) method gas pressure is measured in the seam and this is interpreted in terms of the gas content of the seam by means of a laboratory measured adsorption isotherm graph, (see Chapter 1, Fig. 1.7). In the absence of information for seams in the adjacent strata, a gas content value appropriate to the worked seam is used.

There are two possible interpretations of the quantity referred to as gas content of a coal seam or coal sample. The first of these, which is used in Belgium, France and Germany, is the quantity of gas (m^3/t) which will desorb down to atmospheric pressure. According to this theory, methane desorbs from coal until it is in equilibrium with free methane in its crack system at atmospheric pressure. The alternative interpretation is based on the observation that large blocks of coal can degas completely. This is used in the United Kingdom in the application of Airey's theory and is the quantity which can desorb down to zero absolute methane partial pressure; at the end of desorption no methane is retained in the coal and the crack system is completely empty of methane which is replaced by air or other gases. The magnitude of the difference in gas content value is of the order of 1 m^3/t, the UK figure being higher.

A 3.1.4 The Zone of Gas Emission

Details of the Gas Emission Zones for each method are given in Table A 3.1.1, together with the Degree of Emission which is discussed in the next paragraph. The methods of Gunther, Jeger, Flügge, Schulz and Lidin consider various geometrical configurations to represent the gas emission zones in roof and floor where total or partial emission of gas takes place. In the cases of Flügge and Schulz the vertical height of these zones depends upon the face length, while that of Lidin depends upon the worked thickness of the seam. For roof strata the Gunther method assumes an absolute limit within which total emission is considered to take place, while Winter and Airey specify no limits; reduction in emission from distant seams is specified in these cases entirely by the degree of emission function.

A 3.1.5 The Degree of Gas Emission

Details of this function for each method are also specified in Table A 3.1.1 and shown graphically in Figures A 3.1.1 to A 3.1.4. Gunther is alone in specifying total emission for roof strata up to a certain distance. For floor strata Koppe has calculated a curve based on practical measurements; Gunther however takes a

Table A 3.1.1 Emission from Adjacent Seams.

Method	Emission Zone		Degree of Gas Emission (%)	
	Roof	Floor	Roof	Floor
Gunther	rectangular block $h = 100$ m	rectangular block $h = 100$ m	100	$100 - h$
Jeger	rectangular block $h = 165$ m	rectangular block $h = 55$ m	90 up to ≈ 30 m * $\frac{C\ \text{initial} - 2}{C\ \text{initial}} 100$ from 30 to 120 m $\frac{C\ \text{initial} - 2}{C\ \text{initial}} 2\,(170 - h)$ from 120 to 170 m	90 down to 10 m* then $2\,(55 - h)$ from 10 to 55 m
	N. B. Modifications are used for different strata.			
Flügge	Prism width l $h = 0.5\, l / \tan \alpha_F$		$\frac{100\, l - 200\, h \cot \alpha_F}{l}$	
Schulz	half cylinder diameter l	rectangular block $h = 20$ m	$\frac{100}{l} \sqrt{(l^2 - 4\, h^2)}$	100 down to 5 m then $133 - 6.7\, h$
Winter	unlimited block; practical limit taken at 10 % emission level		100 up to 20 m then $100 \exp[-\mu_W (h - 20)]$	100 down to 8 m then $100 \exp[-\mu_W (h - 8)]$
Lidin	rectangular block $h = 60\, M\, (1.2 \pm \cos \alpha_f)$ gives maximum extent: + above; — below.		$100\,(1 - h/h_{max})$	
Airey	unlimited block		See Figure A 3.1.3	

* Depending on the thickness of the seam and nature of strata.
Notes on symbols follow Table A 3.1.2.

function which decreases linearly with distance from the worked seam, as do Flügge, Schulz, Jeger and Lidin. Flügge and Lidin also use linear functions for degree of emission from sources in the roof where Schulz takes a convex function falling to zero at a height equal to half the face length. For both roof and floor strata, Winter and Airey both use functions which decrease exponentially with distance from the worked seam, Airey's curves being dependent upon the depth of the working as well as the age of the district. Jeger's curve for roof strata is based on practical measurements.

A 3.1.6 Emission from the Worked Seam

Table A 3.1.2 shows the degree of emission for the worked seam according to each method. Airey's value depends on the rate of advance of the face and this function is plotted on Figure A 3.1.5; for typical advance rates the magnitude predicted is of the order of 50 % which is the value chosen by Gunther and Jeger. All the other methods assume total degassing (100 %). It is clear that further research is required on this subject.

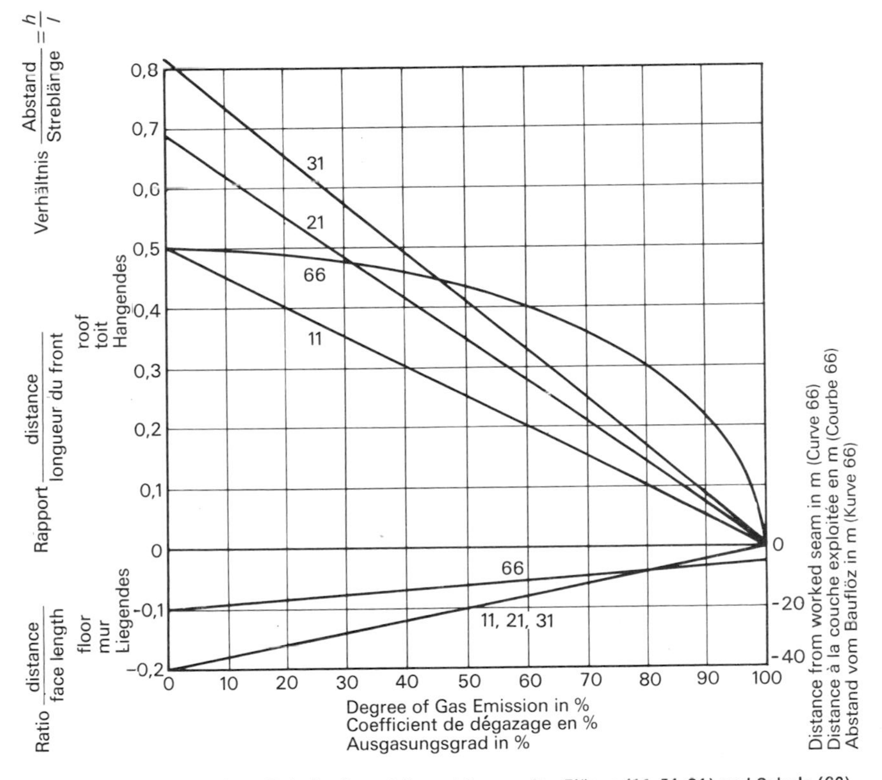

Fig. A 3.1.1 Degree of Gas Emission from Adjacent Seams after Flügge (11,21,31) and Schulz (66).

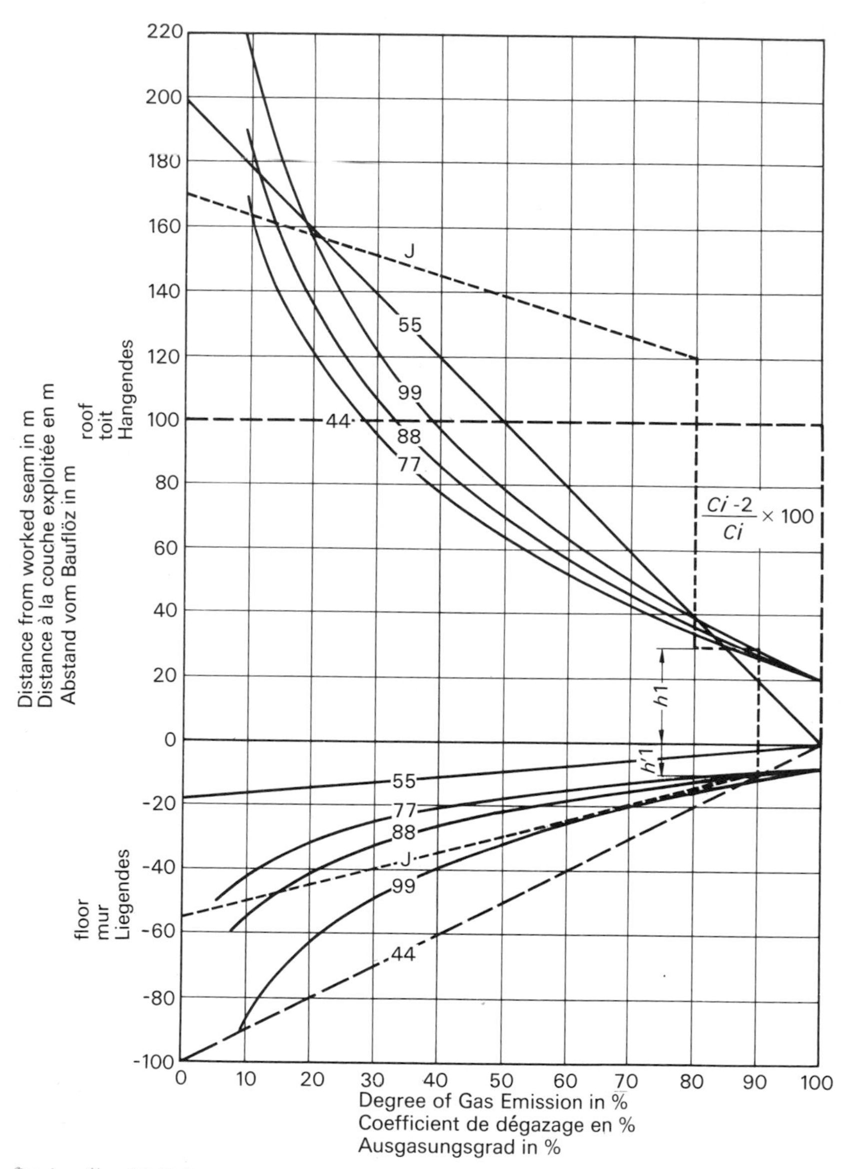

For J: $Ci = C$ initial

$h1, h'1 = f$ (thickness of the seam and nature of the strata)

Fig. A 3.1.2 Degree of Gas Emission from Adjacent Seams after Gunther (44) and Jeger (J), after Lidin (55) for 1,5 m thick level seam and after Winter (77, 88, 99).

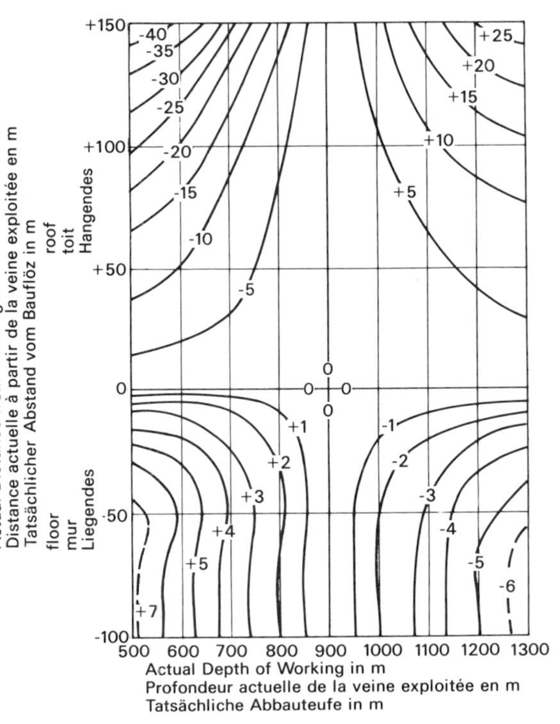

a Height Correction in m before using 900 m curves

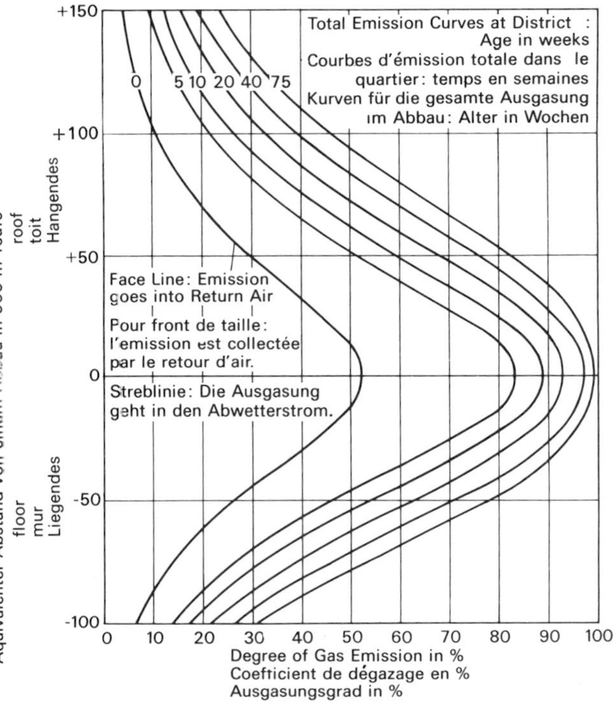

b Degree of Gas Emission at 900 m

Fig. A 3.1.3 Degree of Gas Emission from Adjacent Seams after Airey.

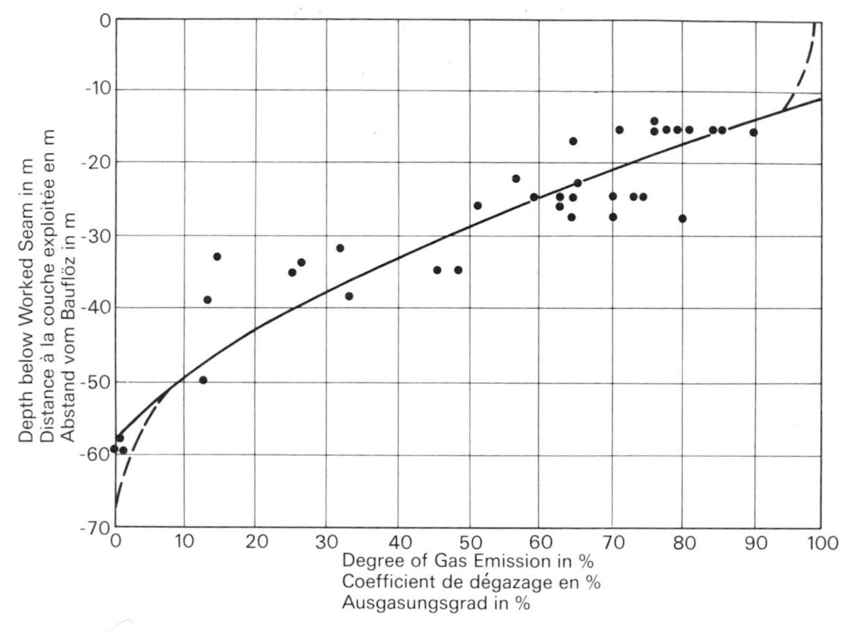

Fig. A 3.1.4 Degree of Gas Emission in the Floor based on 35 Measurements after Koppe.

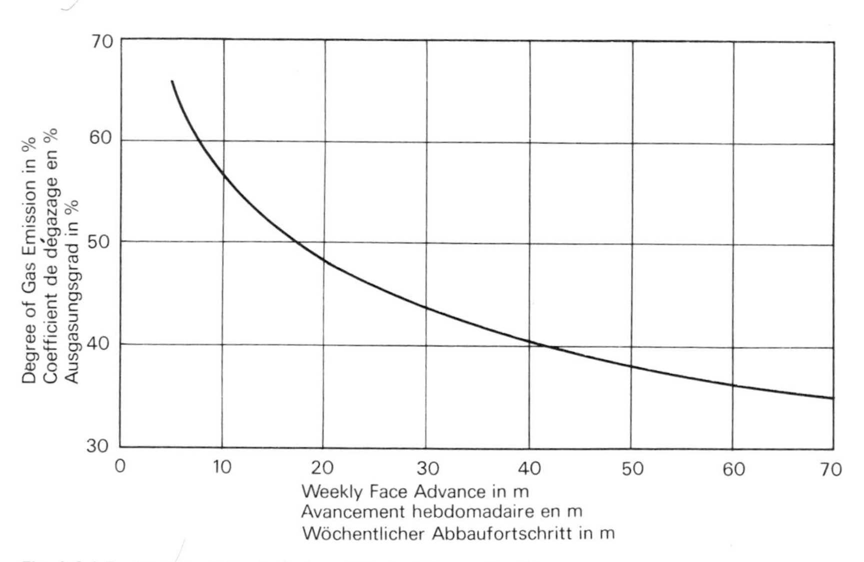

Fig. A 3.1.5 Degree of Gas Emission of Worked Seam after Airey.

Table A 3.1.2 Emission from Worked Seam.

Method	Degree of Gas Emission (%)
Gunther/Jeger	50
Flügge	100
Schulz	100
Winter	100
Lidin	100
Airey	$100\left[1-\exp\left\{-\left(\frac{x_0+l_1}{w\,t_0}\right)^n\right\}\right]$

Notes on Symbols, Values and Units:

All	h	distance normal to the bedding planes excepts in Lidin method where h is vertical distance from worked seam (m)
	l	face length (m)
Flügge	α_F	angle of prism (45°, 54° or 58¹/₂° roof; 22¹/₂° floor)
Winter	μ_W	constant (0.016, 0.014 or 0.012 roof; 0.07, 0.05 or 0.03 floor)
Lidin	M	seam thickness (m)
	α_f	slope of seam (°)
Airey	x_0	constant (say 4 m)
	l_l	face line to front abutment distance (say 2 m)
	W	rate of advance (m/s)
	t_0	63 % emission time constant of minimum size lumps (at maximum stress line) in seam (say 5×10^5 s for bituminous coal)
	n	constant (0.333 for bituminous coal)

A 3.1.7 Emission from Strata between Seams

Gunther and Jeger make allowance for strata between the known seams to hold and emit gas. Within the zone of emission Gunther calculates emission on the basis of 100 m of stone being equivalent to 1 m of coal. Jeger considers the thicknesses equivalent to 1 m of coal to be 100 m of shale or fine sandstone with shaly partings, and 10 m of coarse sandstone.

A 3.1.8 Procedures for Calculation

An example of prediction of gas emission for a working district is given in Table A 3.1.3 sheets 1, 2 and 3 (see p. 220/22). This table is arranged so that the gas make can be calculated for each gas source from the product of the gas content, the relative thickness and degree of gas emission divided by 100. The example given assumes the strata to be previously undisturbed.

Firstly on sheet 1 in column 1 the seams contributing to emission are listed in sequence. For the purposes of Gunther's method, strata between seams is also included. In column 5 the gas content of each seam is written; where this is not known for adjacent coal seams (as in this example), the value for the worked seam is used. As noted in section A 3.1.3 the value used in Airey's method is taken as 1 m^3/t greater than for the other methods. The 'relative thickness' is recorded in column 4; for each seam this is the ratio of the actual thickness (column 2) to the thickness extracted from the worked seam (for intervening stone the 'equivalent thickness' in column 3 is first calculated as 1 % of the actual thickness of stone).

The distances of all seams and intervening strata from the worked seam are written in column 6 and these are used in conjunction with Figures A 3.1.1 to A 3.1.3 to obtain the percentage values of the Degree of Emission Function, which are recorded on sheet 2, each column being for a different method or variation of a method.

Finally on sheet 3 is recorded the gas make or specific gas emission (m^3/t) calculated for each source from the product of the gas content (column 5), the relative thickness (column 4) and the degree of emission (sheet 2) divided by 100. Totals are obtained for roof and floor strata, and an overall total finally worked out for each method.

A 3.1.9 Calculating Emission from Partially Degassed Strata

The above prediction methods have so far been applied only to virgin conditions, but if the gas content of each source in partially degassed strata is known, a prediction for this situation may be attempted. The resulting prediction is likely to be less accurate because errors may be compounded in successive calculations, but the problem is of less importance than the virgin strata case.

The Degree of Emission Function (Table A 3.1.3 sheet 2 and Figures A 3.1.1 to A 3.1.4) enables the remnant gas content at any level to be found so that if a second seam is worked, emission into that working from already partially degassed strata may be calculated. The method based on Airey's theory is suitable for this since it gives the degree of emission as a function of the age of the working.

The distribution of gas content throughout the different levels of strata may thus be calculated for the time at which the second mining operation commences.

A 3.1.10 Selected Bibliography on Prediction of Gas Emission

1. Schulz, P.: Captage et Utilisation du Méthane des Charbonnages (Grisou), OECE, 1956, pp 95/103.

2. Stuffken, J.: De Mijngasafgifte van Kolenlagen Thèse, Uitgeverij Excelsior, 's Gravenhage 1957.
English (NCB) Translation A 1342.

3. Stuffken, J.: Een Berekeningsmethode voor de Mijngasafgifte van Steenkoollagen. Geologie en Mijnbouw (1958) pp 223/32.

4. Winter, K.: Derzeitiger Stand der Vorausberechnung der Ausgasung beim Abbau von Steinkohlenflözen. Bergbaufreiheit 23 (1958) pp 439/54.

5. Schulz, P.: Le Dégagement de Grisou du Charbon causé par l'exploitation. Une étude sur les Possibilitiés quantitatives de Captage et sa Prédétermination. Revue Univ des Mines 102 (1959) pp 41/58.

6. Stuffken, J.: Ein Berechnungsverfahren zur Bestimmung der Ausgasung von Steinkohlenflözen. Bergbau-Archiv 21 (1960) pp 40/48.

7. Lidin, G. D. et al: Determination of the Gassiness of Coal Seams and Methods for the Prediction of Methane Emission in Coal Mines of the USSR. Restricted Int. Conf. of Directors of Safety in Mines Research, Sheffield 1965; English (SMRE) Trans 5158.

8. Gunther, J.: Mécanisme et Prévision du Dégagement grisouteux. Cerchar, Documents Techniques 11 (1965) pp 697/703.

9. Gunther, J. et Belin, J.: Prévision du Dégagement Grisouteux en taille pour les Gisement en plateure. 12th Int. Conf. Mine Safety Research Est., Dortmund 1967.

10. Noack, K.: Untersuchungen über Form und Größe des Ausgasungsraumes um Abbaubetriebe in flacher oder mäßig geneigter Lagerung des Ruhrkarbons. Glückauf-Forschungshefte 31 (1970) pp 121/32.

English (NCB) Translation A 2963.

11. Flügge, G.: Die Anwendung der Trogtheorie auf den Raum der Zusatzausgasung. Glückauf-Forschungshefte 32 (1971) pp 122/29.

12. Airey, E. M.: A Theory of Gas Emission in Coalmining Operations. Int. Conf. of Safety in Mines Research, Donezk/USSR 1971.

13. Koppe, U.: Der Ausgasungsgrad von Begleitflözen im Liegenden der flachen Lagerung. Glückauf-Forschungshefte 36 (1975) pp 138/44.

14. Winter, K.: Reichweite der Ausgasung im Einwirkungsbereich des Abbaus. Glückauf-Forschungshefte 37 (1976) pp 22/27.

15. Curl, S. J.: Methane Prediction in Coal Mines. IEA Coal Research Report No. ICTIS/TR 04. London 1978.

Table A 3.1.3 Prediction of Gas Emission by Different Methods. Sheet 1

		Gas Source Data				
1		2	3	4	5	6
Seam		Actual Thickness m	Equivalent Thickness (stone) m	Relative Thickness	Gas Content [a] m^3/t	Distance from Worked Seam m
Gustav		2.00		1.33	7	180
Hugo		0.20		0.13	7	110
	stone	39	0.39	0.26	7 [b]	80
Karl		1.35		0.90	7	60
	stone	18	0.18	0.12	7 [b]	50
Blücher		2.00		1.33	7	40
	stone	39	0.39	0.26	7 [b]	20
Roof Total						
Wilhelm (worked)		1.50		1.00	7	0
	stone	5	0.05	0.03	7 [b]	2.5
Johann		0.50		0.33	7	5
	stone	34	0.34	0.23	7 [b]	17.5
Präsident		1.00		0.67	7	40
	stone	{15 J 48	0.15 J 0.48	0.10 J 0.32}	7 [b]	{47.5 J 65}
Dickebank		2.00		1.33	7	90
	stone	10	0.10	0.07	7 [b]	95
Floor Total						
Overall Total		—	—	—	—	—

[a] Desorbable to atmospheric pressure; for Airey's method a quantity desorbable to zero methane partial pressure is used, i. e. 8 m^3/t.

[b] Fictitious value.

Table A 3.1.3 Prediction of Gas Emission by Different Methods. Sheet 3

Gas Make[d] in m³/t										
Flügge 11	Flügge 21	Flügge 31	Gunther 44	Jeger J	Lidin 55	Schulz 66	Winter 77	Winter 88	Winter 99	Airey
0	0	0	0	0	0.84	0	0.74	1.02	1.40	1.81
0	0.18	0.30	0	0.65	0.40	0	0.22	0.25	0.31	0.42
—	—	—	1.82	1.31	—	—	—	—	—	—
2.52	3.56	3.97	6.30	4.54	4.41	5.04	3.34	3.59	3.91	5.40
—	—	—	0.84	0.68	—	—	—	—	—	—
5.59	6.61	7.03	9.31	6.70	7.45	8.57	6.80	7.08	7.35	9.47
—	—	—	1.82	1.64	—	—	—	—	—	—
8.11	10.35	11.30	20.09	15.52	13.10	13.61	11.10	11.94	12.97	17.10
7.00	7.00	7.00	3.50	3.50	7.00	7.00	7.00	7.00	7.00	3.84
—	—	—	0.20	0.19	—	—	—	—	—	—
2.02	2.02	2.02	2.19	2.08	1.69	2.31	2.31	2.31	2.31	2.61
—	—	—	1.33	1.21	—	—	—	—	—	—
0	0	0	2.81	1.41	0	0	0.52	0.94	1.78	4.61
—	—	—	0.78	0.11	—	—	—	—	—	—
0	0	0	0.93	0	0	0	0	0.14	0.84	4.15
—	—	—	0.02	0	—	—	—	—	—	—
2.02	2.02	2.02	8.26	5.00	1.69	2.31	2.83	3.39	4.93	11.37
17.13	19.37	20.32	31.85	24.02	21.79	22.92	20.93	22.33	24.90	32.31

[d] Column 4 × column 5 × $\frac{\text{degree of gas emission}}{100}$.

Table A 3.1.3 Prediction of Gas Emission by Different Methods. Sheet 2

Degree of Gas Emission [c] from each curve in %

Flügge 11	Flügge 21	Flügge 31	Gunther 44	Jeger J	Lidin 55	Schulz 66	Winter 77	Winter 88	Winter 99	Airey (75 weeks)
0	0	0	0	0	9	0	8	11	15	17
0	20	32.5	0	72	44.5	0	24	28	34	40
—	—	—	100	72	—	—	—	—	—	—
40	56.5	63	100	72	70	80	53	57	62	75
—	—	—	100	72	—	—	—	—	—	—
60	71	75.5	100	72	80	92	73	76	79	89
—	—	—	100	90	—	—	—	—	—	—
100	100	100	50	50	100	100	100	100	100	48
—	—	—	97.5	90	—	—	—	—	—	—
87.5	87.5	87.5	95	90	73	100	100	100	100	99
—	—	—	82.5	75	—	—	—	—	—	—
0	0	0	60	30	0	0	11	20	38	86
—	—	—	35	15	—	—	—	—	—	—
0	0	0	10	0	0	0	0	1.5	9	39
—	—	—	5	0	—	—	—	—	—	—
—	—	—	—	—	—	—	—	—	—	—

[c] Face Length 200 m
Worked seam thickness 1.5 m
Dip of worked seam 0°
Advance rate 20 m/week.

Appendix 3.2

Basic Fluid Flow Equations

A 3.2.1 In the sections which follow, basic formulae in SI units for the calculation of pressure and energy losses are given. Pressure loss formulae for standpipes have been given in Chapter 2, Appendix 2.1.

Pressure Loss Equation for Incompressible Flow

A 3.2.2 The equation given below is used when gas pressures in the pipe are at, or near, (say within 10 kPa of) atmosphere pressure, as in the case of some underground, low pressure, water seal and venturi extractor installations.

A 3.2.3 The pressure loss Δp_f is given by:

$$p_1 - p_2 = \Delta p_f = \frac{1}{2} \varrho \frac{\lambda\, l\, Q^2}{d\, A^2} 10^{-6} \quad \text{[A 3.2.1]}$$

where:

$p_1 - p_2 = \Delta p_f$ pressure loss in Pa

ϱ density of drained gas, ie of firedamp/air mixtures, in kg/m^3.
The value of ϱ varies directly with the firedamp concentration in drained gas.

λ dimensionless friction coefficient.
The values of λ will depend on whether smooth or rough pipes are being considered, and can be deduced from formulae and the graph (Figure 3.2.1) given below.

l length of pipe in m

d internal diameter of pipe in m

A cross sectional area of pipe in m^2

Q gas flow rate in l/s.

Pressure Loss Equations for Compressible Flow

A 3.2.4 Pressure loss formulae for compressible flow in pipes allow for the fact that gas density increases with rise in gas pressure. Standard conditions are taken as a pressure of 101.3 kPa and a temperature of 288 K.

A 3.2.5 The formula commonly employed in SI units is:

$$p_1^2 - p_2^2 = 804\,372\, f \frac{\delta\, l}{d^5} Q^2 \frac{T}{288} \quad \text{[A 3.2.2]}$$

where:

p_1 absolute pressures at the upstream (inlet) station in Pa

p_2 absolute pressures at the downstream (outlet) station in Pa

f a coefficient of friction

δ relative density of drained gas (air = 1)

Q gas mixture flow in l/s

T gas temperature in K

d pipe bore in m.

This formula for compressible flow covers systems with large pressure differences, and in which changes in volume and density are too great to be neglected.

A 3.2.6 The value of the coefficient of friction f was obtained from standard f — Re curves, where Re = Reynolds Number of the gas flow as defined below.

A 3.2.7 In order to use the widely accepted dimensionless friction coefficient $\lambda = 4f$, expression [A 3.2.2] above can be written as:

$$p_1^2 - p_2^2 = 201\,093\ \lambda \frac{\delta\, l}{d^5} Q^2 \frac{T}{288} \qquad \text{[A 3.2.3]}$$

The value of λ is determined from the λ-Re curves provided in Figure A 3.2.1 or from expressions given below.

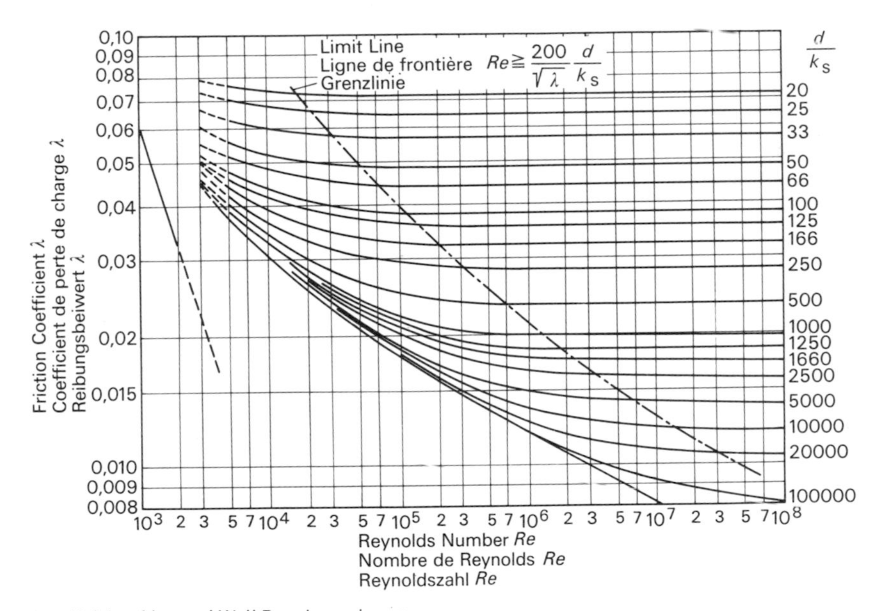

k_s Height of Internal Wall Roughness in mm

d Internal Diameter of Pipe in mm

Fig. A 3.2.1 Relation between Friction Coefficient and Reynolds Number.

A 3.2.8 Formula [A 3.2.3] above refers to horizontal flow systems. Where a difference in level, h (m), exists between the ends of a pipe, an additional expression has to be introduced to allow for the work done against gravity, or by the buoyancy effect. The pressure difference may be positive or negative according to whether gas flow is descensional or ascensional, and whether the gas is heavier or lighter than air. In general:

$$p_h = \delta \varrho_{air} g h \quad \text{[A 3.2.4]}$$

where:

ϱ_{air} density of air in kg/m^3

p_h is in Pa.

For firedamp-air mixtures, δ is less than 1.

A 3.2.9 The value of δ, the relative density of drained gas mixtures, varies with its composition, and is given by:

$$\delta = \varkappa \delta_{air} + (1 - \varkappa) \delta_m \quad \text{[A 3.2.5]}$$

where:

δ relative density of drained methane/air mixture
$\varkappa$ fraction of air in mixture
δ_{air} density of air = 1
δ_m density of methane relative to air (0.55).

Thus, a 60 per cent methane/40 per cent air mixture would have a density:

$$\delta = (0.40 \times 1) + (0.60 \times 0.55) = 0.40 + 0.33 = 0.73$$

A 3.2.10 The density of the drained firedamp/air air mixture at standard conditions of 101.3 kPa and 288 K, is based on that of air at 1.20 kg/m^3. Therefore, the density of the firedamp/air mixture with a relative density of 0.73 would be = 0.73 × 1.20 = 0.876 kg/m^3.

Reynolds Number and the Dimensionless Friction Coefficient

A 3.2.11 The value of the dimensionless friction coefficient λ varies with Reynolds Number Re and the nature of the internal surface of the pipe. The Reynolds Number:

$$Re = \frac{\varrho w d}{\mu} = \frac{w d}{\nu} \quad \text{[A 3.2.6]}$$

where:

ϱ density of drained gas in kg/m^3
d diameter of pipe in m
w mean gas velocity in m/s
μ absolute (dynamic) viscosity of the gas mixture in Ns/m^2
ν kinematic viscosity of the drained gas in m^2/s.

Values of the Friction Coefficient λ for Smooth, Rough and Commercial Pipes

A 3.2.12 The value of the friction coefficient λ can be determined once the Reynolds Number *Re* is known by either using the appropriate formula given below or the λ-*Re* general resistance curves given in Figure A 3.2.1.

a) Turbulent Flow in Smooth Pipes

A 3.2.13 The expression employed to determine the value of λ for turbulent flow ($Re > 2300$) in smooth pipes is:

$$\frac{1}{\sqrt{\lambda}} = 2 \log_{10} \left(Re \sqrt{\lambda} \right) - 0.8 \qquad \text{[A 3.2.7]}$$

This expression has the disadvantage that the dimensionless friction coefficient λ is present on both sides of the equation.

A 3.2.14 The relationships between λ and *Re* for turbulent flow in smooth pipes are also expressed by other equations, such as:

$$\lambda = \frac{0.316}{Re^{0.25}} \qquad \text{[A 3.2.8]}$$

after Blasius, when $Re \geqq 10^5$; and

$$\lambda = \frac{0.172}{Re^{0.18}} \qquad \text{[A 3.2.9]}$$

after Renouard, for *Re* from 2×10^4 to 2×10^6.

b) Turbulent Flow in Rough Pipes

A 3.2.15 The Colebrook and White Expression

This is expressed as:

$$\frac{1}{\sqrt{\lambda}} = -2 \log_{10} \left(\frac{k_s}{3.7\, d} + \frac{2.51}{Re} \sqrt{\frac{1}{\lambda}} \right) \qquad \text{[A 3.2.10]}$$

for the transition between smooth and rough pipes, where k_s is the lineal measure of absolute roughness ie mean height of the pipe roughness, having the same dimensional units as the diameter d.

The factor k_s is sometimes called the absolute roughness characteristic, equivalent to the diameter of uniform sand grains coating the internal surface of the pipe. The Colebrook and White equation suffers from the disadvantage that the friction coefficient appears on both sides of the equation.

A 3.2.16 The Kármán-Prandtl Relationship for turbulent flow in rough pipes

Numerous experimenters have shown that, in the turbulent régime the value of the dimensionless friction coefficient λ for rough pipes is independent of the Reynolds Number $\left(\text{for } Re > \frac{200}{\sqrt{\lambda}} \frac{d}{k_s} \right)$.

The relationship commonly used to determine λ is:

$$\frac{1}{\sqrt{\lambda}} = 2 \log_{10} \left(\frac{d}{k_s}\right) + 1.14 \quad \text{[A 3.2.11]}$$

where k_s = wall roughness in consistent units, as defined above. The ratio $\left(\frac{d}{k_s}\right)$ is sometimes known as the relative smoothness.

Typical values of absolute roughness k_s are given in Table A 3.2.1 below.

Table A 3.2.1 Some values of absolute roughness k_s and relative smoothness d/k_s and λ for a 250 mm diameter pipe.

Material	Broad Description	k_s mm	d/k_s	λ	Remarks
Perfectly smooth drawn pipe	Very smooth	0.0015	166 600	0.0054	Overland pipes
Long distance steel transmission gas grid	Medium smooth	0.018	13 880	0.0108	
Ordinary new steel pipe	Smooth	0.045	5 540	0.0135	Underground pipes
Steel pipe with sand grains	Slightly rough	0.381	656	0.0218	

A 3.2.17 λ-*Re* Curves for Commercial Pipes

The value of the dimensionless friction coefficient λ for commercial pipes can be obtained from standard friction coefficient graphs, such as Figure A 3.2.1, which show the λ-*Re* relationships for pipes of differing roughness.

Equations used for Computer Programs

A 3.2.18 Reglagaz

The equation used is a modified form of equation [A 3.2.2] above:

$$\left(p_A^2 - p_B^2 e^S\right) \frac{s}{e^S - 1} = \frac{16}{\pi^2} \varrho_0 p_0 \frac{T}{T_0} \lambda \frac{Q_0^2}{d^5} / k \quad \text{[A 3.2.12]}$$

where:

$$s = 2 \varrho_0 g \frac{T_0}{T} \frac{h_B - h_A}{p_0} \quad \text{[A 3.2.13]}$$

$$\lambda = \frac{0.172}{Re^{0.18}} \quad \text{[A 3.2.14]}$$

$$Re = \frac{4}{\pi \mu} \cdot \frac{\varrho_0 Q_0}{d} \quad \text{[A 3.2.15]}$$

$$\varrho_0 = \delta \varrho_{0\,air} \quad \text{[A 3.2.16]}$$

where:

p_A absolute pressure at A
p_B absolute pressure at B
p_0 normal pressure (101.3 kPa)
T_0 normal temperature (288 K)
T absolute temperatures of the gas in K
ϱ_0 density of gas at normal conditions
$\varrho_{0\,air}$ density of air at normal conditions
Q_0 gas flow at normal conditions
h_A level at A
h_B level at B
λ friction coefficient
Re Reynolds Number
g gravitational acceleration
k correction factor
μ dynamic viscosity of the gas

A 3.2.19 Resogaz

The basic equations are the same as those used in the Reglagaz program.

A 3.2.20 RAG

The basic formula, which assumes compressible isothermal flows in drainage ranges with a difference in level, ignoring acceleration is:

$$p_1 - p_2 = \left(\lambda \frac{l}{d} + \zeta\right) \frac{10\,332 \times 16\, \gamma_0\, (273 + \vartheta)}{273\, \pi^2\, g\, d^4} \frac{Q_0{}^2}{(p_1 + p_2)} +$$

$$+ p_1 \left(\exp \frac{(h_1 - h_2)\, \gamma_0\, 273}{10\,332\, (273 + \vartheta)} - 1\right) + \Delta p \quad \text{[A 3.2.17]}$$

where:

p_1, p_2 absolute pressure at beginning and end of pipe section in kp/m^2
λ friction coefficient
l length of pipe section in m
d pipe diameter in m
ζ resistance coefficient for additional resistance in the pipe section
γ_0 specific weight at 760 torr and 0 °C in kp/m^3
ϑ temperature in pipe section in °C
g gravitational acceleration in m/s^2
Q_0 standard volume flow (at 760 torr and 0 °C)
h_1, h_2 altitude at beginning and end of pipe section in m below sea level
Δp pressure generated in pipe section in kp/m^3

The first term represents the approximation for the friction losses with compressible isothermal flow, using average specific gravity, see equation [A 3.2.3]; the second term represents the formula for barometric head when there is a change of isothermal state of a stationary column of gas.

The solution for p_2 ($\zeta = 0$; $\Delta p = 0$) becomes:

$$p_2 = \frac{p_1}{2}\left(1 - \exp\frac{h_2 - h_1}{R\,T}\right) \cdot$$

$$\cdot \left[1 \pm \sqrt{1 - \frac{4}{\left(\exp\frac{h_2 - h_1}{R\,T} - 1\right)^2}\left(\exp\frac{h_2 - h_1}{R\,T} - 2 + \lambda\frac{l}{d}\frac{\gamma_0}{2g}\,w_0^{\,2}\,\frac{2}{p_1}\frac{\gamma_0}{\gamma_1}\right)}\,\right] \quad \text{[A 3.2.18]}$$

where:

R	gas constant of gas in m/K
T	temperature in pipe section in K
w_0	velocity at standard conditions 760 torr and 0 °C in m/s
γ_1	specific weight at pressure of p_1 and temperature T in kp/m³

A 3.2.21 TU Clausthal

The basic formula, which assumes compressible isothermal flow in drainage ranges with a difference in level, ignoring acceleration is:

$$l = \frac{1}{2a}\ln\left(\frac{a\,p_1^2 + b}{a\,p_2^2 + b}\right) \quad \text{[A 3.2.19]}$$

with

$$a = \frac{\gamma_1}{p_1}\sin\alpha \quad \text{[A 3.2.20]}$$

$$b = \lambda\,p_1\,\gamma_1\,\frac{1}{d}\frac{w_1^2}{2g} \quad \text{[A 3.2.21]}$$

and

$$\sin\alpha = \frac{h_2 - h_1}{l} \quad \text{[A 3.2.22]}$$

The solution for p_2 becomes:

$$p_2 = p_1\sqrt{\left(1 + \lambda\frac{l}{d}\frac{w_1^2}{2\,g}\frac{1}{(h_2 - h_1)}\right)\exp\left(-2\frac{h_2 - h_1}{RT}\right) - \lambda\frac{l}{d}\frac{w_1^2}{2\,g}\frac{1}{(h_2 - h_1)}} \quad \text{[A 3.2.23]}$$

where:

p_1, p_2	pressure at beginning and end of pipe sections
λ	coefficient of friction in the range
l	length of pipe section in m
d	pipe diameter in m
γ_1	density at pressure p_1 and temperature T in kp/m³

T temperature in pipe section in K
g gravitational acceleration in m/s²
w_1 velocity at pressure p_1 and temperature T in m/s
h_1, h_2 altitude with respect to sea level in m
R gas constant in m/K

The formulae do not apply to level pipes.

A 3.2.22 Pressure Losses in Vertical Shafts

A number of factors need to be taken into consideration.

a) Frictional Pressure Losses

The frictional pressure losses in vertical shafts are determined using equation [A 3.2.2] in Section A 3.2.5.

b) Buoyancy Effect Due to Change in Height Δh

As shown in Section A 3.2.9 and A 3.2.10, drained gas mixtures are lighter than air, giving rise to a buoyancy effect which helps to counter frictional losses. The buoyancy effect can be estimated from the expression:

$$\Delta p_h = g\,(1 - \delta)\,\varrho_{air}\,\Delta h \qquad [A\ 3.2.24]$$

where:

Δp_h buoyancy pressure in Pa
ϱ_{air} density of air in kg/m³
δ relative density of firedamp/air mixture (air = 1)
g acceleration due to gravity in m/s²
Δh vertical difference of shaft column in m

The full buoyancy effect which is theoretically independent of flow and pipe diameter is not always realised because of the super-saturated condition of the drained gas which is cooled as it flows from a lower to a much higher level. The buoyancy effect is of considerable practical value however when the extractors are not operating (ie in the free flow condition) but is constrained when extractors are operating.

c) Pressure losses at the Bottom and Top of the Shaft

Allowance is made for pressure losses due to bends, and possibly changes in pipe section at the bottom or in the shaft, and at the top of the shaft. The necessary information is given in Appendix A 3.3.

d) Net effect in Vertical Shafts

The net effect in vertical shafts when the extractor is not operating is:

$$\Delta p_s = \Delta p_f - \Delta p_h + \Delta p_c \qquad [A\ 3.2.25]$$

where:

Δp_f pipe friction pressure loss
Δp_h buoyancy pressure
Δp_c pressure loss due to bends etc.

When extractors are operating, the buoyancy term is often omitted to give:

$$\Delta p_s = \Delta p_f + \Delta p_c \qquad [A\ 3.2.26]$$

Appendix 3.3

Losses in Valves and Pipe Fittings

Pressure losses in Shaped Fittings and Accessories

The friction coefficient ζ for pressure loss in shaped fittings and accessories is defined in the following equation:

$$\Delta p = \zeta \frac{w^2 \gamma}{2 g} \quad \text{[A 3.3.1]}$$

in which:

Δp pressure loss in a shaped fitting or an accessory
w mean velocity of the fluid in shaped fitting or accessory in m/s
γ specific weight of the fluid in kp/m^3
g gravitational acceleration in m/s^2

In the equation for incompressible flow in pipes

$$\Delta p = \frac{\lambda\, l\, w^2 \gamma}{d\, 2 g} \quad \text{[A 3.3.2]}$$

in which:

λ pipe friction coefficient
l pipe length in m
d pipe diameter in m

By comparison of the equations [A 3.3.1] and [A 3.3.2],

$$\zeta = \lambda \frac{l}{d} \quad \text{[A 3.3.3]}$$

Thus, one can calculate the equivalent length of straight piping to give the pressure loss of installed fittings or accessories knowing the friction coefficient ζ. The additional resistance of fittings can therefore be stated in terms of an increased pipe length. Alternatively we can add the individual coefficients to the pipe coefficient $\lambda \frac{l}{d}$ to give the total friction value $\Sigma \zeta$.

Typical Values of the Friction Coefficient ζ for Various Fittings

a) Bends and branches: See Figure A 3.3.1
b) Gate valves, cocks and butterfly valves $\zeta = 0.3$
c) Throughway valves:

— to DIN specification

Diameter in mm	50	80	100	150	200
Friction coefficient ζ	4.5	4.8	4.8	4.1	3.6

— of larger sizes

Diameter in mm	100	125	150	200	300	400	500
Koswa type ζ	2.5	2.5	2.4	2.4	2.3	2.2	2.1
Rhei type ζ	2.7	2.3	2.0	1.4	1.0	0.8	0.7

d) Non Return and Relief Valves

Diameter in mm	50	80	100	150	200
Friction coefficient ζ	1.4	1.3	1.2	0.9	0.8

e) Sudden Changes in Pipe Cross Section: See Figure A 3.3.2
f) Constriction: See Figure A 3.3.2
g) Sudden Enlargement in Pipe Cross Section: See Figure A 3.3.2
h) Enlargement: See Figure A 3.3.2
i) Measuring equipment: See Figure A 3.3.3
k) Venturis: See Figure A 3.3.3

Smooth bend — Coude régulier — Krümmer gebogen

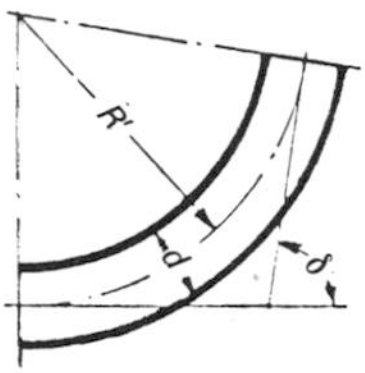

δ		Smooth — Lisse — Glatt					Rough Rugueux Rauh
		15	22,5	45	60	90	90
$R' = d$	$\zeta =$	0,03	0,045	0,14	0,19	0,21	0,51
$= 2d$	$\zeta =$	0,03	0,045	0,09	0,12	0.14	0,30
$= 4d$	$\zeta =$	0,03	0,045	0,08	0,10	0,11	0,23
$= 6d$	$\zeta =$	0,03	0,045	0,075	0,09	0,09	0,18
$= 10d$	$\zeta =$	0,03	0,045	0,07	0,07	0,11	0,20

Segmented bend — Coude par segments soudés — Krümmer segmentgeschweißt

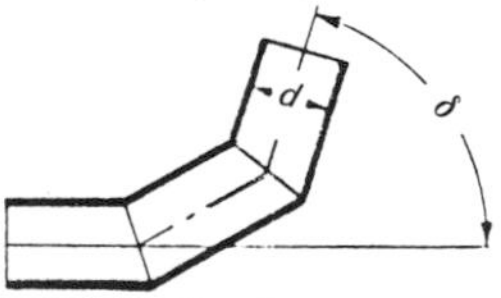

δ	15	22,5	30	45	60	90
Number of joins Nombre de sondure Anzahl der Rundnähte	1	1	2	2	3	3
ζ	0,06	0,08	0,1	0,15	0,2	0,25

Folded 90° bend — Coude plié 90° — Faltenrohrbogen 90°

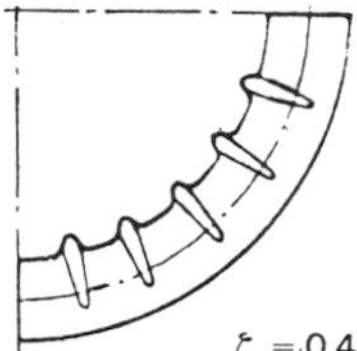

Long 90° bend — Coude coulé 90° — Gußkrümmer 90°

Nominal Diameter Diamètre Nennweite	50	100	200	300	400	500
ζ	1,3	1,5	1,8	2,1	2,2	2,2

Elbows — Condes — Kniestücke

$\zeta = 0,4$

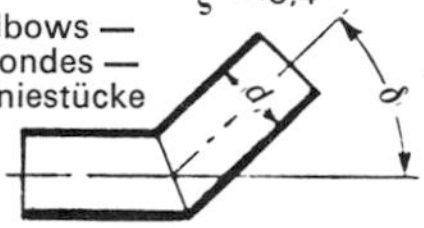

δ	22,5	30	45	60	90
Smooth — Lisse — Glatt	0,07	0,11	0,24	0,47	1,43
Rough — Rugueux — Rauh	0,11	0,47	0,32	0,68	1,27

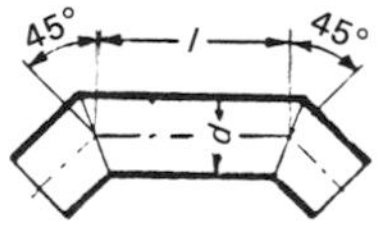

l/d	0,71	0,943	1,174	1,42	1,86	2,56	6,28
Smooth — Lisse — Glatt	0,51	0,35	0,33	0,28	0,29	0,36	0,40
Rough — Rugueux — Rauh	0,51	0,41	0,38	0,38	0,39	0,43	0,45

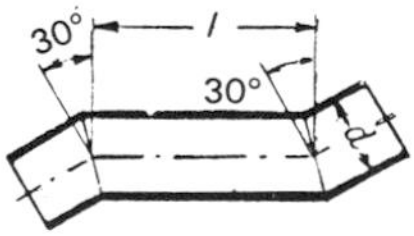

l/d	1,23	1,67	2,37	3,77
Smooth — Lisse — Glatt	0,16	0,16	0,14	0,16
Rough — Rugueux — Rauh	0,30	0,28	0,26	0,24

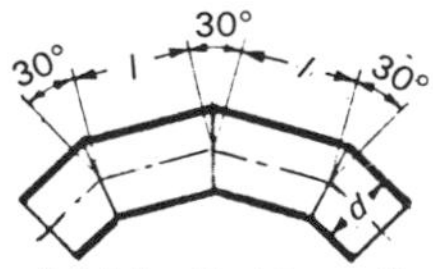

l/d = 1,7 to — à — bis 6,0 — ζ = 0,15 to — à — bis 0,2; ζ = 0,3 to — à — bis 0,4

Fig. A 3.3.1 Resistance Coefficients of Pipe Fittings after F. Herning.

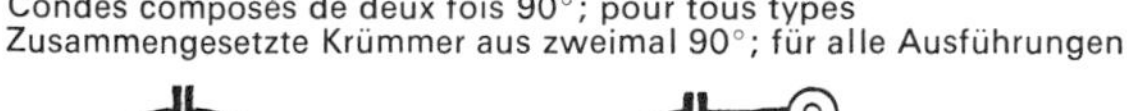

Composite bends made of two 90° bends; for all forms
Condes composés de deux fois 90°; pour tous types
Zusammengesetzte Krümmer aus zweimal 90°; für alle Ausführungen

$\zeta \approx 0{,}5$

T-pieces (reduced flow) — Té — T-Stück (Stromtrennung)

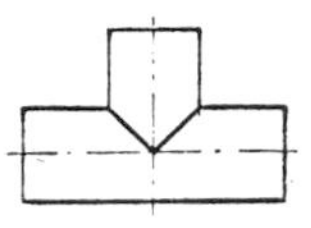

Square —
A angles vifs —
Scharfkantig
$\zeta = 1{,}3$

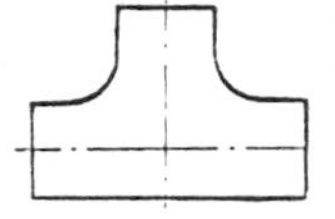

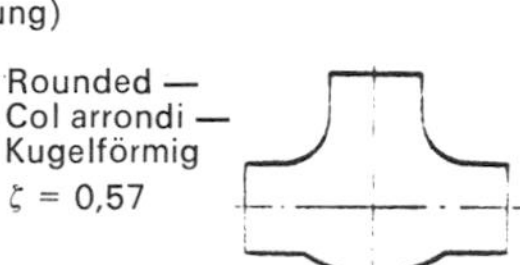

Rounded —
Col arrondi —
Kugelförmig
$\zeta = 0{,}57$

Spherical —
Col arrondi et
fond droit —
Abgerundet mit
geradem Boden
$\zeta = 0{,}73$

Branches — Derivations — Abzweigstücke	Flow leaving — Séparation — Trennung				Flow entering — Réunion — Vereinigung			
	Q, Q_a (90° branch)		Q, Q_a (45° branch)		Q_a, Q (90° branch)		Q_a, Q (45° branch)	
Q_a/Q	ζ_a	ζ_d	ζ_a	ζ_d	ζ_a	ζ_d	ζ_a	ζ_d
0	0,95	0,04	0,90	0,04	— 1,2	0,04	— 0,92	0,04
0,2	0,88	— 0,08	0,68	— 0,06	— 0,4	0,17	— 0,38	0,17
0,4	0,89	— 0,05	0,50	— 0,04	0,08	0,30	0,00	0,19
0,6	0,95	0,07	0,38	0,07	0,47	0,41	0,22	0,09
0,8	1,10	0,21	0,35	0,20	0,72	0,51	0,37	— 0,17
1,0	1,28	0,35	0,48	0,33	0,91	0,60	0,37	— 0,54

Q Total flow — Débit total — Gesamtstrom
Q_a Flow in branch pipe — Arrivée ou départ — ab- bzw. zufließender Strom
ζ_d Resistance coefficient, main pipe — Résistance de la conduite principale — Widerstand im Hauptrohr
ζ_a Resistance coefficient, branch pipe — Résistance des dérivations — Widerstand im Abzweigrohr
— Negative indicates pressure gain — Signe moius indique gain de pression — Minuszeichen bedeutet Druckgewinn

Composite pipe sections — Elements composés — Zusammengesetzte Leitungsstücke

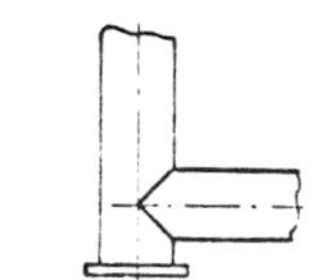

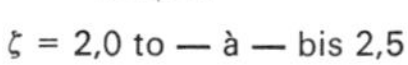

$\zeta = 2{,}0$ to — à — bis 2,5

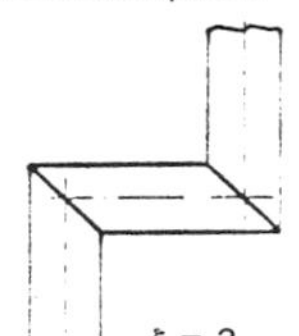

$\zeta = 3$

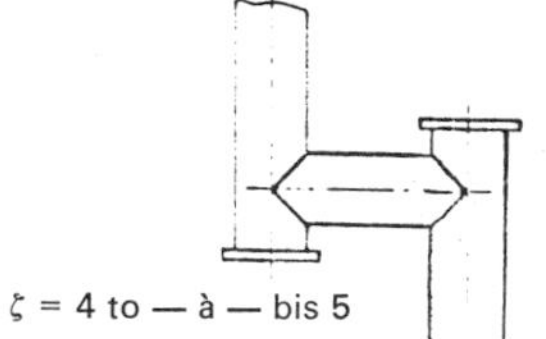

$\zeta = 4$ to — à — bis 5

Expansion sections — Elements compensateurs — Ausgleichsstücke

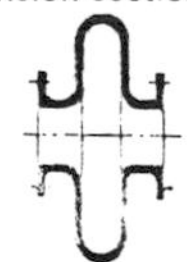

Corrugated pipe
Element compensateur ondulé
Wellrohrausgleicher
$\zeta = 0{,}2$

Smooth loop
Element compensateure on lyre
Glattrohr-Lyrabogen
$\zeta = 0{,}7$

Folded loop
Element compensateure on lyre
Faltenrohr-Lyrabogen
$\zeta = 1{,}4$

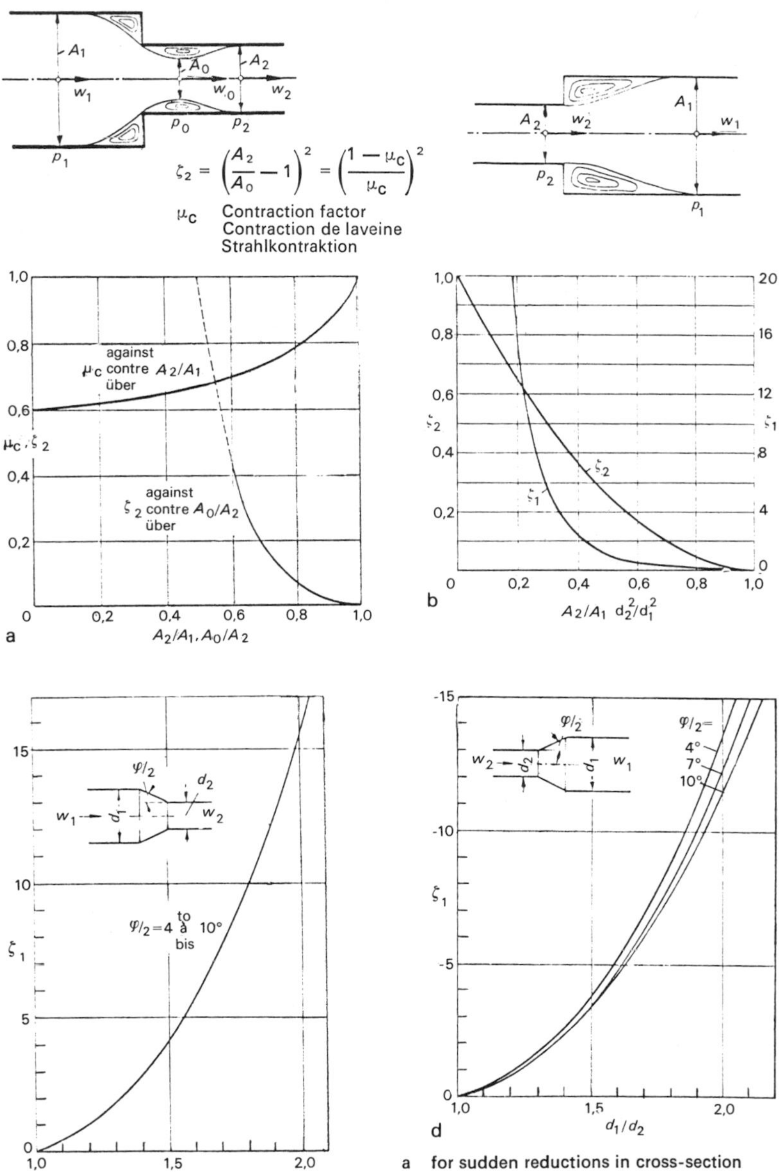

a for sudden reductions in cross-section
b for sudden increases in cross-section
c for gradual reductions in cross-section
d for gradual increases in cross-section

Fig. A 3.3.2 Resistance coefficients.

a

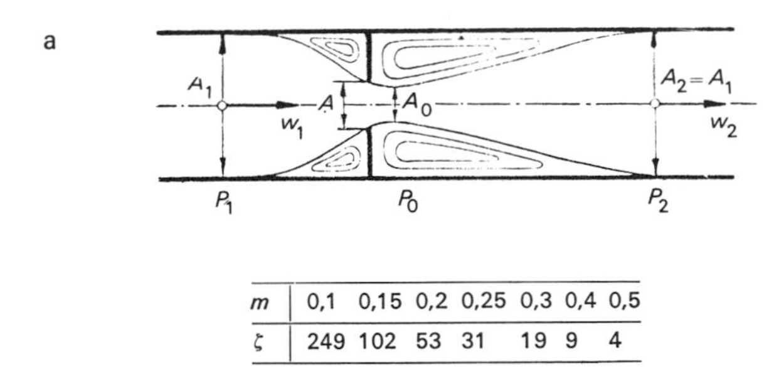

m	0,1	0,15	0,2	0,25	0,3	0,4	0,5
ζ	249	102	53	31	19	9	4

b

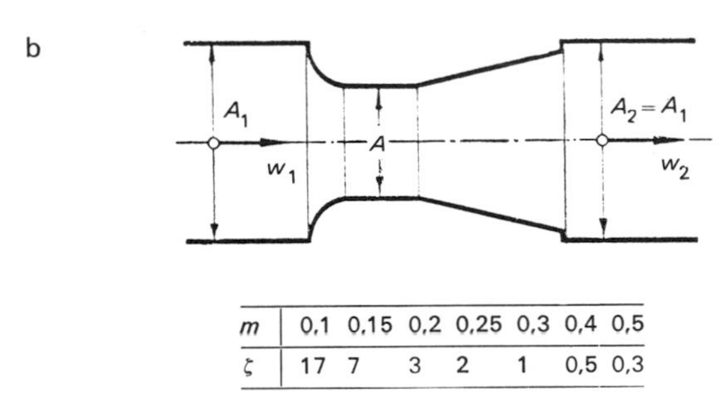

m	0,1	0,15	0,2	0,25	0,3	0,4	0,5
ζ	17	7	3	2	1	0,5	0,3

$m = A/A_1$ Orifice Ratio
Rapport des sections
Öffnungsverhältnis

Fig. A 3.3.3 Resistance Coefficients for Standard Orifice Plates (above) and for Standard Venturi Tubes (below).

Appendix 3.4

Purpose Designed Calculators for Gas Drainage Network Calculations

Two purpose designed calculators for gas drainage network calculations are described below. Instructions for use of each calculator are given on the calculator itself.

A 3.4.1 The NCB/Mears Methane Drainage Pipe Calculator

The NCB/Mears Methane Drainage Pipe Calculator (see Figure 3.1) is a small hand calculator, 200 mm in diameter, regularly employed in the United Kingdom for:

▷ rapid calculation of pressure losses in existing firedamp drainage pipes,

▷ rapid assessment of the effects of changes in gas pipe networks,

▷ assessment of vacuum and/or pressure requirements in particular gas pipe networks,

▷ assessments of forward planning requirements.

SI Units are employed. Reference conditions are a temperature of 288 K and a pressure of 101.3 kPa. The values of the friction factor are obtained from Appendix 3.2.

The calculator is made by M. H. Mear and Co., Huddersfield, United Kingdom.

The NCB/Mears Methane Drainage Pipe calculator has a number of main advantages:

a) Calculations are easily and quickly made.

b) The calculator is portable, thus enabling calculations to be carried out anywhere, such as at the office or at a colliery at any time.

c) It is simple and easily used by colliery staff.

d) It is cheap.

e) It is eminently suitable to assess the effects of suggested changes in gas systems.

f) It is eminently suitable for analysing existing gas grid systems and for identifying measures that will lead to improvements in those systems.

g) It is widely used for forecasting underground gas system requirements.

h) Time delay awaiting solutions is minimal.

The main disadvantage is that the accuracy of the calculation is limited by the scales on the calculator. In practice, however, this limitation has not been found to be of significance.

A 3.4.2 Gaz de France Slide Rule

The Gaz de France slide rule is illustrated in Figure 3.2, and can be used for incompressible and compressible gas flow systems. The equations employed are similar to those given in Appendix 3.2. Empirical modifications have been made to the indices of Q and d. The Règle Gaz de France is distributed by Graphoflex, 21 Rue de Montsouris, Paris 14. The Gaz de France slide rule has a number of main advantages:

a) It is readily used.

b) For a length of pipe, one of the following parameters can be calculated — flow, length, diameter, $(p_A^2 - p_B^2)$ or $(p_A - p_B)$ knowing the other four.

c) The $(p_A^2 - p_B^2)$ scale allows pressure determination by stages, and relatively quickly with the assistance of a calculator giving x^2 or $\sqrt{x}$.

d) The coefficient of roughness can be calculated knowing the four parameters.

The main disadvantages are that:

a) It can only be used for horizontal pipes.

b) Gas is assumed to be at 288 K.

c) The calculation may be very long, with risk of errors, when used on a large firedamp drainage system.

Appendix 3.5

Surface Firedamp Extraction Plant

A 3.5.1 Example of a Surface Extraction Plant (NCB Design)

a) The illustration in Figure A 3.5.1 shows a simplified general layout, and gas and water flow circuits for a surface firedamp extraction plant to National Coal Board design. The particular illustration shows three extractors E, of the water seal H7 or H10 Nash type, driven by electric motors, M. The extractor bypass arrangement B, and the drained gas pipe lines to atmosphere F and to the utilisation plant D are indicated. The delivery gas sampling lines are shown as G. Two photographs Figures A 3.5.2 and A 3.5.3 show the extractors and instrument panel.

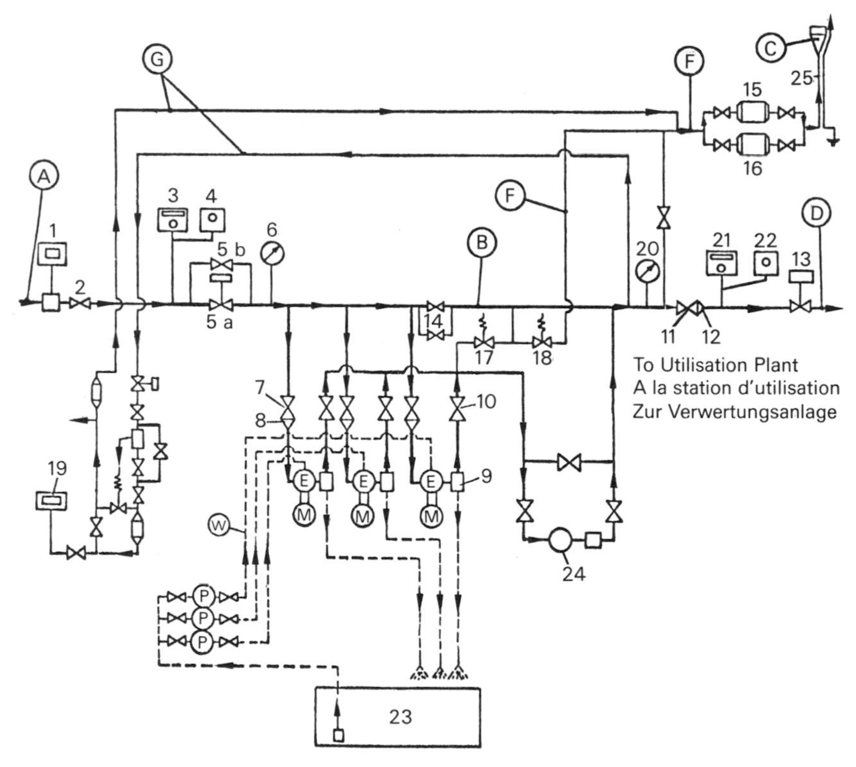

Fig. A 3.5.1 Simplified Standard Layout for Surface Firedamp Extraction Plant with Water Seal Extractors.

b) Firedamp/air mixtures extracted from the mine pass from shaft A, through a 255 or 300 mm nominal bore steel pipe (or two such pipes in parallel), a stop valve 2, a magnetic valve 5a, into one or more of the water seal extractors E, which are connected up in parallel. The magnetic valve is provided with a small bypass and small diaphragm valve 5b. Each water seal extractor E, is provided with an inlet stop valve 7, an inlet non-return valve 8 and a delivery stop valve 10.

c) Firedamp is discharged from each water seal extractor through a tangential gas separator 9 (see Figure 3.10) and a diaphragm outlet valve 10 (see Table 3.6), into a common delivery gas line. A diaphragm outlet valve 11, and a non-return valve 12, are inserted in the delivery pipe D, to the utilisation plant. A hand-opening magnetic safety cut out valve 13, is installed in the utilisation pipe line also.

d) A common bypass B is provided for the extractors so that, in the event of all extractors being stopped (say because of power failure or for maintenance), gas drained from underground workings can flow out of the mine to atmosphere through a steel or brick chimney C, provided with a lightning conductor 25. This bypass is provided with a stop valve 14 and also a small bypass to enable some gas recirculation to be achieved if necessary.

Key for Fig. 3.5.1

1 High range methanometer — Indicateur de méthane haute teneurs — Methanometer für hohe Konzentrationen
2 Manual diaphragm valve — Vanne manuelle à diaphragme — Handbetätigtes Membranventil
3 Gas flow vacuum and temperature recorder — Enregistreur de débit, dépression et température — Gasstrom-, Unterdruck- und Temperaturschreiber
4 Gas flow indicator/integrator — Indicateur de débit et compteur — Gasstromanzeiger und -integrator
5a Suction hand opening magnetic safety cut out valve — Vanne magnétique manuelle de coupure de sécurité — Von Hand zu öffnendes saugseitiges Magnet-Sicherheitsventil
5b By pass and valve — Bipasse et vanne — Bypass und Ventil
6 Low pressure diaphragm gauge with electric contacts — Indicateur basse pression à diaphragme et contacts électrique — Niederdruck-Membranmanometer mit elektrischen Kontakten
7 Diaphragm inlet valve (manual) — Vanne d'entrée à diaphragme — Handbetätigtes eintrittseitiges Membranventil
8 Inlet non return valve — Clapet de non retour — Eintrittseitiges Rückschlagventil
9 Water separator — Séparateur d'eau — Wasserabscheider
10 Diaphragm outlet valve — Vanne de sortie à diaphragme — Austrittseitiges Membranventil
11 Delivery diaphragm valve with micro switches — Vanne de sortie avec micro-interrupteur — Druckseitiges Membranventil mit Mikroschaltern
12 Delivery non return valve — Clapet de non retour — Druckseitiges Rückschlagventil
13 Delivery hand opening magnetic safety cut out valve — Vanne magnétique manuelle de coupure de sécurité — Von Hand zu öffnendes druckseitiges Magnet-Sicherheitsventil
14 By pass stop valve — Vanne de bipasse — Bypass-Absperrventil
15 Flame arrestor — Coupe-flammé — Flammensperre
16 Flame arrestor — Coupe-flammé — Flammensperre
17 Differential pressure relief valve — Vanne de charge — Differenzdruck-Entlastungsventil
18 Differential pressure relief valve — Vanne de charge — Differenzdruck-Entlastungsventil
19 Sigma recording calorimeter — Calorimètre enregistreur Sigma — Schreibendes Sigma-Kalorimeter
20 Delivery pressure gauge — Indicateur de pression de refoulement — Druckseitiges Manometer
21 Gas flow pressure and temperature recorder and orifice plate — Enregistreur de débit, pression et température — Gasstrom-, Druck- und Temperaturschreiber sowie Meßblende
22 Gas flow indicator/integrator to match item 18 — Indicateur de débit et compteur — Gasstromanzeiger und -integrator
23 Water sump — Réservoir d'eau — Wassersumpf
24 Gas cooling plant — Refroidisseur — Gaskühler
25 Lightning conductor — Paratonnerre — Blitzableiter

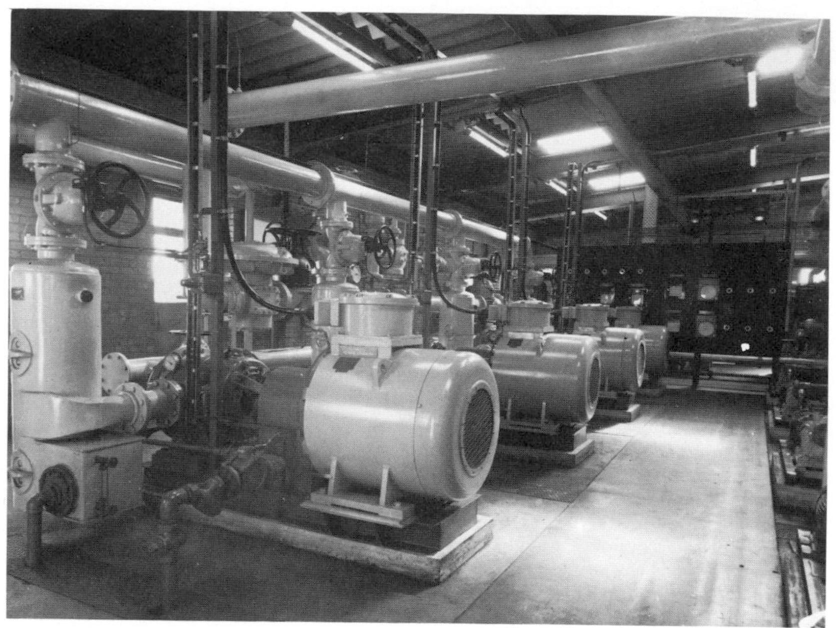

Fig. A 3.5.2 Surface Extraction Plant: Extractors.

e) The gas main F, to the discharge chimney C, is divided into two separate parallel streams. Each of the separate parallel streams is provided with a flame trap 15 and 16. Stop valves are sited on either side of each flame trap to ensure that inspection and maintenance of one flame trap can be undertaken when the plant is operating continuously. These flame traps are usually either 250 mm or 310 mm in diameter and consist of one or more steel wire gauzes or elements and supporting frame (see Chapter 3, Section 3.7). Gauzes or elements of the flame traps may be examined at two or three monthly intervals or more frequently. Automatic pressure relief valves 17 and 18, which are provided in the gas main to the discharge chimney C, operate in the event of delivery gas pressures exceeding prescribed values.

f) The purity of inlet drained gas is monitored continuously by a high concentration methanometer 1, of the acoustic, thermal conductivity (BM2H) or industrial infra-red type. The purity of drained gas is shown on an indicator in the extractor house, where it is also recorded on paper chart or transmitted to a central monitoring station remote from the extractor plant. Inlet gas flow rates, inlet gas pressures (vacuum) and inlet gas temperatures are shown on indicators and paper chart recorders 3 and 4, for analysis of plant and firedamp extraction performance. This information may also be relayed to the central monitoring station. The bourdon-type vacuum gauge 6 indicates the vacuum and is provided with contacts for alarm on excess suction.

g) Gas delivered to the utilisation plant is monitored continuously for calorific value by a Sigma flame calorimeter 19 when drained gas is sold to an external customer. Alternatively, the purity of drained gas to the utilisation plant is measured continuously either by an acoustic, thermal conductivity (BM2H) monitor, or an industrial type infra-red analyser. These monitors are connected to the gas sampling lines G, which are 12 mm in diameter. Calorific values and purities of drained gas are recorded locally on paper chart, indicated on a meter, and may also be transmitted to the central monitoring station. The delivery pressure is indicated by local bourdon-type pressure gauge 20, which is provided with contacts for alarm on excess pressure. Outlet gas flow rates, pressures and temperatures are indicated on meters and recorded on paper chart 21 and 22, and may also be transmitted to the central monitoring station. In addition, an outlet flow standard electric analogue signal may be relayed to the central monitoring station.

h) Monitoring of the atmosphere in and near the surface extractor house is achieved by a multiheaded pellistor type low concentration methane monitor with up to eight channels. All rooms in which a gas escape might occur are monitored continuously, including the main exhauster room and the calorimeter room, as are the external water sump and some cable ducts. If firedamp concentrations in the extractor house, or at any of these monitoring positions, exceed a prescribed value (usually 0.25 per cent), an alarm is sounded and the electrical power is automatically cut off.

i) Seal water circulating pumps for the extractors are shown as P. Water pipe lines are indicated by dotted lines W. Water is taken from, and returned to, the circulating water sump 23.

k) The electrical equipment in the hazardous area is required to be either intrinsically safe or flameproof to relevant UK regulations (Group 1 standards of the Health and Safety Executive) and to be installed in accordance with the conditions of certi-

Fig. A 3.5.3 Surface Extraction Plant: Monitoring Panel.

fication. Adequate segregation of circuits is required when several intrinsically safe electrical supplies are employed.

l) Fully automatic shut down and alarm controls are used. Two levels of automatic action are provided on inlet gas purity. An alarm is actuated at a certain firedamp percentage, and at some lower percentage the plant is automatically shut down. The plant shut-down setting is usually not less than 25 per cent. The methane alarm level is often set at about 27 per cent. Where drained gas is utilised, the delivery side of the plant is automatically shut down if the purity of drained gas falls below the statutory value of 40 per cent inflammable gas. The corresponding alarm level is about 42 per cent inflammable gas.

Other automatic shut-down and alarm features are incorporated. Any failure or substantial reduction in water circulation rate through the water seal extractor(s) stops the relevant extractor and operates an alarm. Any unusual rise in vacuum in the main inlet pipe or any unusual pressure rise on the outlet side actuates an alarm. The outlet valve of each extractor must be opened before that extractor can be started. Visual or audible alarms are automatically sounded if pressure relief valves are operated. An alarm operates in the event of high gas temperature arising at the outlet of the delivery gas cooling plant 24.

A 3.5.2 Principal Differences from other EEC Surface Extractor Plants

The principal differences between the UK and other EEC surface extractor plants are outlined below.

a) In the UK, only water seal gas extractors are employed, whereas, dry and water seal gas extractors are used in Germany and France and only dry extractors in Belgium (see Table 3.10).

b) In the UK, a flame trap is not used on the inlet side of water seal extractors. In Germany, Belgium and France, drained firedamp air mixtures pass through an explosion-proof flametrap (with an extinction device in Germany only) before entering the gas extractors. The flame trap is intended to prevent the spreading of a fire or an explosion into the mine in the event of the drained gas igniting, eg through the extractor.

c) In the UK duplicate flametraps and isolating valves are installed near the bottom of the chimney through which drained gas is discharged to atmosphere. In Germany, powder-type and CO_2-type flame suppressors are also used near or at the flametraps in the discharge chimney, in order to make the traps fireproof (Figure A 3.5.4). Modern installations are built without mechanical flametraps. Instead protection is afforded by an automatic flame extinguisher at the foot and at the outlet of the discharge chimney (Figure A 3.5.5).

d) In the UK, flame traps are installed at, or near, the point of utilisation, as for example near each drained gas supply to the burners of boilers. In Germany, two types of protective systems are installed in the main delivery pipe line to the utilisation plant: first a system without a flametrap but with a 'slam-shut' valve and automatic powder flame quencher/suppressor; and second a system with a flametrap, automatic flame quencher/suppressor and a 'slam-shut' valve.

e) Powder type flame suppressors are used in German mines on the inlet and outlet sides of the surface extraction plant; in modern installations they are also used in discharge chimneys. Figure A 3.5.4 shows an electrically triggered powder extinguisher (Halone) and an automatic rope-triggered carbon dioxide extinguishers in a modern drainage installation.

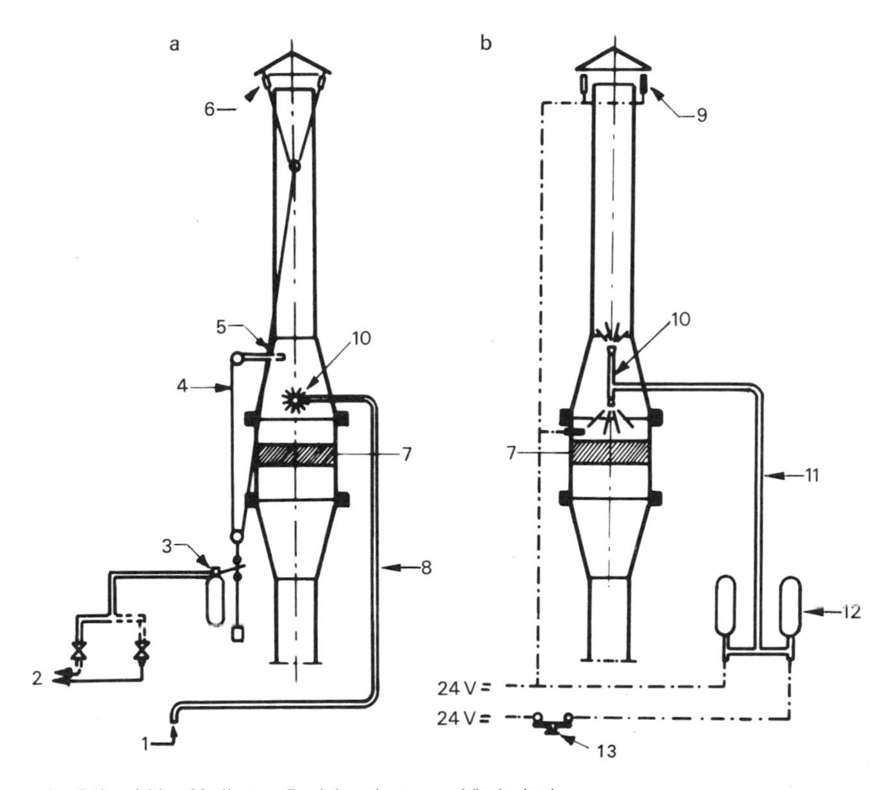

1 Extinguishing Medium — Produit extincteur — Löschmittel
2 To CO_2 Supply — Vers alimentation en CO_2 — Zur CO_2-Batterie
3 Control Flask — Bouteille de commande de vanne — Steuerflasche
4 Rope Traction — Câble de traction — Seilzug
5 Fusible Line Piercer — Bouchon fusible — Schmelzlotstopfen
6 Fusible Link — Element fusible — Schmelzlotglied
7 Flametrap — Coupe-flammé — Flammensperre
8 Extinguisher Pipe line — Arrivée du produit extincteur — Löschleitung
9 Heat Sensor — Capteur de témperature — Wärmefühler
10 Extinguishing nozzle — Dispositif extincteur — Löschdüse
11 Extinguisher Pipe line — Arrivée du produit — Löschleitung
12 Extinguishing medium — Produit extincteur — Löschmittel
13 Manual release — Déclenchement manuel — Handauslösung

a Rope triggered extinguishing medium (CO_2)
Extincteur à CO_2 avec systeme de déclechement
Seilauslösung, Löschmittel: CO_2

b Electrically tripped extinguishing medium (Powder)
Extincteur à poudre declenché électriquement
Elektrische Auslösung, Löschmittel: Halone/Pulver

Fig. A 3.5.4 Extinguishing Equipment for Atmospheric Discharge Chimney.

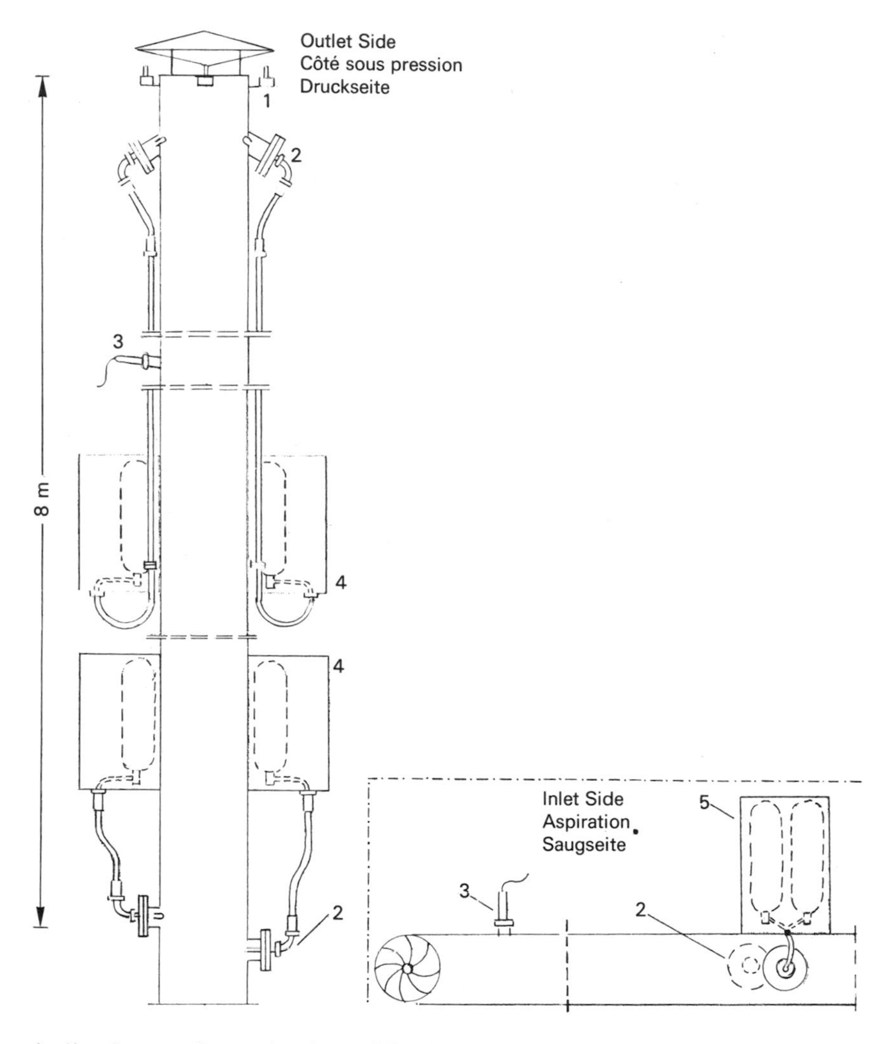

1 Heat Sensor — Capteur thermique — Wärmefühler

2 Socket with fan nozzle and gauze — Conduit de raccordement à pulvérisateur en éventail — Anschlußstutzen mit Fächerdüse

3 IR-Detector — Détecteur IR — IR-Detektor

4 2 pressurized vessels in protective casing — 2 bouteilles dans le coffret protecteur — 2 HDR-Flaschen im Schutzkasten

5 2 pressurized vessels in protective casing — 2 coffrets protecteurs avec à 2 bouteilles — 2 Schutzkästen mit je 2 HRD-Flaschen

Fig. A 3.5.5 Layout of Flame Arrestors in a Modern Firedamp Drainage System.

f) In the Federal Republic of Germany, measures are required to be taken at boreholes and other methane extraction points to increase the methane concentration of drained gas if the concentration falls to 20 per cent. Measures are also required to be taken to increase the methane concentration of drained gas at the ends of the gas collecting mains and in the main gas pipeline if the methane concentration in drained gas falls to 30 per cent. If the methane concentration in drained gas to the extractor falls to 25 per cent, a warning signal must be given, and the extractor is automatically stopped in the event of the methane concentration in drained gas falling to 20 per cent.

g) In Germany, drained firedamp is utilised down to a methane concentration of 25 per cent, in boiler houses and power stations. Below this concentration the gas supply to utilisation plants must be isolated by means of a 'slam-shut' valve. In the UK, France and Belgium, gas employed for utilisation must not contain less than forty per cent inflammable gas, and below this value the gas supply to the utilisation plant is automatically cut off.

A 3.5.3 Gas Main from Outlet side of Extraction Plant to Utilisation Plant

a) In the United Kingdom, delivery pipe lines forming part of a gas grid usually have diameters ranging from 200 to 700 mm according to the utilisation application, distances involved, pipe layout, gas flow rates, and purity of drained gas. Such pipe lines can be thin wall (6.25 to 7.5 mm on larger sizes), hot-finished seamless mild steel, to specification API 5L Grade B (27th Edition 1973 and Supplement 1 1974) with welded joints. Tubes would be supplied in random lengths of 5 to 8 m with bevelled ends. The joints may be butt welded (by either conventional or stove pipe welding to API 1104) under strict welding inspection conditions. The external protective coating could include cold and hot applied coal-tar enamel primer with glass wrap and a final hot flood-coat of enamel on the outside of which external glass wrap is applied. The coating thickness is usually between 3 and 6 mm. The gas mains are usually cathodically protected.

b) Gas from the water seal extractors/compressors passes through a cooler and demister to remove a high proportion of the water content and thereby to protect pipes against internal corrosion. However, condensation could still occur in the pipe in cold winter months with subsequent rust formation. Pipes are, therefore, descaled by pickling, then phosphate treated and internally painted with epoxy red oxide. The pipeline is buried and the joints wrapped (as above), the joints X-rayed and pressure tested, and the whole given cathodic protection. In addition, drained gas in some surface ungraded gas grids in the UK is dried before being passed into a grid, using di-ethylene glycol or absorption refrigeration systems.

c) The material selected for overland gas grids may also be ductile iron, coated internally and externally with bitumen for corrosion prevention. Pipes with internal diameters of either 250, 300 or 400 mm are supplied in 5.5 metres lengths. They have ultimate strengths of 420 N/mm^2 and a minimum elongation of 10 per cent and are allied with the flexibility of Stanlock self anchoring joints. The pipes are rated for the transmission of gas or liquids at pressures up to 700 kPa. A most important advantage over an all welded steel main is the ability of the grid or pipeline to accommodate subsidence without fracture. In addition, each mechanical (Stanlock) joint allows flexibility to be built in and whereas the recommended maximum angle of deflection is given as 2 degrees, some practical tests have shown that joints remained airtight and resistant to blow out at the maximum designed operating pressure when deflected through 20 degrees.

Another advantage is the ability of the pipe to withstand external corrosion in ground of particularly aggressive nature. In such situations, the pipes are fitted with polyethylene sleeving immediately prior to laying and may be surrounded by inert sand infill.

d) Full-bore manual valves are installed at each entry and exit position to a grid and approximately at intervals of 3 km on grid systems — and wherever else (eg rail crossings) where they might be required by another authority. Automatic shut-off valves may be installed to shut off the gas flow completely in the event of a line burst or damage, or serious leakage.

Chapter 4

Firedamp Drainage Monitoring, Control and Experience

0. Preface

It is necessary to know suctions applied to the network, purities of the drained gas and flow rates so that a correctly installed firedamp drainage system can be managed most effectively. For this purpose measurements must be made regularly in different parts in the network (see Section 1).

It is also necessary to consider the following points:

a) Commissioning the network, extending ranges and connecting boreholes (Section 2).

b) Regulating suctions at boreholes and in districts (Section 3).

c) Maintaining the network, locating and eliminating air inleakages and water blockages (Sections 4 and 5).

1. Underground and Surface Measurements

1.0 Introduction

The description of instruments is divided into those for underground use (Section 1.1) and surface use (Section 1.2), and is limited to models currently available within the Community. Each is described under the broad headings of physical principle, applications, and characteristics.

Underground instruments have been classified as portable, transportable, fixed and/or recording and the physical principles of measurement are given.

A summary of the instruments described and their principal characteristics is given in Table 4.1.

Table 4.1 Characteristics of Measuring Instruments. Sheet 1

Abbreviations:
Po portable instrument;
T transportable instrument;
F fixed station instrument.
WG water gauge.
IS intrinsically safe.

Conversions from SI units:
1 MPa = 10 bar ≈ 102 m WG
100 kPa = 1 bar ≈ 1 atmosphere ≈ 10 · 2 m WG
1 kPa = 10 mbar ≈ 7.5 mm Hg ≈ 102 mm WG
10 Pa ≈ 1 mm WG
100 ppm = 0.01 %

Pressure Underground.

Parameter Measured	Place of Use	Po, T or F	Instrument	Paragraph Reference	Range and Precision of Measurement	Remarks
Low suctions or pressures	Boreholes, Drainage ranges and Stoppings	Po, F	Inclined water U-tube, Water U-tube	1.1.1.1		
Medium suctions or pressures			Mercury U-tube			
	Stoppings		Single mercury tube		0 to 46 kPa	
	Drainage ranges	F	Ring balance	1.1.1.2	0 to 33 kPa	Recorder
		Po, F	Lugameter St AM	1.1.4.2		
		F	Tricapteur TCC 69	1.1.5	0 to 40 kPa	also measures concentration and flow of methane; remote transmission

Table 4.1 Pressure Underground. Sheet 2

Parameter Measured	Place of Use	Po, T or F	Instrument	Paragraph Reference	Range and Precision of Measurement	Remarks
Large suctions or pressures	Reservoirs, Drainage ranges	F	Differential manometer Ty 501	1.1.1.5	Suction down to 100 kPa, Pressure up to 60 MPa	remote transmission (IS in GFR)
	Boreholes, Drainage ranges, Extraction units	F	Bourdon tube manometer	1.1.1.6	suction $\leqq$ 100 kPa, pressure $\leqq$ 1.5 MPa (= 150 m WG)	also measures air or water pressure in the drilling machine
Atmospheric pressure	Airways	Po, F	Barolux Aneroid Barometer	1.1.1.7	66 to 123 kPa, precision 0.013 kPa	used in GFR and Belgium
		Po	Portable Barometer	1.1.1.8	80 to 120 kPa	
Vacuum Alarm	Drainage ranges, Underground extraction units	F	Vacuum (and differential pressure), Indicator and Alarm	1.1.1.9	0 to 3 kPa, 0 to 17, 0 to 34, 0 to 100 kPa	approved in UK
Vacuum and Differential pressure Alarm					typically 0 to 1 kPa 0 to 2 kPa	

Table 4.1 Methane Concentration Underground. Sheet 3

Parameter Measured	Place of Use	Po, T or F	Instrument	Paragraph Reference	Range and Precision of Measurement	Remarks
High concentration of methane	Drainage ranges, Boreholes	Po	Auer M 510 B	1.1.3.1	5 to 100 % CH_4	IS in GFR, Continuous measurement, Suction $\leqq$ 20 kPa, Absorbent train used for CO_2
	Drainage ranges, boreholes, layers, etc.		MSA HC II	1.1.3.2	0 to 100 %	IS in UK, Sampling by squeeze bulb, Life: 10,000 measurements of 10 s
	Drainage ranges, Boreholes		Fyrite	1.1.3.3	0 to 100 % low precision	Used in Belgium, Sampling by squeeze bulb, Absorption train life: 60 measurements, CO_2 correction or use second Fyrite
			Interferometer	1.1.3.4	0 to 100 %	IS throughout EEC except UK, Reading corrected to standard conditions, Correction for CO_2

Table 4.1 Methane Concentration Underground. Sheet 4

Parameter Measured	Place of Use	Po, T or F	Instrument	Paragraph Reference	Range and Precision of Measurement	Remarks
High concentration of methane (continued)	Drainage ranges	Po	CK 68	1.1.3.5	0 to 100 % Precision ± 3 % absolute	IS in France and Belgium, can also be used to measure explosion risk
High concentration with Alarm	Drainage ranges, Boreholes	T, F	Auer A 2	1.1.3.6	Three scales: 5 to 100 % CH_4, 0 to 2 % CH_4, 0 to 50 % of lower limit of inflammability	IS sought in GFR, Continuous measurement possible, Life: 8 to 70 h depending on use
High concentration with remote transmission	Drainage ranges	F	CKA 678 C Thermal Conductivity Head	1.1.3.10	0 to 100 % CH_4	in connection with surface control station

Table 4.1 Methane Concentration Underground.

Sheet 5

Parameter Measured	Place of Use	Po, T or F	Instrument	Paragraph Reference	Range and Precision of Measurement	Remarks
High concentration with Alarm, Cut-off and Remote Transmission	Drainage ranges, Stoppings, Extraction-Plant	F	Acoustic Methanometer	1.1.3.8	0 to 100 % CH_4	IS in UK, Orifice plate in the drainage range
			BM2H	1.1.3.9	0 to 100 % $\pm$ 3% CH_4	as above, Continuous measurement
	Particularly drainage ranges		GTM 67	1.1.3.7	0 to 100 $\pm$ 4 % CH_4	IS France and Belgium, Probe in the drainage range, Measures every 1 or 4 min or manually, Life: 1 day to 1 week
			UNOR	1.1.3.11	0 to 100 $\pm$ 2 % CH_4	IS in GFR, Continuous measurement, Over-pressure in the drainage: $\leqq$ 2 kPa. Power supply: elec. or compressed air
High concentration with Remote Transmission	Drainage ranges		Tricapteur TCC 69	1.1.5	0 to 100 % CH_4	Also measures suction and methane flow

Table 4.1 Firedamp Drainage Flow Underground. Sheet 6

Parameter Measured	Place of Use	Po, T or F	Instrument	Paragraph Reference	Range and Precision of Measurement	Remarks
Differential pressure	Drainage pipes	F	Orifice plate and apparatus to measure differential pressure	1.1.4.1	0 to 1 kPa 0 to 2 kPa	
			Lugameter St AM	1.1.4.2	0 to 10/0 to 20/ 0 to 40 m/s (depending on the jet). Minimum reading 0.3 m/s, Precision 1.5 % of maximum	Also used with a recorder, Flow obtained using calculator, —29 kPa to +100 kPa
Normal flow of methane with remote transmission			Tricapteur TCC 69	1.1.5	0.6 to 9 or 1.2 to 20 m/s	IS (France and sought in Belgium), Remote transmission by TCC or TF 24
Velocity	Boreholes only		Anemometer probe	1.1.7	0 to 2/0 to 6/ 0 to 20; 0 to 4/ 0 to 12/0 to 40; 0 to 20/0 to 40/ 0 to 80; 0 to 30/ 0 to 60/ 0 to 120 m/s, ± 1.5 % of reading	IS in GFR with recording

Table 4.1 Pressure at the Surface. Sheet 7

Parameter Measured	Place of Use	Po, T or F	Instrument	Paragraph Reference	Range and Precision of Measurement	Remarks
Differential pressures and suctions	Drainage pipes and/or utilisation systems	F	Underground Instruments	1.1.1		
			Diaphragm Pressure Transducer CMR 15.240	1.2.1.3	0 to 2/0 to 2.5/ 0 to 6/0 to 10/ 0 to 25/0 to 40/ 0 to 60/0 to 100/ 0 to 200 kPa	Facility for recording and remote transmission
Absolute pressure (notably atmospheric)			CMR 15.741 Diaphragm Pressure Transducer	1.2.1.1	0 to 5/0 to 10/ 20 to 40/70 to 90/ 80 to 100/ 90 to 110 kPa	
			Bell & Howell 4—385	1.2.1.2	normally 85 to 115 kPa	not for hazardous areas
Differential Pressure			Differential Pressure Transmitter 5 PdH	1.2.1.4	5 to 60 kPa	Static pressure $\leqq$ 10 MPa
			Furness Type 050	1.2.1.5	Typically (kPa): vacuum 0 to 30/ 0 to 60, positive 0 to 35/0 to 70/ 0 to 140, differential 0 to 0.5/0 to 2	not for hazardous areas
Differential and absolute pressure			Teleperm M 730	1.2.4.2		See Firedamp Drainage Flow at the surface (Sheet 9)

Table 4.1 Gas Concentration at the Surface. Sheet 8

Parameter Measured	Place of Use	Po, T or F	Instrument	Paragraph Reference	Range and Precision of Measurement	Remarks
High concentrations of methane	Drainage pipes and/or utilisation systems	F	Underground instruments	1.1.3		
			Infra-red analyser	1.2.2.2	0 to 75 or 0 to 100 % methane	Used in UK, recording, continuous
			Uras 2T-Ex	1.2.2.3	0 to 100 % methane	
Concentration of carbon monoxide			UNOR	1.2.3.1 and 1.1.3.11	0 to 300 ppm (minimum: 0 to 100 ppm)	Recording, continuous, filter (for high % methane)
Concentration of oxygen			Paramagnetic analyser 'Magnos'	1.2.3.2	0 to 2/0 to 3/ 0 to 5/0 to 6/ 0 to 10/0 to 21/ 0 to 50/ 0 to 100 % O_2 (2 scales on each apparatus), Precision $\pm$ 2 % of scale	Flameproof, used in France, pipework must be horizontal, Gas pressure $\leqq$ 100 kPa. If $<$ 2 kPa a pump is necessary
			Paramagnetic analyser 'Servomex'	1.2.3.2	0 to 10/0 to 25/ 0 to 100 $O_2 \pm$ 1 % of span	

Table 4.1 Firedamp Drainage Flow at the Surface. Sheet 9

Parameter Measured	Place of Use	Po, T or F	Instrument	Paragraph Reference	Range and Precision of Measurement	Remarks
Differential pressure (for flow calculation), Absolute pressure	Drainage pipes and/or utilisation systems	F	Underground Instruments	1.1.4		
			Téléperm M 730 with orifice plate	1.2.4.2	0.4 to 2.0/ 1.5 to 6.0 kPa or 2.5 to 15/5 to 64/ 50 to 200 kPa	
Differential pressure (for flow calculation)			Differential Pressure Transmitter TEC 5 QB With orifice plate	1.2.4.3	0.5 to 2.5/ 0.15 to 1.0 kPa	connected to a flow calculator, used in France, static pressure $\leqq$ 200 kPa
Flow			Fluxi Meter	1.2.4.1	8 types (70 to 1800 l/s), Precision $\pm$ 1 to 2 % scale	
			Furness 050	1.2.4.4 and 1.2.1.5	0 to 0.5 kPa 0 to 2 kPa	

Table 4.1 Other Measuring Instruments at the Surface. Sheet 10

Parameter Measured	Place of Use	Po, T or F	Instrument	Paragraph Reference	Range and Precision of Measurement	Remarks
Calorific value	Calorimeter Room	F	Reineke 66 Calorimeter	1.2.5.1		used in GFR, occupies $\geqq 15\ m^2$ plus $7\ m^2$ for ancilliary equipment, gas pressure 0.7 to 2.5 kPa, needs surveillance (naked flame)
Calorific value and Alarm and Cut-off			Sigma Calorimeter	1.2.5.2	3 to 37 MJ/m^3	used in UK when gas is sold; alarm, and cut-off if $<$ 15 MJ/m^3 (naked flame)
Density			Debro Densimeter	1.2.5.3	0.1 to 2.5 Precision $\pm$ 1 % of scale	used in France, pressure $\leqq$ 1.5 kPa remote transmission

Table 4.1 Monitoring and Control Systems. Sheet 11

System	Place of Use	Po, T or F	Instrument	Paragraph Reference	Range and Precision of Measurement	Remarks
Remote Monitoring and Control	Surface and Underground	F	Télécontroleur centralisé de captage (TCC)	1.2.7.1 and 1.2.7.5	0 to 40 kPa, 0 to 100 % methane, 0 to 9 or 0 to 20 m/s	IS in France, collects data from 'tricapteur' sensing heads, 4 min interrogation, connected by telephone to measuring point
			SCI 76	1.2.7.2		IS in Belgium, data transmission from 'tricapteurs' by Funke and Huster system TF 24, 4 ½ min cycle, battery life 14 h
			Central Time Division Multiplexing (TDM) System	1.2.7.3		IS in UK, 1 sec to >1 min interrogation cycle
Remote Monitoring			Tube Bundle system	1.2.7.4		used in UK for remote sampling of mine and drained gases

1.1 Underground Measurements

1.1.1 Pressure Measurement

1.1.1.0 Introduction

Three types of pressure measurement are made,

a) difference in pressure between a point in the network and its surroundings: eg suction (or pressure) at a borehole or in the drainage range,

b) difference in pressure or 'differential pressure' between two points in a drainage range or across an orifice plate (Section 1.1.4.1, measurement of flow by orifice plates),

c) absolute pressure, principally barometric pressure.

The description and limitations of instruments are summarised in the above order in Table 4.1. It should be noted that the majority of them have several different uses.

Measurement of suction in the range and atmospheric pressure p_0 at the measuring point enable flow in a drainage range to be calculated for standard conditions. The following formula is usually used to calculate p_0 (kPa).

$$p_0 = p_{OS} + 0.012\,h \qquad [4.1]$$

where:

p_{OS} the surface pressure in kPa

h the depth of measuring point in m

Atmospheric pressure can also be measured directly using a portable barometer (Sections 1.1.1.7 and 1.1.1.8).

It should be noted that measuring points in a drainage range must be located well away from any disturbance (valve, change of direction, etc. Chapter 3, Sections 3.1.3 and 3.2.3).

1.1.1.1 U-tubes or Single Arm Manometers (Water or Mercury)

Principle

In a U-tube, the difference in vertical height h between the level of liquid in the two branches is a measure of the pressure difference Δp. The latter is derived from the expression:

$$\Delta p = K \varrho h \qquad [4.2]$$

where ϱ is the density of liquid (water for small differences; mercury for large) and K is a constant, its value depending on units used.

For example if h is measured in mm mercury (ϱ = 13.6 kg/l), the pressure difference

$\Delta p = 0.00981 \times 13.6 \times h$ in kPa,

$K = 0.00981$ for the units used.

For very small pressure differences, the sensitivity is increased by inclining the U-tube at an angle α to the horizontal. In this case,

$$\Delta p = K \varrho l \sin \alpha \quad [4.3]$$

where l is the observed difference between the length of liquid in the two columns; $l \sin \alpha$ replaces h in Equation [4.2].

Applications

Vertical and inclined gauges are used to measure small suctions, pressures and pressure differences at boreholes, in drainage ranges or at stoppings. Mercury gauges are employed to measure high suctions at the same positions and are occasionally used for measuring pressure differentials.

Characteristics

Because the U-tube manometer is so well known only the single tube manometer is described below (Figure 4.1). The reservoir R containing a liquid, eg mercury, connects with the tube t. When the pressure connections 1 and 2 are both at atmospheric pressure the

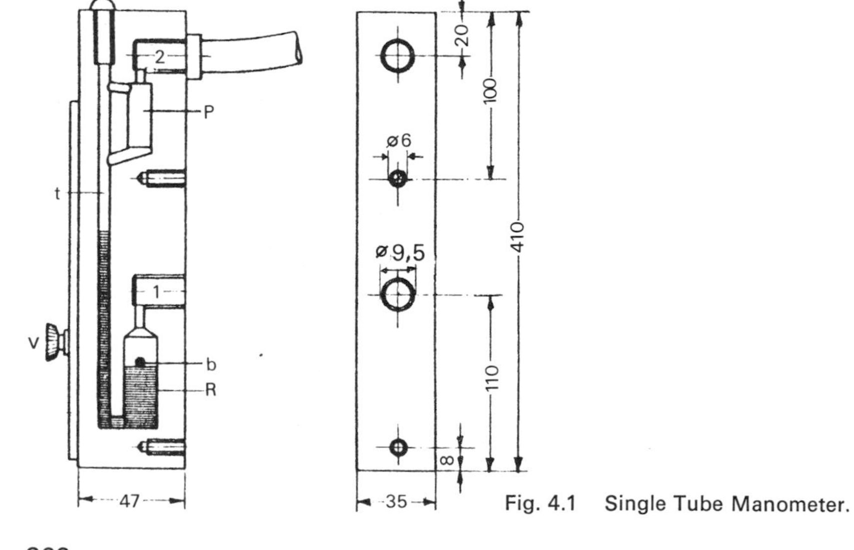

Fig. 4.1 Single Tube Manometer.

level of liquid is the same in the reservoir and the tube. The adjusting screw v allows the zero of the scale to be set to the meniscus of the liquid in the tube.

Pressure connection 2 is connected to the drainage system by means of flexible tubing. A stop cock between the instrument and the drainage system is used to isolate the manometer when suction exceeds the useable limit — eg 46 kPa with the mercury manometer illustrated. As soon as suction is applied to the manometer, the mercury rises in tube t giving the suction measurement. The upper reservoir P prevents spillage of mercury. The ball b prevents the loss of mercury to atmosphere when the manometer is subjected accidentally to a large positive pressure.

1.1.1.2 Ring Balance Suction Indicator and Recorder

This apparatus can be used as an indicator and recorder and consists essentially (Figure 4.2) of a hollow ring of circular cross section, supported on knife edges placed at the axis of the ring. This ring, which has closed ends, is partially filled with a liquid (eg mercury)

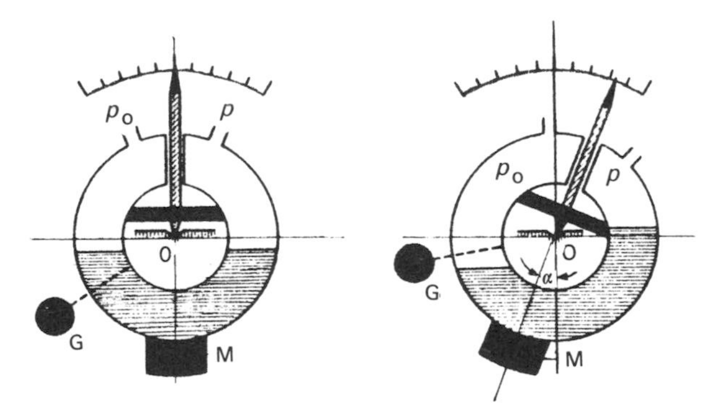

Fig. 4.2 Ring Balance Suction Indicator and Recorder.

which forms a hydraulic connection between two chambers to which atmospheric pressure p_0 and the suction of the drainage system p are applied. The ring turns through an angle proportional to the pressure difference. A constant mass M ensures stable equilibrium in the absence of pressure difference. The counterweight G provides the opposing force of the couple. The range of measurement is between 0 and 33 kPa.

1.1.1.3 Lugameter

Also for flow measurement: see Section 1.1.4.2.

1.1.1.4 Tricapteur

See Section 1.1.5.

1.1.1.5 Capsule Type Gauges

Principle

The pressure or suction to be measured changes the shape of a resilient capsule. A system of levers and wheels transmits this change to an indicator. The reading may also be transmitted remotely to an external dial or recorder by means of a transducer fixed to the pressure gauge (Figure 4.3).

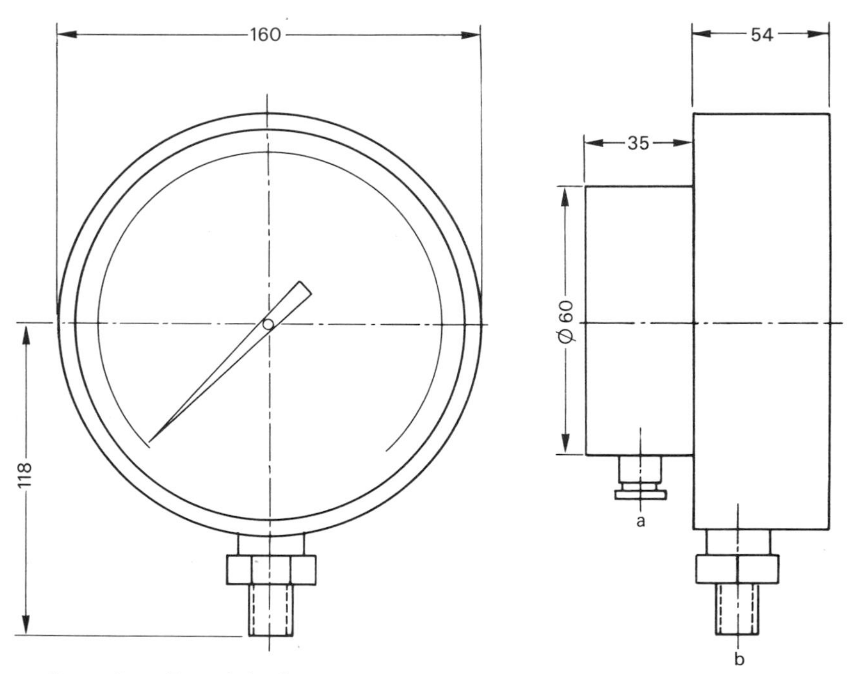

a Connection to Transmission System
b Pressure/Suction Connection

Fig. 4.3 Capsule Type Pressure Gauge.

Applications

It is suitable for measuring pressure and suction and is used for continuous monitoring at a given point.

The transmitter version of the pressure gauge is approved as intrinsically safe. Without the transducer it is a simple mechanical pressure gauge which does not require approval. It is installed mainly on drainage ranges to measure the suction at that point and also provide a remote read-out of this measurement.

Characteristics

The Funke and Huster instrument is housed in a robust cast-iron casing. The remote transmission system version comprises a resistance coil and connecting terminals in a watertight case with a connection for the transmission cable. The pressure gauge can be connected to any intrinsically safe remote transmission system (eg Funke and Huster TF 24 in Germany).

Manufacturer:	Funke and Huster (GFR)
Type:	Ty 501 with remote transmission
Dimensions: pressure gauge	diameter 160 mm; depth 54 mm
transducer	diameter 60 mm; depth 35 mm
Measuring scale: suction	down to —100 kPa
pressure	as required (up to + 60 MPa)
Resistance of the transducer	0 to 10 kΩ

1.1.1.6 Bourdon Tube Gauges

Principle (Figure 4.4)

A thin walled tube, elliptical in section, is bent into an arc of a circle of approximately 270°; one end is fixed and the other (free) end is sealed. Pressure or suction is applied to the inside of the tube with the result that positive pressures tend to straighten it whereas suctions tend to bend it further. The displacement of the free end is linked to the movement of a recorder pen/pointer.

Applications

They are used for the measurement of high values of suctions or pressures at boreholes, in drainage ranges and in exhauster stations. Gauges can also be used to measure the pressure of compressed air and water at a drilling machine.

Characteristics

Limits: suctions $\leqq$ 100 kPa; pressure $\leqq$ 1500 kPa.

Fig. 4.4 Bourdon Tube Type Pressure Recorder.

1.1.1.7 'Barolux' Precision Aneroid Barometer

Principle (Figure 4.5)

The deformation of the aneroid capsule 1 is transmitted by means of the lever 2 and the spindle 3 to a finely graduated scale 4. This scale is illuminated by bulb 5 via a condenser 6; the greatly magnified image is projected on to the focusing screen 11 via the small lens 7 and

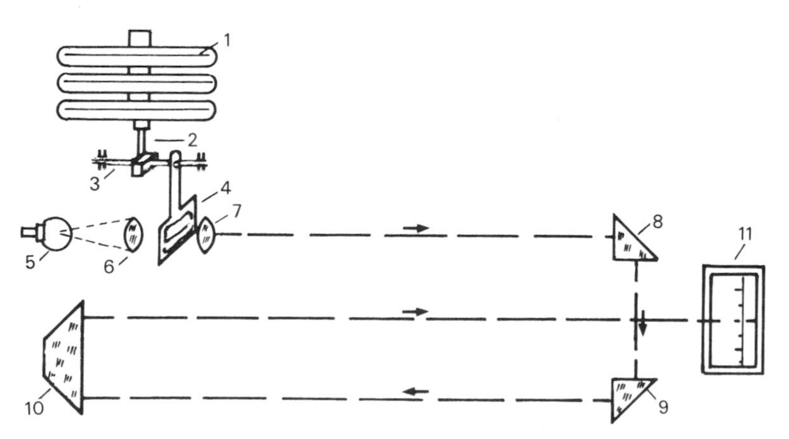

Fig. 4.5 Diagram Showing Principle of the "Barolux" Barometer.

three reflecting prisms 8, 9 and 10 which serve to lengthen the path. The scale image is focused on a ground glass screen, and the pressure indicated by a fixed pointer.

It is compensated for temperature by the bimetallic system between 2 and 3.

Applications

It is used to measure the absolute pressure of mine air and is carried in a leather case (Figure 4.6)

Fig. 4.6
"Barolux" Precision
Aneroid Barometer.

Characteristics

Manufacturer:	Fuess (GFR)
Dimensions:	316 mm height, 133 mm depth, 130 mm breadth
Weight (with case):	2.5 kg
Measuring range:	66 to 123 kPa
Scale graduation:	0.03 kPa
Accuracy:	0.015 kPa
Total length of scale image:	3 m (1 mm of scale represents 0.02 kPa)
Bulb:	4 V/0.3 A powered by normal dry battery or accumulator, or transformer when used from a fixed position.

Focusing of the image is obtained by an adjustment knob which is independent of the barometric zero adjustment and does not affect the accuracy of the instrument. The instrument can read correctly in any position and is not affected by vibration or wear and tear during transport.

1.1.1.8 Small Portable Barometers

Principle

Aneroid barometer.

Fig. 4.7
Small Portable Barometer.

Applications

They are used to take spot measurements of barometric pressure. It is necessary to keep the instruments horizontal because they are calibrated in that position. Readings are corrected by means of an instrument calibration curve.

Characteristics

Manufacturer	Fuess (GFR) (Figure 4.7)	Negretti & Zambra (UK)	T. Wheeler (UK)	C. F. Casella (UK)
Height in mm	80	66	66	58
Diameter in mm	130	130	130	207
Weight in kg	0.8	1.39	1	1.66
Range in kPa	80 to 120	85 to 115	85 to 115	85 to 115

The instruments are easy to use, insensitive to knocks and are compensated for temperature.

1.1.1.9 Devices for Alarm and/or Automatic Cut-Off

1.1.1.9.1 Huwood Vacuum Indicator and Alarm (Figure 4.8)

Principle

If the suction as measured by capsule or bourdon tube (principle: Section 1.1.1.6), is less than an adjustable predetermined value, a switch operates a separate external visual alarm (red lamp) which remains on until the suction is restored.

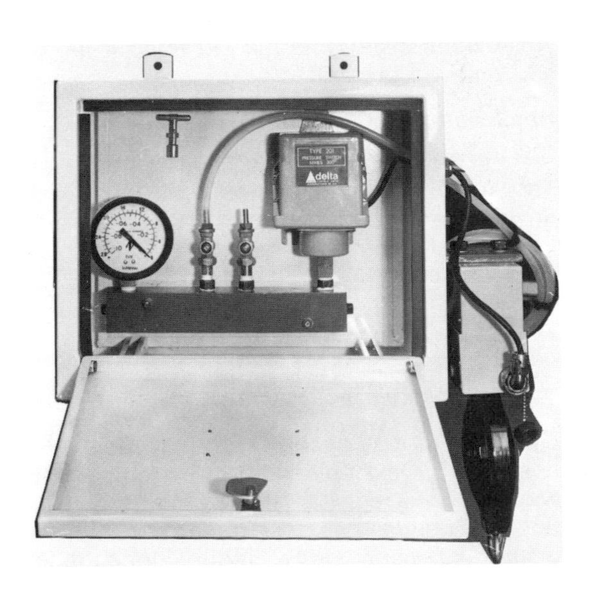

Fig. 4.8
Huwood Vacuum Indicator and Alarm.

Applications

The instrument is connected to district drainage ranges, near the face or at the outbye end of one or both gate roadways, to limbs of firedamp drainage systems, at the shaft side, stoppings and at underground exhauster stations. The device can be connected to a data transmission system.

Characteristics

Approved:	In UK
Manufacturer:	Huwood (UK)
Measuring range:	0 to 3 (Capsule type), 0 to 17, 0 to 34, 0 to 100 kPa

The capsule or bourdon tube and the adjustable vacuum switch are located in a locked steel box, within which are housed the manifold, pressure connections and cocks, a vacuum gauge and the adjusting mechanism for the vacuum switch. The gauge is read through an observation window.

1.1.1.9.2 Huwood Combined Vacuum and Differential Pressure (Flow) Indicators and Alarm (Figure 4.9)

Principle

In addition to the features previously described in Section 1.1.1.9.1 this alarm possesses a bellows and switch for differential pressure. This switch also lights the red lamp if the differential pressure (flow) falls below a prescribed value.

Applications

See previous section.

They are used in conjunction with orifice plates, venturi tubes, or other devices generating pressure differences from gas flow.

Characteristics

See previous section for vacuum details.

Typical operating differential pressure ranges: 0 to 1 kPa to 0 to 2 kPa.

1.1.2 Sampling by Hand Pumps

Gas samples may be taken from the drainage range either for laboratory analysis, for example where firedamp contains carbon dioxide and hand held instruments such as interferometers would require a correction (Appendix 4.1), or to analyse directly using an underground instrument such as a high concentration methanometer, when

Fig. 4.9 Huwood Combined Vacuum and Differential Pressure (Flow) Indicators and Alarm.

suctions are too high to allow the use of a rubber squeeze bulb or its built-in pump. A rubber squeeze bulb, for example, is usually adequate for suctions up to 13 kPa.

The expedient of partially closing a valve during sampling to reduce the suction in the range, may falsely increase methane concentrations by reducing air inleakage in the range, or may decrease it due to the effect of suction on the instrument.

Hand pumps designed to overcome these problems are manufactured in different countries.

Principle

One method of taking a sample from a range makes use of a tube inserted in a rubber stopper which is forced into a tapping and is then connected by flexible tubing to the pump. Both the stopper and the end of the tube must be sufficiently air-tight and the sampling end of the tube must reach the centre of the pipe. The sample of gas is collected in either a metal capsule or glass tube for despatch to the laboratory.

a) Sampling with glass tubes

One sampling arrangement is shown in Figure 4.10. The sample is first pumped into a bladder in the following sequence. With tap in

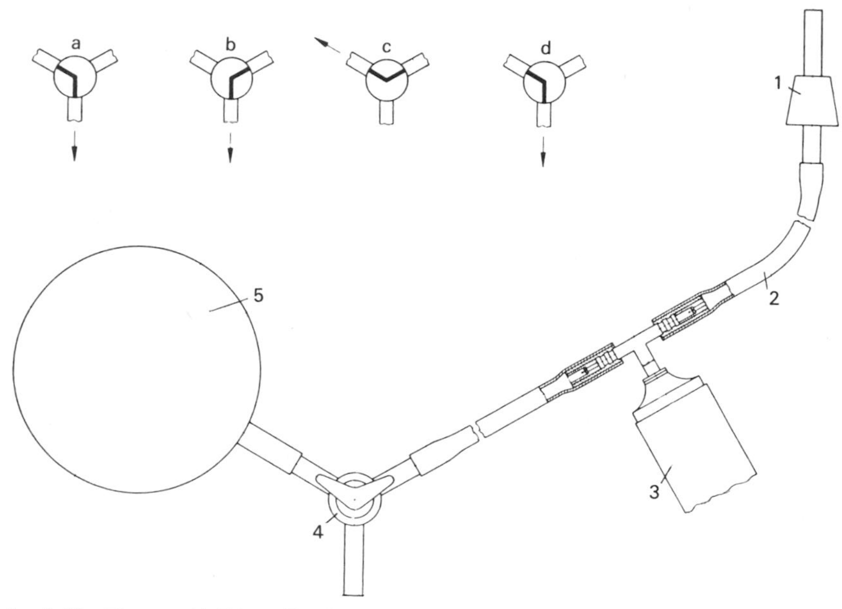

1 Rubber Stopper with Tube — Bouchon en caoutchouc avec tuyau — Gummistopfen mit Tülle und Schlauch
2 Flexible Tube — Tuyau flexible — Schlauch
3 Hand pump — Pompe à main — Saug-Druck-Kolbenpumpe
4 120 degree Tap — Robinet à 120° — 120°-Hahn
5 Bladder — Ballon en caoutchouc — Blase aus Gummi oder Kunststoff

Fig. 4.10 A Method of Using a Hand Pump to Sample from a Drainage Range.

position (a) the bladder is emptied by squeezing. With tap in position (b) the connection between pipe and tap is flushed by means of the hand pump. With tap in position (c) the bladder is refilled until it is well inflated. With tap in position (d) and after a brief purging of the tap and the flexible connection, the glass sample tube is connected and filled with the aid of the bladder.

In France, tubes which are evacuated on the surface are connected to the drainage ranges and given a slight pressure by means of a suitable hand pump.

b) Sampling using metal capsules

One or two capsules are coupled directly to the pump by a bayonet connection (Figure 4.11).

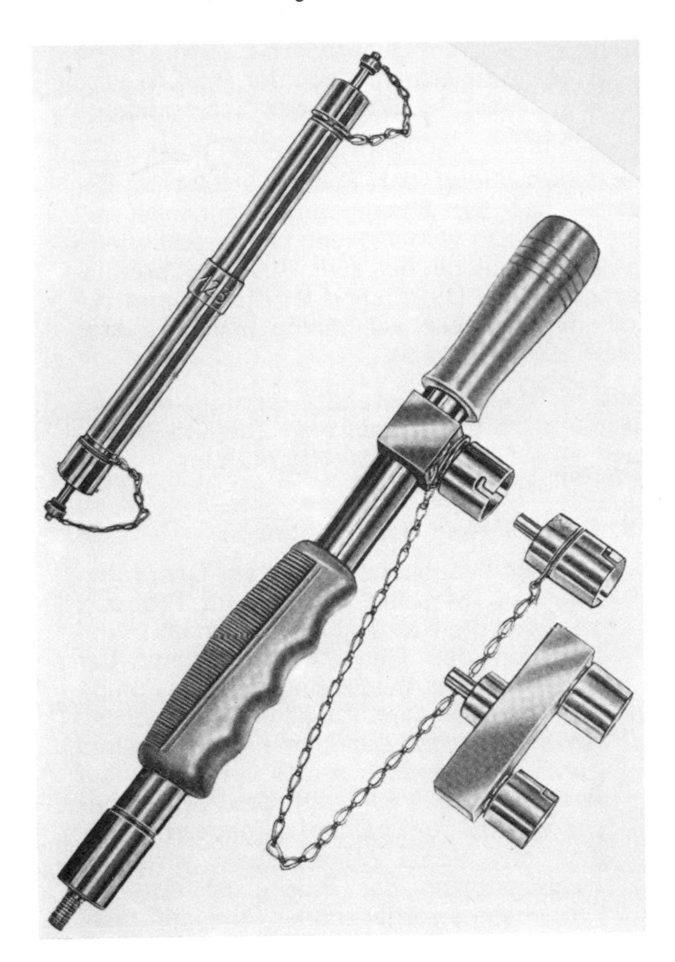

Fig. 4.11
Metal Capsule
and Hand Pump.

c) Sampling using bladders (Lorraine)

When gas has a high carbon dioxide content, the methane reading given by portable instruments (interferometers, for example) requires a large correction, for which it is necessary to know the carbon dioxide concentration (cf Appendix 4.1). In the Lorraine coalfield, daily gas samples are taken from the drainage range using plastic bladders, purged by squeezing and refilled by inflating with a hand pump. Bladder samples must be analysed the same day.

Applications

In addition to those applications given at the beginning of the section, the hand pump can be used to take samples of the atmosphere at surface or underground extractor stations.

Characteristics

Piston Pumps

Manufacturers:	CERCHAR (France) GfG (GFR) Gresham Engineering (UK)

Glass Tubes

Capacity:	150 or 500 ml
Dimensions:	155 mm length and 42 mm diameter; 220 mm length and 65 mm diameter.

The gas is released by a tap.

Metal Capsules

Capacity:	15, 30, 50 ml Those of 15 and 30 ml, used only in UK, are filled to 1 MPa with 15 to 20 strokes of the pump after purging twice.
Approximate Dimensions:	120/165/250 mm length and 20 mm diameter.

The gas is released by a Schrader valve.

1.1.3 Measurement of Drained Methane Concentration

In this section, instruments are described in the following order, portable then transportable/fixed and finally large and complex instruments.

1.1.3.1 Auer M 510 B Methanometer (Hand held)

Principle

Two identical preheated thermal conductivity filaments which form two branches of a Wheatstone bridge are initially in equilibrium. One of these filaments, the detector, receives the gas sample to be analysed, whilst the other filament, is in fresh air. Because methane conducts heat better than air does, the detector filament is cooled compared with the reference filament. As a result the electrical resistance decreases, causes an imbalance in the Wheatstone bridge and the out-of-balance current produced gives a measure of the methane concentration in the gas.

Applications

A hand held instrument for the measurement of methane concentration in pipes and boreholes.

Characteristics (Figure 4.12)

Approval:	In GFR, intrinsically safe for mines and industries where there is an explosion risk: (Sch)i, s (Ex) i, sG5
Manufacturer:	Auer Gesellschaft (GFR)
Dimensions:	140 mm height, 80 mm length, 47 mm depth
Weight:	0.52 kg
Measuring range:	5 to 100 % methane
Accuracy:	± 2 % methane.

The sample is aspirated through the instrument by means of an electrically driven, built-in pump, capable of overcoming suctions up to 20 kPa. A switch is operated progressively in two steps by applying

Fig. 4.12
Auer 510 B Methanometer.

pressure on a button, gently at first and then more firmly. The instrument works continuously. For samples containing carbon dioxide it is necessary to insert an absorbent train.

1.1.3.2 MSA HC II High Concentration Methanometer (Hand held)

Principle

Based on thermal conductivity (Section 1.1.3.1).

Applications

A hand held instrument for measuring high methane concentrations in various situations (boreholes, pipe ranges, stoppings, extractor plants).

A detachable telescopic probe facilitates remote sampling.

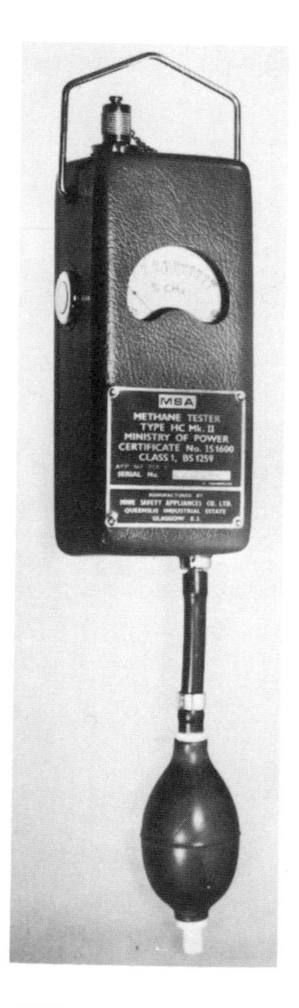

Fig. 4.13 MSA HC II Methanometer.

Characteristics (Figure 4.13)

Approval: Intrinsically safe in UK
Manufacturer: MSA (UK)
Dimensions: 170 mm high, 70 mm breadth, 64 mm depth
Weight: 0.98 kg
Measuring range: 0 to 100 % methane
The sample is drawn in by a squeeze-bulb.
Power: 14 Ah mercury cells, giving a life of 10 000 samples, each of 10 s duration. The state of the batteries is tested by pressing two side buttons simultaneously.
The voltage can be regulated and there is a mechanical zero adjustment.

1.1.3.3 Fyrite (Hand held, Figure 4.14)

The instrument consists of two chambers 1 and 2 (in the Figure) joined by a cylindrical tube 3. The lower chamber 1, whose base

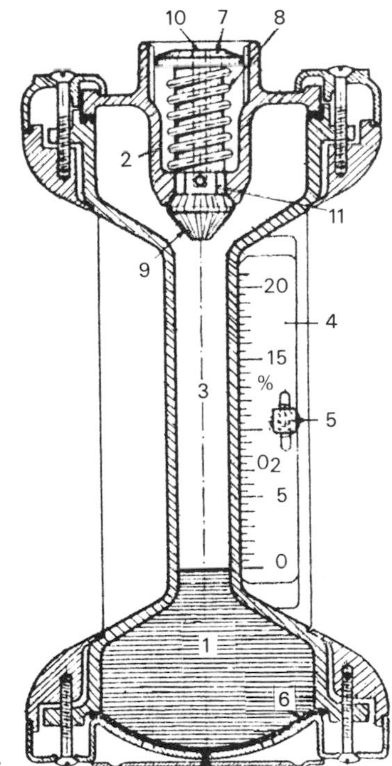

Fig. 4.14 Fyrite Apparatus.

consists of a rubber membrane 6, contains an oxygen absorbing liquid such as a mixture of the chlorides of chromium and zinc, and hydrochloric acid.

a) Calibration at the Surface

On inverting the apparatus 3 or 4 times the liquid absorbs the oxygen from the air (21 % in normal air) by mixing. The rubber membrane 6, subjected on the one side to atmospheric pressure and on the other to a reduced internal pressure, causes the liquid to rise up the graduated scale 4, to a maximum reading of 21 %. The zero of the scale is adjusted to the level of the liquid meniscus by means of screw 5. To re-establish pressure equilibrium air is re-admitted to the instrument by pushing the spring loaded valve 7.

b) Measuring underground

To introduce the sample to be analysed, a rubber squeeze-bulb is used connected on the one side to the sample of firedamp (through a flexible tube fitted with a moisture absorption train) and on the other side to the Fyrite apparatus (through a flexible tube with a rubber cap at its end). On pressing this cap, the spring valve 7 is pushed in until the point 9 comes up against a stop; at this point the head forms a sealed joint, and the upper chamber is isolated from the reagent liquid. Three or four pump strokes are made to thoroughly purge the air in the chamber through the lateral slots 11. The valve 7 is then released, isolating the apparatus from the exterior. Three or four inversions cause the oxygen to be absorbed. The oxygen reading gives the concentration of methane by difference. For example when the oxygen concentration is 4 per cent the methane concentration would be given by:

$$100\% - 4\%\ (O_2) - 4 \times 4\%\ (N_2) = 80\%\ (CH_4)$$

After disconnecting the apparatus, pressure equilibrium is again established by depressing valve 7 momentarily.

Applications

A hand held instrument used for measuring methane concentration at different positions in the network (pipe system, borehole orifice).

Characteristics

Manufacturer:	Bacharach Industrial Instruments (USA)
Instrument:	Simple but of low accuracy
Liquid absorbant charge:	Sufficient for 60 samples only, provided the O_2 concentration $< 10\%$.

Correction for carbon dioxide

When the firedamp contains CO_2, it is necessary to make use of another Fyrite apparatus containing CO_2 absorbing reagent (charge valid for 200 reactions if the CO_2 concentration is less than 20%). For accurate measurements it is essential that the Fyrite apparatus is given sufficient time to adjust to ambient temperature.

1.1.3.4 Interferometers (Hand held)

Principle

The measurement is obtained by comparing the refractive indices of the firedamp to be analysed with that of pure air.

A light source S (Figure 4.15) followed by an optical condenser C produces across the width of a slit F a narrow band of parallel light rays which are reflected by the parallel sided glass plate L. The rays reflected by the external face traverse the upper chamber A, undergo double internal reflection in the prism P, then pass back through the lower chamber A and are further reflected by the glass plate L. Those

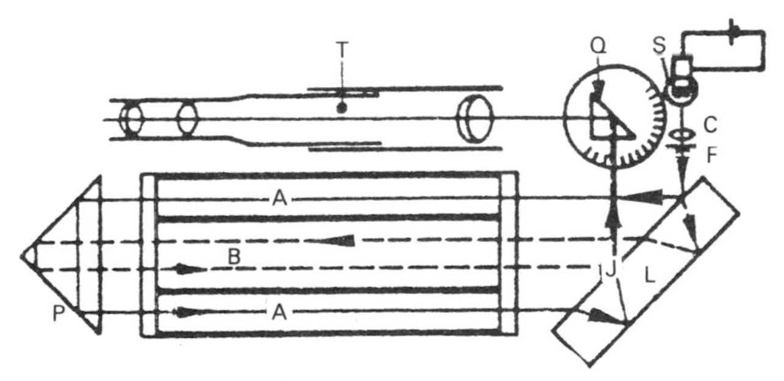

Fig. 4.15 Interferometer Optical System.

reflected by the lower face of L traverse chamber B, also undergo a double internal reflection in the prism P, pass again through chamber B and in their turn are reflected by the glass plate L. The two light beams recombine at J and fall on the second internally reflecting prism Q which projects them into the telescope T. The difference in optical path length between the two light beams produces a system of interference fringes, the central part of which is observable in the telescope T as shown in Figure 4.16.

If the chamber B is then filled by a gas whose refractive index differs from that of air, the optical path of the traversing light beams is modified, causing the displacement of the system of interference

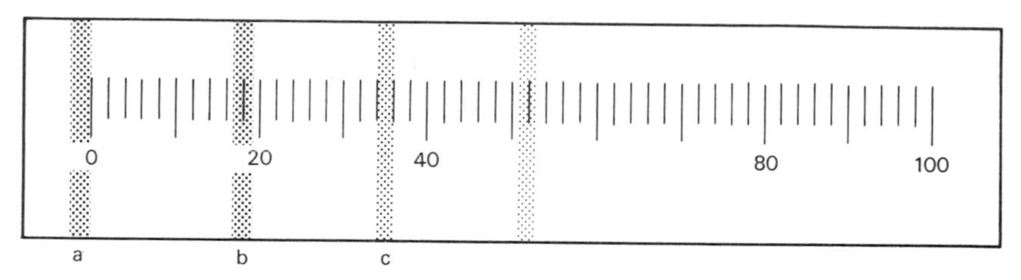

a Black fringe indicating the reading (0 % methane) — Noir — Schwarz
b Blue/Red — Bleu/Rouge — Blau/Rot
c Green/Red — Vert/Rouge — Grün/Rot

Fig. 4.16 Interferometer Scale and Fringes.

fringes observed in the telescope. This displacement is proportional to the difference in optical paths. The new position of the central fringe is read on the scale of the telescope eyepiece, which is directly graduated in percentage methane.

Applications

As for preceding instruments.

a) *Zero Adjustment at the Surface:*

The chamber B is filled with fresh air by means of 5 or 6 operations of the squeeze bulb and the central interference fringe is made to coincide with the zero by rotating an adjustment knob.

b) *Measuring Underground:*

The chamber B is well flushed with the methane sample by 5 or 6 pumps of the squeeze-bulb (Figure 4.17 and Appendix 4.1).

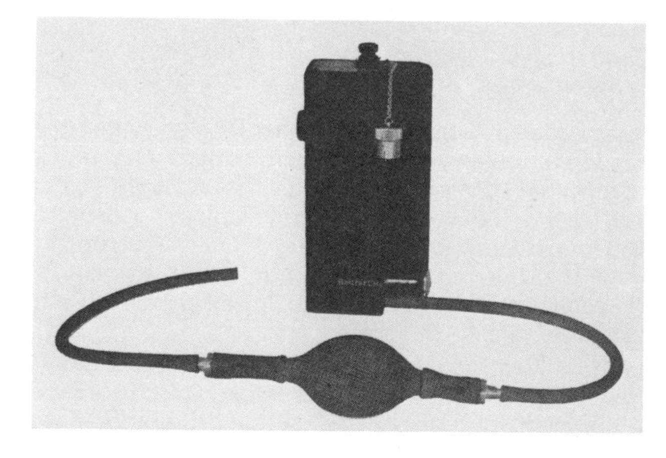

Fig. 4.17 Zeiss Interferometer.

The reading I_1 (in % methane), is brought to conditions of zero adjustment (p_0, T_0) using the expression:

$$I_0 = \frac{p_0\, T_1}{T_0\, p_1}\, I_1 \quad [4.4]$$

where I_0 is the corrected reading, and p_1 and T_1 are the absolute pressure and temperature underground. When the reading is taken, the pressure in the chamber B is equal to p_1 and in general the temperature T in the drainage system is close to the ambient temperature T_1 which it rapidly reaches. The reading I_1 is near to the true value I. The method of correcting for carbon dioxide is given in Appendix 4.1.

Characteristics

Approval:	In different countries of the community, except the UK
Manufacturers:	Zeiss (GFR), no longer manufactured; Riken-Keiki (Japan)
Dimensions:	40 mm breadth, 190 mm height, 100 mm depth
Weight:	≈ 1.5 kg
Measuring range:	0 to 100% methane
Accuracy:	Incorrect interpretation of fringes can contribute an error of 15% in readings. This can be avoided by choosing one edge of the fringe initially.

A high standard of maintenance is essential.

1.1.3.5 CK 68 Katharometer (Hand held)

Principle

(Thermal conductivity: Section 1.1.3.1).

The instrument can also burn methane catalytically, when used as an explosimeter, in which case, the filaments are run at a higher temperature.

Applications

A hand held instrument used to measure methane concentrations in drainage ranges, boreholes and stoppings.

a) *Zero Adjustment at the Surface:*

Zero adjustments are made using two potentiometers K and C (Figure 4.18). However because they interact with one another it

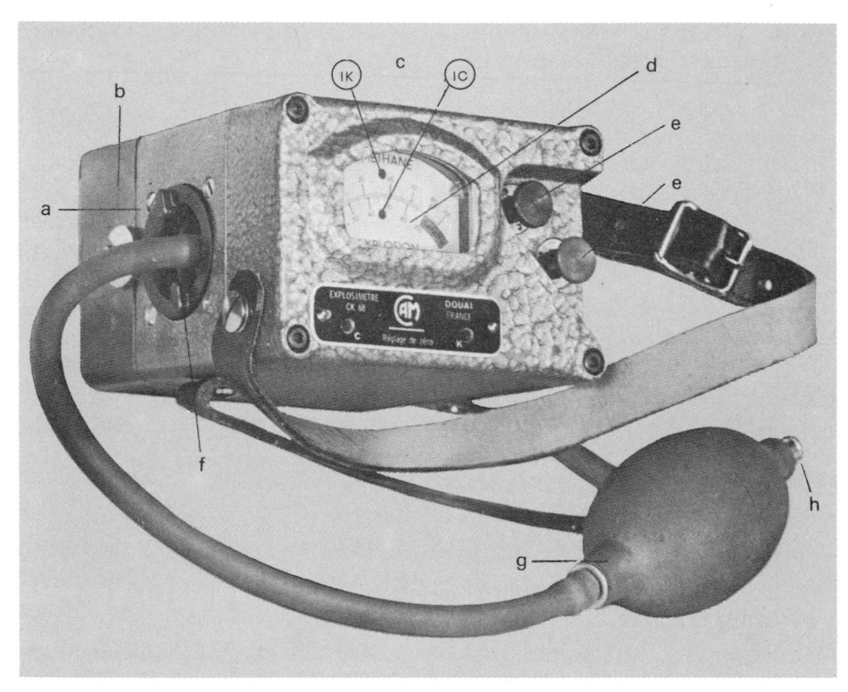

a Locking Button — Bouchon verrouillage — Verriegelungsschraube
b Battery Compartment — Compartiment des piles — Batteriegehäuse
c Illuminated Indicators — Voyants lumineux — Leuchtdioden
d Meter — Galvanomètre — Galvanometer
e Operating Buttons — Boutons de mesure — Meßknöpfe
f Interchangeable Plug- in Detector Head — Cellule de détection embrochable — Steckbare Detektor-Zelle
g Squeeze-bulb — Poire d'injection des gaz — Gummiball
h Sampling Probe Connection — Vers la sonde prélèvement — Zur Probe-Entnahmestelle

Fig. 4.18 CK 68 Katharometer.

is necessary to repeat the operation until the adjustment is complete. This adjustment becomes necessary every 200 to 300 measurements and in any case when in fresh air the instrument reads 5 % on the lower explosimeter scale IC.

b) Measuring Underground:

The red button is depressed for two seconds and the reading taken on the upper scale IK. Continuous measurement may be made by holding down the button and supplying the cell with gas by applying steady pressure on the squeeze-bulb.

Characteristics

Approval: Intrinsically safe in France and Belgium
Manufacturer: Societé Oldham (France)
Dimensions: 120 mm breadth, 80 mm height, 125 mm depth
Weight: 1.4 kg
Measuring range: 0 to 100 % methane
Accuracy: ± 3 % methane
No correction is needed for carbon dioxide
Power: 3 batteries of 1.5 V

Two illuminated indicators automatically show the state of the batteries and which scale is to be read.

Other possible uses include determination of methane concentration in natural gas, and the detection of danger of explosion of other combustible and explosive gases (natural and manufactured gas, propane, butane, petrol vapour etc.).

1.1.3.6 Auer A 2 Methane Measuring System (Transportable)

Principle

Thermal conductivity for high methane concentrations (Section 1.1.3.1) and catalytic combustion for lower concentrations of 0 to 2 % methane in air (Section 1.1.3.5).

Applications

Used as a transportable instrument and at fixed stations for measurements at boreholes and surveillance of drainage ranges. The instrument has a meter and emits an alarm (visual and audible) in the presence of abnormal concentrations.

Characteristics (Figure 4.19)

Approval: Intrinsically safe in GFR
Manufacturer: Auer Gesellschaft (GFR)
Dimensions: 177 mm width, 117 mm breadth, 154 mm height
Weight: 3.15 kg

Three measuring ranges are provided by exchanging modules:

▷ 5 to 100 % methane (thermal conductivity) with two levels of alarm adjustable over the whole range, latching,

- ▷ 0 to 2% methane (catalytic combustion) with one alarm level, adjustable from 0.3 to 2%, latching,
- ▷ 0 to 50% of the lower limit of inflammability or explosibility when used as an explosimeter (catalytic combustion); one level of alarm adjustable between 0.5 and 50%, latching.

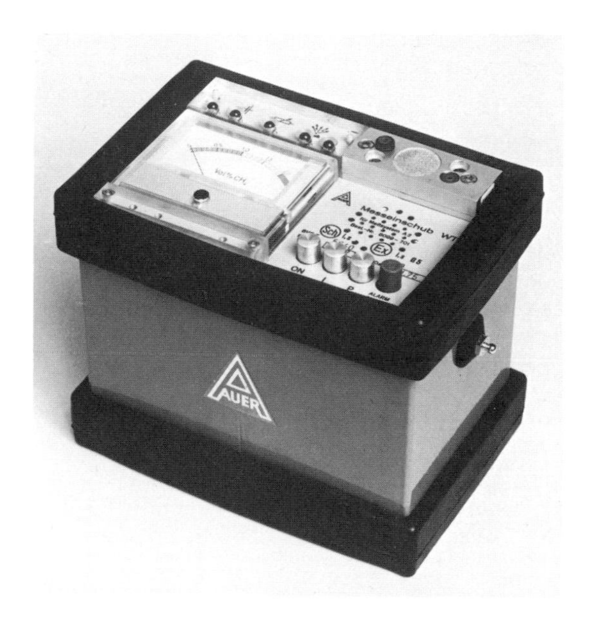

Fig. 4.19
Auer A 2 Methane Measuring System.

The instrument can be used continuously or intermittently. The sample goes through an internal or external diffusion head, or is aspirated by a built-in electric pump (8.3 ml/s).

A battery life of approximately 12 h is obtained with continuous use of the diffusion head and of approximately 8 h with continuous use of the pump. When used intermittently, a battery life of approximately 70 h is obtained sampling automatically every 180 s or approximately 1400 manual 30 s measurements may be taken.

Alarms include the visual type with two red flashing diodes for alarm and three diodes permanently red for instrument failure (drop in battery voltage, damage to measuring head, etc.); and intermittent audible alarm using a piezo-electric transmitter.

Its modular construction enables the positions of the principal components (battery, measuring cell, diffusion head) to be interchanged.

1.1.3.7 Multipurpose Methanometer GTM 67 (Transportable)

Principle

Thermal conductivity (Section 1.1.3.1).

Applications

It is a transportable instrument, which can also be installed at a fixed station. It is used for the surveillance of methane concentrations in firedamp drainage pipes with local indication, local or remote recording; it may also be employed for cutting off electrical machinery and operating an alarm (audible or visual) at preset levels.

Characteristics (Figure 4.20)

Approval:	Intrinsically safe in France and Belgium
Manufacturer:	Societé Oldham (France), under CERCHAR licence
Dimensions:	220 mm breadth, 210 mm height, 90 mm depth
Weight:	4 kg
Measuring Range:	0 to 100 % methane, intermittent measurement
Accuracy:	± 4 % methane

A selector permits a choice of either automatic interrogation (15 or 60 per hour) or manual interrogation by push button.

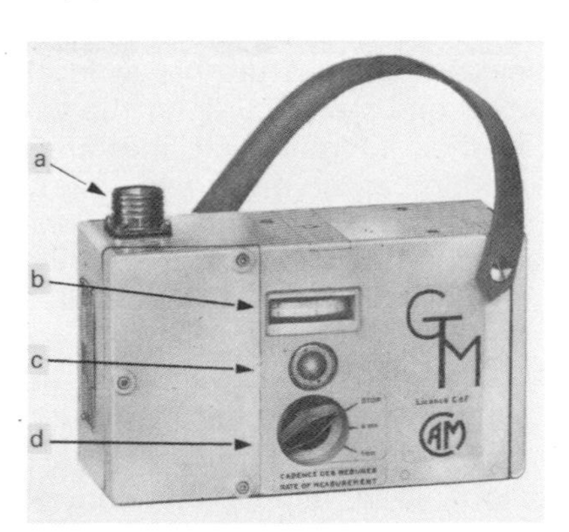

Fig. 4.20
GTM 67 Multipurpose Methanometer.

The sensing head is type CKA 678, model C (Figure 4.21) which contains a probe and is screwed on to the drainage pipe. The length of connecting cable to the control position must not exceed 5 m. Power is usually supplied from the mains but when abnormal methane concentrations are present in the general body, is obtained from a built in 3.5 Ah battery which is rechargeable from the mains and interchangeable on site. Battery life exceeds 1 day at 60 measurements per hour, and lasts a week at 15 measurements per hour or 1 and 3 weeks respectively if a supplementary battery is used.

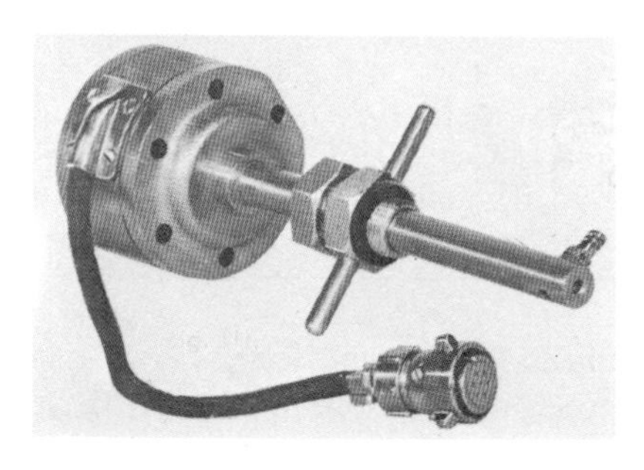

Fig. 4.21 CKA 678 C Sensing Head.

Each principal or auxiliary function, is achieved using a separate printed circuit board. The principal circuit boards are referred to as A and D and the connection circuit board as C. These three boards are always necessary. The power cut-off circuit board B is adjusted to a preset level within 15 and 65% on the scale; when this level is reached an oscillator is triggered activating an audible alarm of 90 dB intensity or a flashing lamp (either on the instrument or up to 100 m away) and causing a relay to trip which leads to a shut-down. Another board G enables the preset level to be obtained between the wider range of 15 and 85% on the scale. When boards B and G are used together, additional facilities are provided. On reaching a first level, a warning can be given requiring preventative action (card B, closing a valve) and on reaching a second level, automatic shut-down of the drainage network can be achieved using board G. The recording circuit is provided by board E. The recorder cannot be sited more than 500 m away, and only one cut-out level board (B) can be used.

Signals can be transmitted to the surface up to distances of 10 km by a two wire system, either by a 2.6 Hz frequency coder (board F) to a central control unit, or by a special circuit giving a 0 to 10 V output to a remote monitoring station (télévigile) using a TF 24 transmission system for example.

1.1.3.8 Acoustic Methanometer Type 218 A (Fixed)

Principle

The velocity of propagation of sound in methane is greater than that in air (430 m/s compared with 330 m/s).

This velocity w may be expressed by:

$$w = \sqrt{\frac{y\,p}{\varrho}} \quad \ldots \ldots \ldots \ldots \quad [4.5]$$

where:

y the ratio of specific heats

p the gas pressure

ϱ the gas density.

The sound is produced by an oscillator. Though initially sinusoidal in form, (a) in Figure 4.22, it is changed to rectangular form (b), and then further modified leaving only the peaks (c). Negative peaks are used only as a time base. The sound reaching the microphone receiver is advanced in phase relative to the emitter, causing a change to

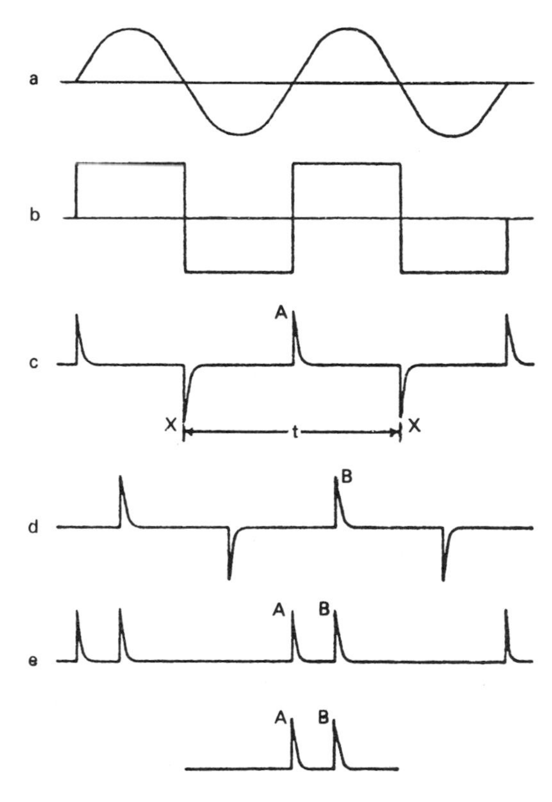

Fig. 4.22 Acoustic Methanometer Wave Forms.

form (d). The phase shift A — B in (e) gives an estimate of the methane concentration. Possible variations in frequency (or velocity) due to variations in the pressure *p* of the gas require no correction.

Applications

It is used as a fixed monitor for surveillance of firedamp drainage systems and stoppings, and for giving an alarm and cut-off at extractor plants.

Characteristics

Approval:	Intrinsically safe in the UK	
Manufacturer:	Norbury Instruments (UK), no longer manufactured but still in use	
	Detector Head	Control Module
Dimensions:	300 mm length, 100 mm depth, 187 mm height	214 mm length, 180 mm depth, 330 mm height
Weight:	10 kg	12.3 kg
Range:	0 to 100 % methane	

The sensing head, consisting of the transducer unit and oscillator, is housed in a solid steel case clamped to the drainage range. It is connected across an orifice plate using standard tappings or alternatively using a pitot tube.

Electrical pulses are fed continuously over signalling cables to a remote control station equipped with an indicator and recorder which may be many kilometres away.

1.1.3.9 BM 2H High Concentration Methane Monitor (Fixed, Figure 4.23)

Principle

Thermal conductivity (Section 1.1.3.1).

Applications

As for the Acoustic Methanometer (Section 1.1.3.8) which it is replacing.

Characteristics

Approval:	Intrinsically safe to latest UK standards
Manufacturer:	J & S Sieger (UK)

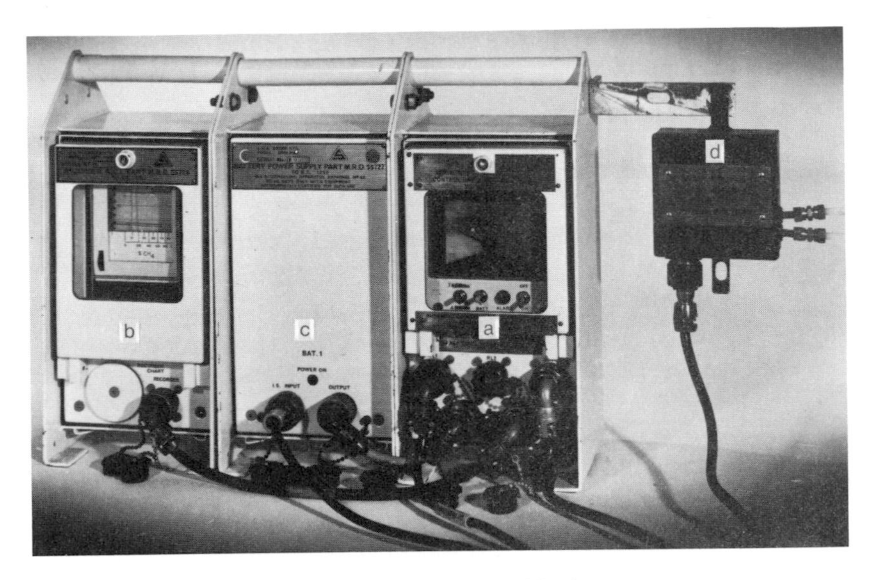

Fig. 4.23 BM 2H High Concentration Methane Monitor.

Certification:	Intrinsically Safe to BS 1259 Class 1. Approval IS 1859
Range:	0 to 100 %
Accuracy:	Better than ± 5 % methane
Dimensions:	360 mm height, 480 mm width (3 modules), 160 mm depth
Weight:	24.5 kg (total for 3 modules)

In addition to the sensing head it consists of (a) a control module containing the electronics, the indicator and the input power and output sockets, (b) a recorder module, (c) a rechargeable battery module which may be either 7 Ah charged underground or 20 Ah charged on the surface, and (d) a filter unit. The apparatus may be powered from the mains using a DC 3 power supply with the 7 Ah stand-by rechargeable battery, a DC 2 power supply unit or the 20 Ah rechargeable battery.

The sensing head is connected to a drainage range using two tappings one on either side of an orifice plate. The output voltage from the Wheatstone bridge is 2 V full scale, which can be transmitted to the surface or other central station by a two wire system or a time division multiplexing data transmission system (Section 1.2.7.3).

1.1.3.10 CKA 678 C Thermal Conductivity Head (Fixed, Figure 4.21)

The CKA 678 C sensing head used in the GTM can also be connected directly through an outstation to a central CERCHAR methanometer transmission system installed at the surface.

1.1.3.11 UNOR Infra-Red Gas Analyser (Fixed)

Principle

Infra-red radiation is selectively absorbed by all gases except the elementary ones, particularly the nitrogen and oxygen components of air. Each gas is characterised by absorption bands of well defined wavelengths.

The source a (Figures 4.24 and 4.25) emits infra-red radiation of different wavelengths. A chopper c driven by a synchronous motor b is perforated in such a way that the radiation is directed alternately and for a brief instant into either part d_2 of the tube containing a non-absorbing substance (elementary gas or fluorite) or part d_1 containing a sample of a gas mixture containing gas A whose concentration is to be determined. A gas-tight seal is provided between d_1 and d_2. A diffuser h distributes the radiation over the whole section of the detector cell which must be filled only with the gas whose concentration is to be measured. Chambers e and f of the detector are separated by a partition which is transparent to the radiation, and by a flexible thin metallic membrane which forms the second plate of a capacitor g.

Phase 1

Radiation passes through d_2 without being absorbed. The gas A contained in the upper chamber e absorbs that part of the radiation which occupies the centre of its absorption bands. The rest of the radiation, from the edges of the absorption bands, reaches the lower chamber f where it is absorbed. The gas A heats up, and the increase in temperature is practically the same in both chambers as a result of their carefully chosen dimensions.

Phase 2

One part of the radiation occupying the centre of the absorption bands is absorbed only by gas A contained in the sample in d_1 and the remainder is absorbed in chamber e. The other part of this radiation, ie from the edges of the absorption bands, reaches chamber f where it is absorbed. The gas A heats up more in the chamber f than in e because of the previous absorption in d_1. The difference in temperature

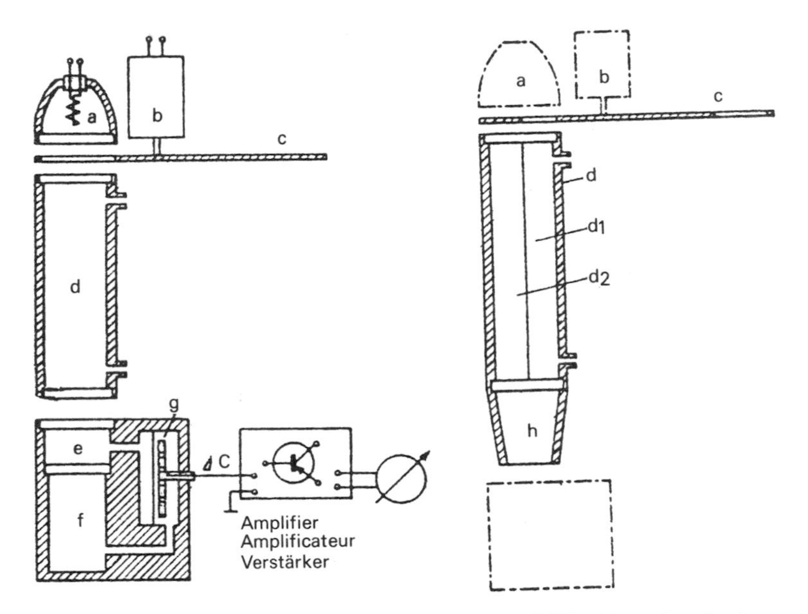

Fig. 4.24 Diagram of Unor Gas Analyser.

Fig. 4.25 Unor Gas Analyser Sample Tube Details.

produces a difference in pressure between the two chambers causing deflection of the membrane and a change in capacitance of the capacitor g. The periodic pulsing produced is amplified and rectified to give a reading on a voltmeter which may be calibrated directly in concentration of the gas A, because the signal depends only on this concentration. The signal may also be fed to a recorder.

Note:

Since the heating effect is small, the measurement must be made by comparison between two chambers. Measurement is continuous. The system is insensitive to drift, because the radiation is pulsating (a result of the action of chopper c) and the amplifier only responds to periodic capacitance variations. For similar reasons, when there is an external source of heat, the system does not produce a signal even if the dimensions of the chambers are not perfect, since there is no deflection of the membrane.

Applications

Installed at a fixed station for the surveillance of methane concentrations in firedamp drainage systems.

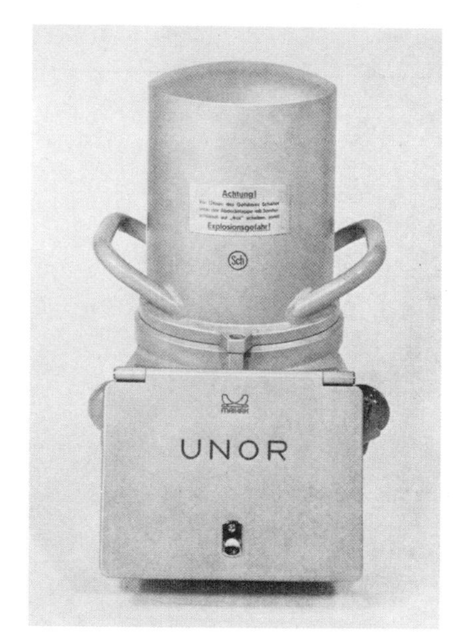

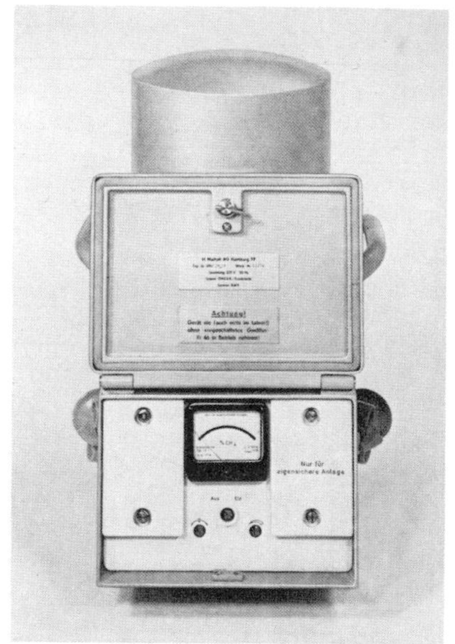

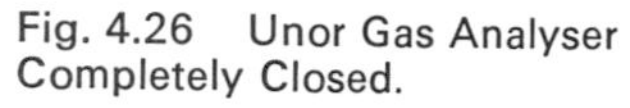

Fig. 4.26 Unor Gas Analyser Completely Closed.

Fig. 4.27 Unor Gas Analyser with Flap Open Showing Meter and Controls.

Characteristics (Figures 4.26 and 4.27)

Approval: In the GFR flameproof with intrinsically safe output signal

Manufacturer: Maihak (GFR)

Dimensions: 340 mm breadth, 340 mm depth, 520 mm height

Weight: 44 kg (including battery)

Range: 0 to 100 % methane (continuous measurement)

Measuring Error: $\leqq \pm 2\%$ methane (with variations in gas pressure, errors of 0.6 % methane per kPa are incurred)

Sensitivity: 0.5 % methane

The time to record a sudden change in concentration is one second (ie to attain 90 % of the change).

Output signal: 0 to 1 mA or 0 to 10 V for 0 to 100 % methane if a 1 kΩ line resistance is used.

Flow of gas through the instrument is achieved by a built-in pump which has an hourly capacity of 30 l; 100 l could be achieved with the external pump recommended for pipe systems. A pressure reducer becomes necessary at pressures above about 2 kPa. Power supply is by mains or, in abnormal general body methane concentrations, a battery of 1.5 h life is used, with automatic change-over and recharging.

With no mains supply, the instrument may be powered by compressed air, provided there is a suitable converter. The warming-up time (to put into service) ranges from 30 to 60 min.

1.1.3.12 Tricapteur

This instrument measures in turn, suction, methane concentration and flow. It is fully described in Section 1.1.5.

1.1.4 Measurement of Flow Rate

1.1.4.0 Introduction

Only the Tricapteur (Section 1.1.5) gives a direct measurement of methane flow rate. The other instruments measure it indirectly, either by pressure difference across an orifice plate or by velocity (Lugameter) from which the flow rate can be calculated.

1.1.4.1 Orifice Plates

The flow of gas mixture through an orifice plate (Figure 4.28) in a drainage range may be expressed (Appendix 4.2) by:

$$Q = K_C \, K_J \, K_E \, A_2 \sqrt{\frac{2\,(p_1 - p_2)}{\varrho}} \qquad [4.6]$$

where:

K_C the flow rate coefficient

K_J the universal correction coefficient (for viscosity, roughness, type of orifice, compressibility of the mixture)

K_E a function of the cross-sectional areas of pipe and orifice

A_2 the cross-sectional area of the orifice plate, and ϱ is the gas density.

Because all the coefficients are known, the measurement of flow rate can be reduced to the measurement of $(p_1 - p_2)$ the differential pressure across the orifice plate between points 1 and 2 (Figure 4.28).

If a less accurate value is acceptable, Equation 4.6 can be simplified to:

$Q = K_A\sqrt{p_1 - p_2}$ in m³/h at standard conditions . . . . [4.7]

K_A is calculated for a mean value of concentration, absolute pressure and temperature in the range downstream of the orifice plate (Appendix 4.2). The error is $\pm$ 15 %.

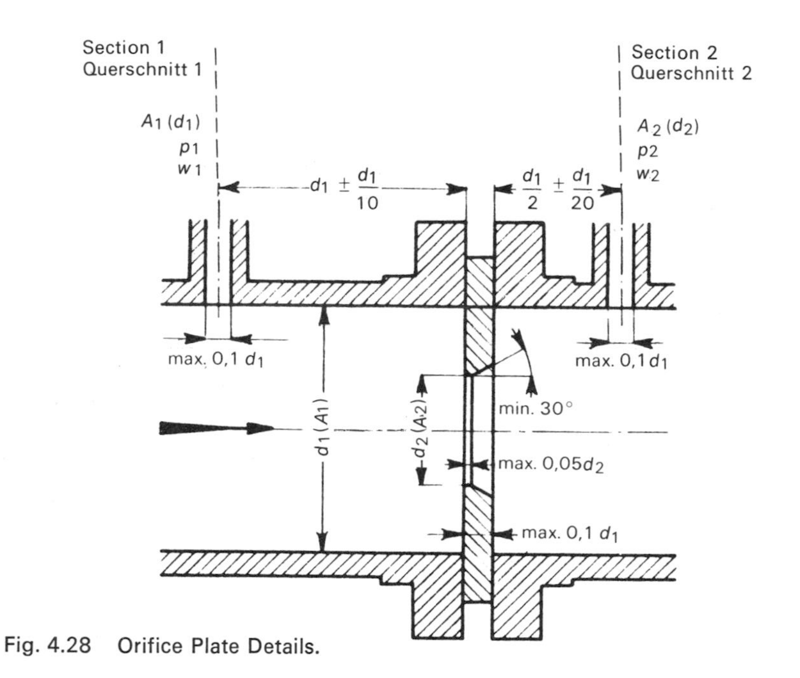

Fig. 4.28 Orifice Plate Details.

Note:

The insertion of an orifice plate in the range creates a small permanent loss of pressure equivalent to between 0.6 $(p_1 - p_2)$ and 0.9 $(p_1 - p_2)$.

Applications

Orifice plates can be used to measure flow rates in firedamp drainage ranges. Special calculators may be used to obtain the flow rate (Appendix 4.3).

The orifice plate must be placed in a straight section of pipe which must also be free from water blockage (eg at a high point), otherwise measurements will be incorrect.

Characteristics

If d_1 is used to denote the diameter of the straight section, (Figure 4.28), for accurate measurement,

the length upstream should be $\geqq 20\ d_1$ (in UK $\geqq 10\ d_1$),
the length downstream should be $\geqq 10\ d_1$ (in UK $\geqq 5\ d_1$),
the tapping upstream should be at $d_1 \pm 0.1\ d_1$ and
the tapping downstream should be at $\frac{d_1}{2} \pm 0.05\ d_1$

Any suitable pressure differential measuring device already described may be used (Table 4.1).

In a drainage range, measurements with orifice plates may become inprecise for example due to dirt or scale affecting the measurement. In the UK when problems are encountered with orifice plates, venturis are used.

1.1.4.2 Lugameter 'St AM' (Hand held)

Principle

The instrument (Figure 4.29) consists essentially of a cylindrical probe put in the pipe for measurement and a velocity indicator. The special probe is inserted in the range and because of the pressure difference between inlet and outlet a flow is generated through the velocity indicator.

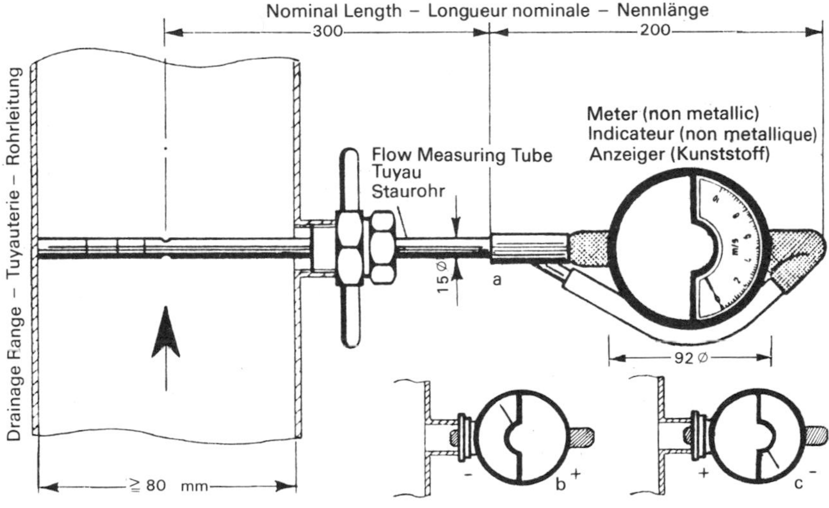

Fig. 4.29 Lugameter StAM.

The velocity indicator itself consists of a box containing a small moving vane on the axis of which is fixed a pointer and a spiral spring which maintains the pointer in the zero position as long as there is no gas flow acting on the vane. As soon as a flow of gas impinges on the vane however, it rotates about its axis, moving the pointer to a position of equilibrium between the action of the gas current and the reaction of the spiral spring. The pointer displacement depends on γw^2 (where γ is the specific weight of the gas and w the velocity).

Recorder

The position of the Lugameter pointer may be transmitted through a linkage system and recorded (Figure 4.30) as dots on a chart (chart speed 20 mm per hour).

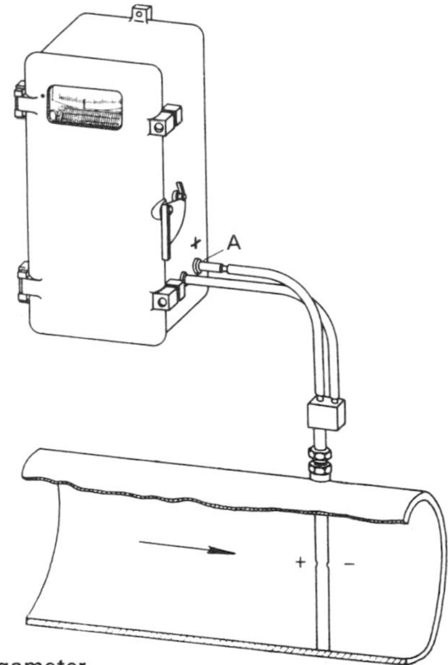

Fig. 4.30 Recording Lugameter.

Applications

The instrument may be used as a portable instrument (Figure 4.29) or with a recorder at a fixed position (Figure 4.30). To measure suction the negative side is connected to the range; for positive pressure the positive side is used (Figure 4.29). For measuring velocity (flow) it is connected through the top of the range by a pressure tapping in a G $^3/_4$ socket.

The holes in the probe must be aligned to the axis of the pipe range; correct alignment is obtained by an extension screwed on the end of the probe. When using a recorder, it is necessary to couple the flexible tubes between the instrument and the range correctly (ie positive to positive connections, Figure 4.30).

Calculation of Flow Rate (with indicating Lugameter)

The flow of mixture (m^3/min at 273 K and 101.3 kPa) is obtained by multiplying the corrected velocity (m/s) by four coefficients:

C_D: depending on the diameters of the pipe and the probe.

K_c : depending on the concentration of methane in the range; in general the effect of carbon dioxide may neglected, because it is balanced by that of methane, the constants of these gases being mutually opposed.

K_w: depending on the corrected velocity in the range and on the probe diameter.

K_e : depending on the density of the air (kg/m^3) at the time of measurement (hardly variable).

The product thus obtained is divided by two coefficients:

K_p : depending on the absolute pressure in the range.

K_t : depending on the dry-bulb temperature in the range.

Values of the six coefficients may be obtained from Figure 4.31.

The correction to be added to the indicated velocity to give the corrected velocity used in the above calculation, is obtained from a calibration curve. Because the calibration curve differs from one instrument to another, each Lugameter must be calibrated individually.

Except when velocities are near the limit of use of the instrument, the correction is generally negligible. For example (Figure 4.32) the correction is:

—8 % at 10 m/s with nozzle 10,
—5 % at 20 m/s with nozzle 20,
—6 % at 34 m/s with nozzle 40.

Calculation of Flow Rate (with Recorder)

The calculation is more convenient (but less precise) by starting with established formulae.

The velocity w (m/s) is deduced from the recorder chart and the corresponding total flow rate may be written:

$$Q_b = w\,(1 + k)\,U_{\alpha D} \qquad [4.8]$$

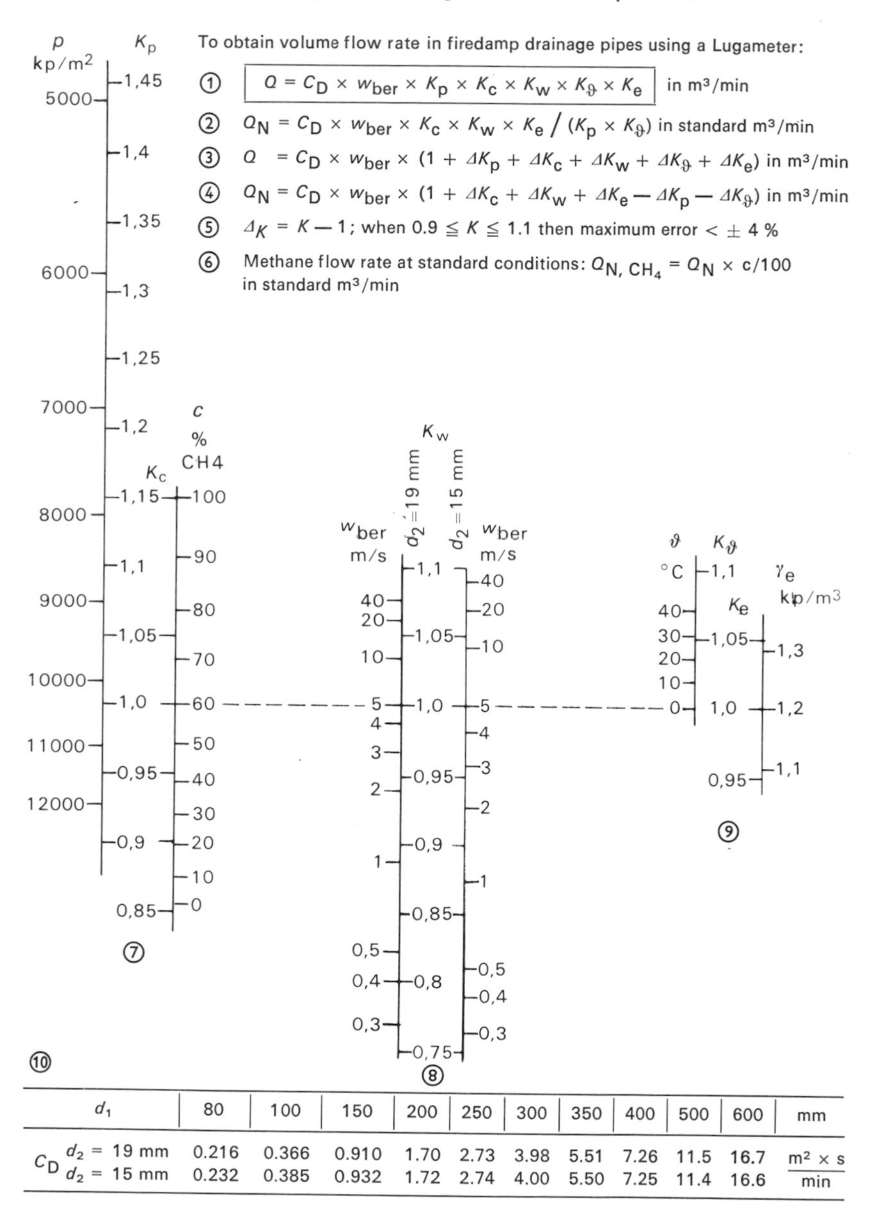

d_1	80	100	150	200	250	300	350	400	500	600	mm
C_D d_2 = 19 mm	0.216	0.366	0.910	1.70	2.73	3.98	5.51	7.26	11.5	16.7	m² × s / min
C_D d_2 = 15 mm	0.232	0.385	0.932	1.72	2.74	4.00	5.50	7.25	11.4	16.6	

Figure 4.31 Chart used in Germany for a Lugameter to obtain Drainage Flow Rates Showing Examples of the Calculations.

Symbols:			
	Q	Flow rate under measured conditions	in m^3/min
	Q_N	Flow rate at standard conditions of $p_N = 10\,330$ kp/m^2 and $\vartheta_N = 0$ °C	in m^3/min
	d_1	Pipe diameter	in mm
	d_2	Probe diameter	in mm
	C_D	Constant depending on d_1 and d_2	in $m^2 s/min$
	p	Absolute pressure in the pipe	in kp/m^2
	c	Purity	in %
	w_{ber}	Corrected velocity (pipe centre)	in m/s
	ϑ	Dry-bulb temperature of the pipe	in °C
	γ_0	Density (specific weight) of Lugameter calibration	in kp/m^3

Example 1:

given that:

$d_1 = 150$ mm, $d_2 = 15$ mm	then from	⑩		C_D	= 0.932
$p = 7\,200$ kp/m^2	then from	⑦	left	K_p	= 1.20
$c = 80$ % CH_4	then from	⑦	right	K_c	= 1.07
$w_{ber} = 5.0$ m/s	then from	⑧	right	K_w	= 1.00
$\vartheta = 30$ °C	then from	⑨	left	K_ϑ	= 1.05
$\gamma_e = 1.25$ kp/m^3	then from	⑨	right	K_e	= 1.02

from ①: $Q = 0.932 \times 5.0 \times 1.20 \times 1.07 \times 1.00 \times 1.05 \times 1.02 = 6.41$ m^3/min

from ②: $Q_N = 0.932 \times 5.0 \times 1.07 \times 1.00 \times 1.02 \,/\, (1.20 \times 1.05) = 4.04$ m^3/min

---

Example 2: $p = 11\,000$ kp/m^2, then from ⑦ left $K_p = 0.97$
the remaining values are the same as Example 1

from ③: $Q = 0.932 \times 5.0\,[1 + (-0.03) + 0.07 + 0 + 0.05 + 0.02] = 5.17$ m^3/min

from ④: $Q_N = 0.932 \times 5.0\,[1 + 0.07 + 0 + 0.02 - (-0.03) - 0.05] = 4.99$ m^3/min

---

Example 1 can also be calculated using a mixed method:

$$Q = C_D \times w_{ber} \times K_p\,(1 + \Delta K_c + \Delta K_w + \Delta K_\vartheta + \Delta K_e) =$$
$$= 0.932 \times 5.0 \times 1.2 \times (1 + 0.07 + 0.05 + 0.02) = 6.36 \; m^3/min$$

$$Q_N = C_D \times w_{ber} \times (1 + \Delta K_c + \Delta K_w + \Delta K_e - \Delta K_\vartheta) \,/\, K_p =$$
$$= 0.932 \times 5.0 \times (1 + 0.07 + 0 + 0.02 - 0.02) \,/\, 1.2 = 4.15 \; m^3/min$$

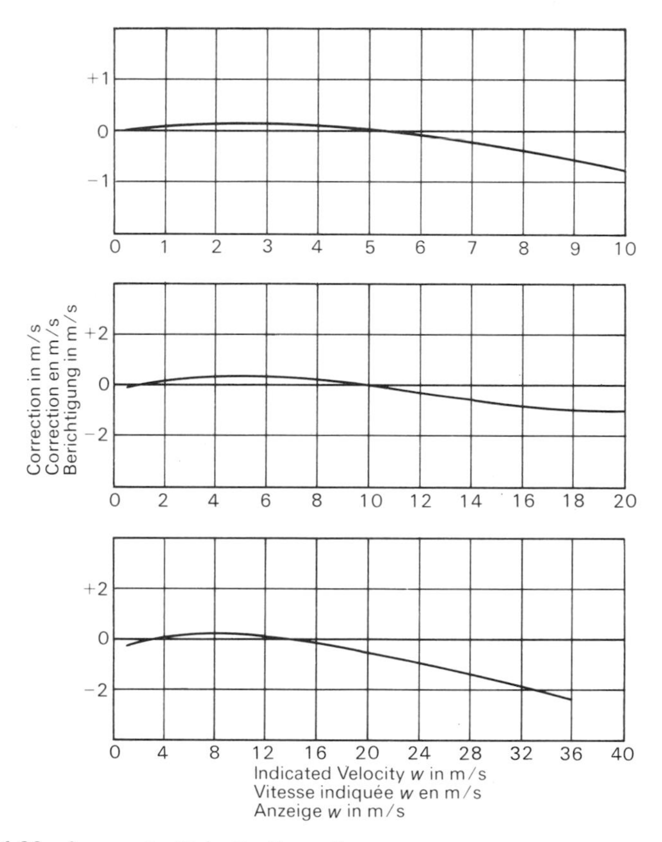

Fig. 4.32 Lugameter Velocity Correction.

where, in equation [4.8]:

k is a coefficient depending on the methane concentration and

$U_{\alpha D}$ is a multiplier giving the flow in m^3 per hour depending on the diameter of the range and the effect of the probe.

The normal hourly flow, in m^3 at standard conditions, may be written as:

$$Q_N = Q_b \; K_F \qquad [4.9]$$

where:

K_F depends on the dry-bulb temperature and absolute pressure in the range, being the algebraic sum of the barometric pressure, the suction and the saturated vapour pressure of water.

These coefficients are given by the tables in Figure 4.33.

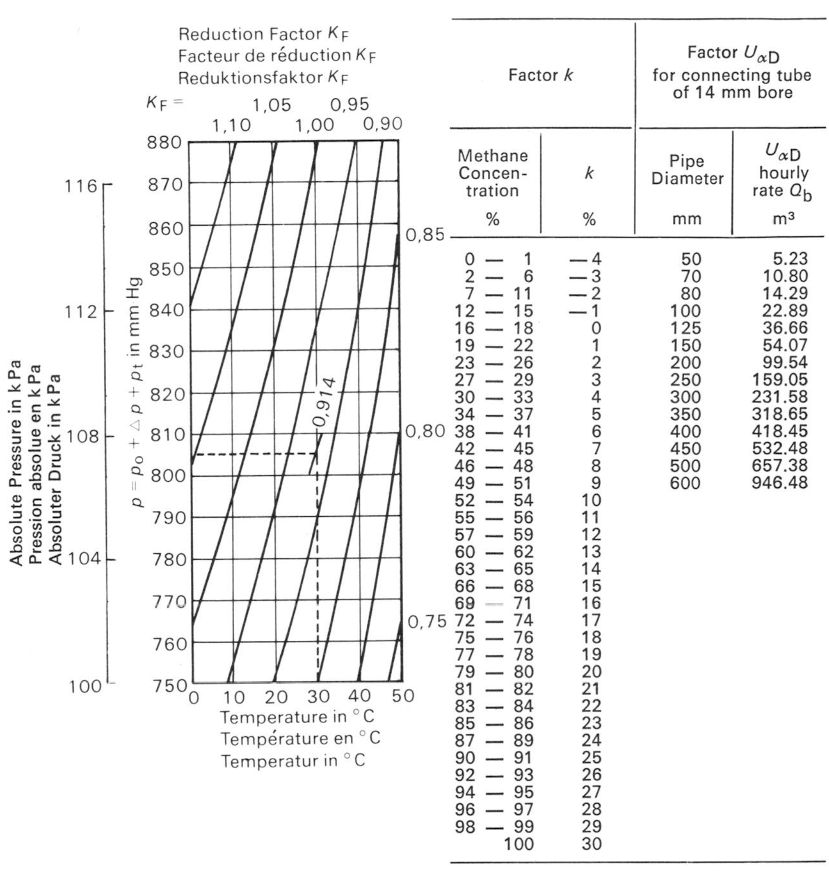

Factor k		Factor $U_{\alpha D}$ for connecting tube of 14 mm bore	
Methane Concentration %	k %	Pipe Diameter mm	$U_{\alpha D}$ hourly rate Q_b m³
0 — 1	—4	50	5.23
2 — 6	—3	70	10.80
7 — 11	—2	80	14.29
12 — 15	—1	100	22.89
16 — 18	0	125	36.66
19 — 22	1	150	54.07
23 — 26	2	200	99.54
27 — 29	3	250	159.05
30 — 33	4	300	231.58
34 — 37	5	350	318.65
38 — 41	6	400	418.45
42 — 45	7	450	532.48
46 — 48	8	500	657.38
49 — 51	9	600	946.48
52 — 54	10		
55 — 56	11		
57 — 59	12		
60 — 62	13		
63 — 65	14		
66 — 68	15		
69 — 71	16		
72 — 74	17		
75 — 76	18		
77 — 78	19		
79 — 80	20		
81 — 82	21		
83 — 84	22		
85 — 86	23		
87 — 89	24		
90 — 91	25		
92 — 93	26		
94 — 95	27		
96 — 97	28		
98 — 99	29		
100	30		

Figure 4.33 Lugameter Factors k, $U_{\alpha D}$ and K_F used to obtain Flow Rate.

Characteristics

Manufacturer:	Paul Gothe (GFR)
Graduation:	m/s
Diameter of the Probe:	15 or 19 mm
Ranges of measurement:	0 to 10, 0 to 20, 0 to 40 m/s depending on the nozzle used
Accuracy:	1.5 % of full scale reading
Internal diameter of pipe:	$\geqq$ 80 mm
Scale:	From 0.3 m/s
Pressure range:	Between —29 kPa and + 100 kPa

1.1.5 Suction, Methane Concentration and Flow Rate Measurement Apparatus Tricapteur TCC 69 (Fixed)

Principle

The head of the Tricapteur (Figure 4.34) is fixed on the firedamp drainage range and allows successive measurement of:

Δp suction in the range relative to underground pressure at the point of measurement

c the methane concentration

Q the flow rate of methane at 293 K and 101.3 kPa.

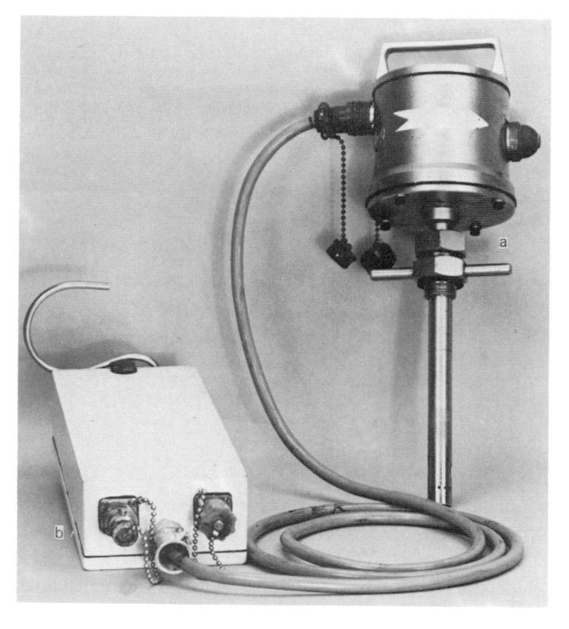

a Tricapteur Head — Tricapteur-
b Coder — Codeur — Kodiersender

Fig. 4.34
Tricapteur TCC 69.

The instrument has three measuring thermistors for Δp, c and Q and a reference thermistor R. The reference thermistor for each measurement is placed in the air flowing in the roadway.

The temperature of the thermistors in use (around 570 K) eliminates the effect of carbon dioxide.

a) *Measurement of Suction (Figure 4.35)*

The velocity of inleakage of filtered air from the airway which is controlled by the capillary d (diameter 0.2 mm, and protected by

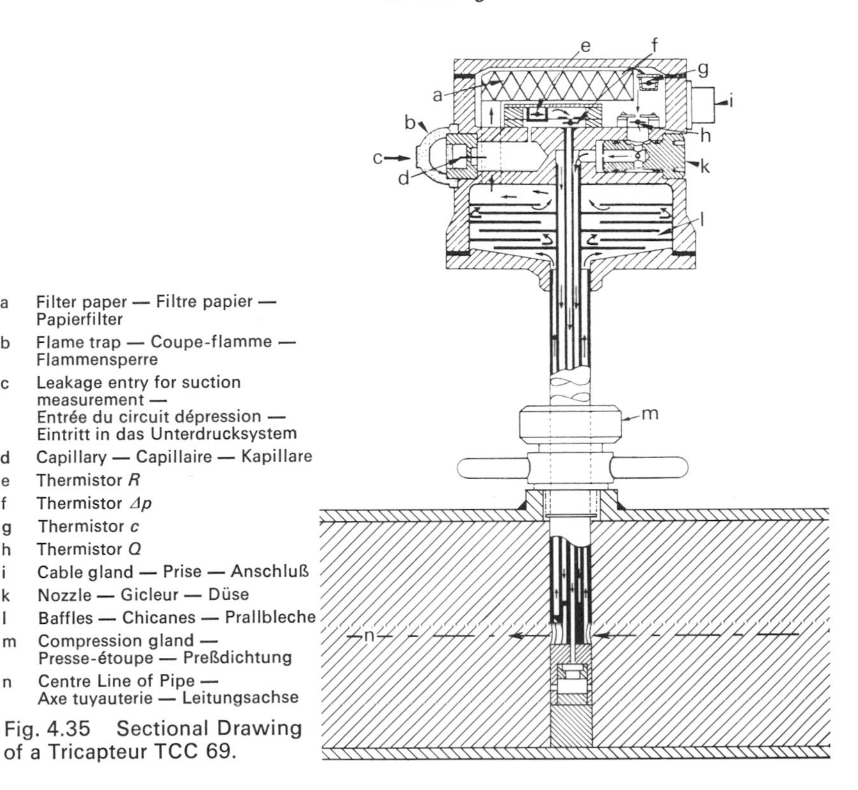

a Filter paper — Filtre papier — Papierfilter
b Flame trap — Coupe-flamme — Flammensperre
c Leakage entry for suction measurement — Entrée du circuit dépression — Eintritt in das Unterdrucksystem
d Capillary — Capillaire — Kapillare
e Thermistor R
f Thermistor Δp
g Thermistor c
h Thermistor Q
i Cable gland — Prise — Anschluß
k Nozzle — Gicleur — Düse
l Baffles — Chicanes — Prallbleche
m Compression gland — Presse-étoupe — Preßdichtung
n Centre Line of Pipe — Axe tuyauterie — Leitungsachse

Fig. 4.35 Sectional Drawing of a Tricapteur TCC 69.

a flame trap of sintered metal), is measured by passing it over the thermistor f (Δp) which is fixed behind an orifice plate. This air then flows into the drainage range through the central tube of the probe. The velocity of inleakage increases with suction causing more cooling of the thermistor.

b) Measurement of the Methane Concentration and Flow Rate

A system resembling a Pitot tube ensures that part of the flow in the range passes in succession through the outer annular space of the probe, baffles l and paper filter a; baffles l are used for cooling and removal of moisture. The gas then reaches the thermistor g which measures the concentration and which has been placed in a sintered metal casing to avoid the velocity cooling effect. Thus a measurement of thermal conductivity is made which depends only on the concentration — the higher the concentration, the greater the cooling effect on the thermistor. The gas subsequently passes through an orifice to the thermistor h (Q) and then to the drainage range through a flow limiting nozzle k and the interior annular space of the probe. The flow rate Q' over the thermistor h is proportional to the flow in the drainage range such that:

$$Q' = k' \sqrt{\Delta p} \qquad [4.10]$$

and as

$$\Delta p = k'' w^2 \qquad [4.11]$$

then

$$Q' = k''' w = k\, Q \qquad [4.12]$$

where:

Q' the flow through the orifice plate

Δp the suction in the range

w the velocity in the pipe

Q the flow in the drainage pipe.

The Tricapteur indicates the flow rate in pure methane over the usual range of drained gas concentrations. If at a constant methane flow, the velocity of the mixture should increase, the temperature of the thermistor h (Q) would tend to fall but a decrease in methane concentration would tend to cause its temperature to rise. Within a certain operating range, these two effects compensate for one another. Thus in normal conditions the equilibrium temperature and the signal depend only on the mass flow of pure methane so that the tricapteur measurement does not require further corrections for pressure or temperature.

Applications

The instrument is used at a fixed position. Its probe is screwed on to the drainage range by means of a standard G $^3/_4$ screwed socket welded on the range in a position complying with the dimensions given in Figure 4.36. To avoid operating problems caused by water, the measuring point must not be placed at a low point in the range.

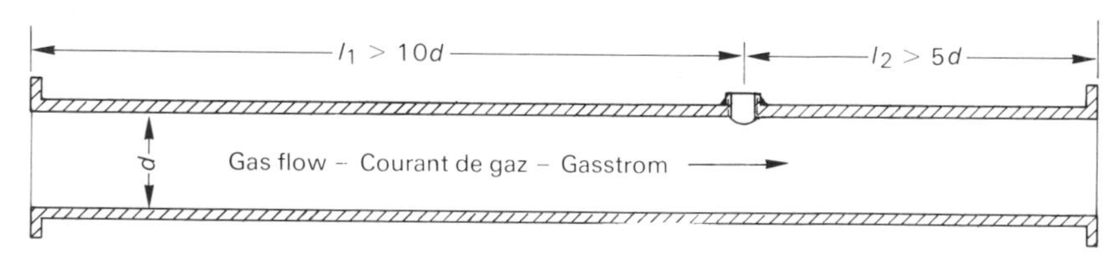

Fig. 4.36 Pipe Dimensions For Installation of Tricapteur Head with G ¾ socket.

The difference in temperature between the gas in the range and the air in the roadway must not exceed 3 K and the socket must be located on top of the pipe.

The Tricapteur must also be correctly aligned so that the axis through the cable gland i and sintered flame trap b (Figure 4.35), must be parallel to and vertically above the longitudinal axis of the pipe. False measurements of flow rate are obtained at all angles greater than 0.17 rad. The flame trap b must be on the downstream side, ie pointing in the direction of flow. (If the flame trap were on the upstream side gas would flow through the Tricapteur without first passing the baffles l and paper filter a, and the thermistors could be damaged).

Signals from the Tricapteur may be transmitted over telephone lines either by a surface remote control system for drainage (TCC) using a coding station (Section 1.2.7.1), or by a remote 'télévigile' monitoring system using a TF 24 transmitter, power supply, measuring station and charging unit (Section 1.2.7.2).

Maintenance

It is sufficient, once a month, to take out the Tricapteur from the pipe range to check the paper filter and nozzle, and to clean the flame trap and orifices of the probe. It is necessary to check and calibrate the instrument in the laboratory annually.

Characteristics

Approval:	Intrinsically safe in France and Belgium
Manufacturer:	CERCHAR (France)
Dimensions:	130 mm diameter, 400 mm height
Weight:	6 kg
Measuring ranges:	0 to 40 kPa suction (10 000 to 6510 Hz)
	0 to 100 % methane (10 000 to 8800 Hz)
	0.6 to 9 m/s (8700 to 6560 Hz) nozzle 9
	1.2 to 20 m/s (8700 to 6450 Hz) nozzle 20

1.1.6 Temperature Measurement

This is mentioned for completeness only.

For occasional measurements, a simple mercury-in-glass thermometer is used. For continuous measurements, more precise electric instruments are employed, eg thermocouples and resistance thermometers of the dial type (Figure 4.37) or with remote transmission facilities.

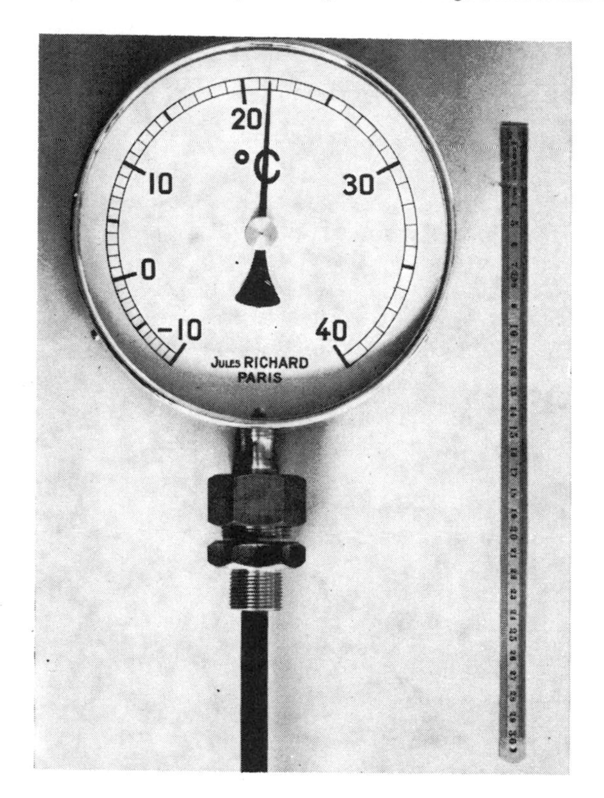

Fig. 4.37
Dial Type Thermometer.

1.1.7 Location and Measurement of Firedamp Flow in Boreholes

Principle

A probe (Figure 4.38 or Figure 4.39) consisting of an anemometer and a methane measuring head is pushed gradually into the borehole by means of a string of push-rods to a known position. It is thus possible to determine the concentration of methane and flow rate of gas at any point in the borehole assuming the cross-sectional area is constant. Sources of firedamp or air inleakage are located at places where the flow or purity of gas changes significantly as indicated in Figure 4.40. Actual measurements are obtained from the rotational speed of the anemometer vane which is converted into electrical pulses by a micro-wave diode and from the thermal conductivity head

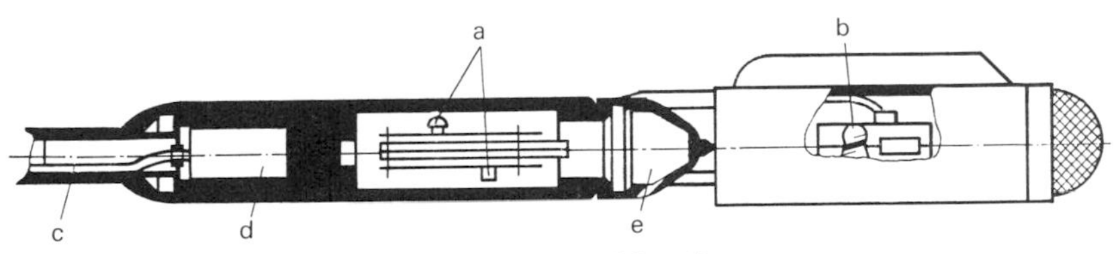

a Electronic Circuitry — Distribution électronique — Elektronik
b Anemometer — Anémomètre — Anemometer
c Output Cable — Câble de mesure — Meßleitung
d Battery — Accumulateur — Akkumulator
e Methane Sensor — Appareil de mesure CH_4 — CH_4-Meßkopf

Fig. 4.38 Borehole Probe For Measuring Methane Concentration and Flow Rate (Centralised Type).

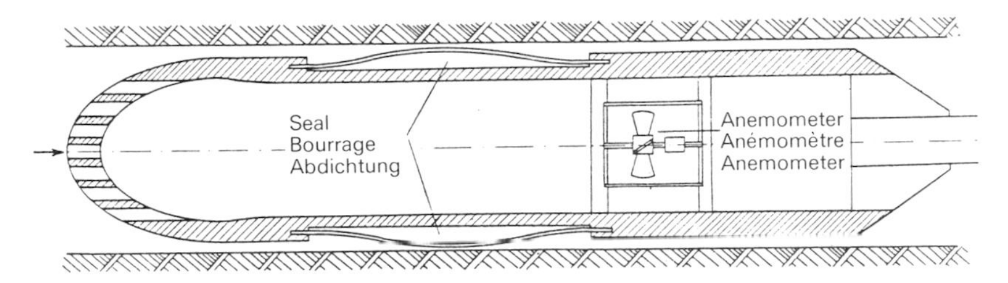

Fig. 4.39 Borehole Probe For Measuring Methane Concentration and Flow Rate (Seal Type).

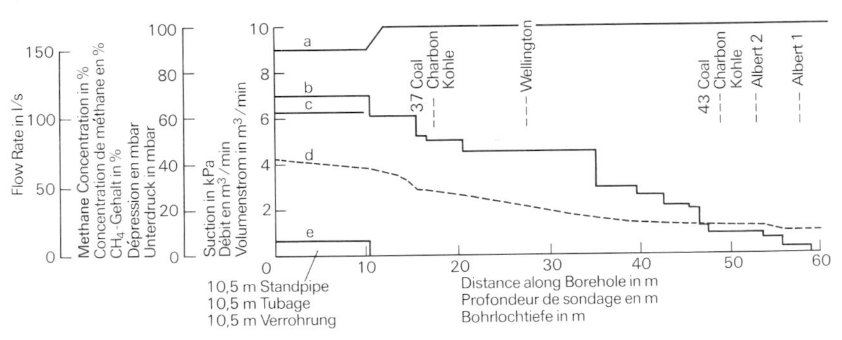

a Purity — Teneur de méthane — CH_4-Gehalt
b Mixture Flow — Mélange — Gemisch
c Pure Methane Flow — Méthane — Methan
d Suction — Dépression — Unterdruck
e Air Inleakage — Air — Luft

Seam — Couche — Flöz Karl
Borehole — Sondage — Bohrloch Nr. 46 S
Date — Mesure — Messung 15. 3. 76
Borehole Length — Longueur de sondage — Gebohrte Länge: 62 m
Probed Length — Longueur sondée — Sondierte Länge: 62 m
Probe used — Sonde utilisée — Verwendete Sonde: 50 mm Dmr.

Fig. 4.40 Borehole Probe Results.

which provides methane concentration measurements. Measuring signals are transmitted to indicators or recorders in the roadway.

Characteristics

Approval:	Intrinsically safe in GFR
Manufacturer:	Höntzsch; Dräger (GFR)
Construction:	Modular, allowing various arrangements
Anemometer:	Diameter 20 mm (AS 20)
Output signal:	0 to 10 V at 10 kΩ (adjustable to existing instruments or transmission systems)
Micro-wave diode:	Hardly affected by dirt; low power consumption (high frequency electromagnetic).

Two types of probe are used

a) The first type (Figure 4.38) is centrally mounted, is made of brass 50 mm diameter and 610 mm in length, and has lateral centralising fins selected according to borehole diameter. This type of probe must be previously calibrated in the laboratory, is easy to handle and creates little additional resistance to flow. Clearly measurement is less accurate if the borehole cross-section is irregular.

b) In the second type (Figure 4.39) an expandable sleeve presses against the walls of the borehole. It is suitable for very small flow rates and permits an easy comparison to be made between different boreholes because the measuring cross-section remains the same.

Indicating Instrument

Ranges of measurement for AS 20:	0 to 10, 0 to 20, 0 to 40 m/s; other ranges are possible
Accuracy:	± 1.5 % of the reading
Graduation:	in m/s
Power Supply:	A built-in 9 V dry battery for measurements of short duration. An external supply is possible through a mains connector.

1.1.8 Calculators

The NCB Flow Calculator has been designed to facilitate firedamp calculations underground (Appendix 4.3).

1.2 Surface Measurements and Control

1.2.0 Introduction

Figure 4.41 shows an example of the monitoring and control circuitry at a modern surface firedamp drainage extraction plant using water seal pumps. The following parameters are measured and recorded:

- ▷ temperature, flow rate, methane concentration and absolute pressure of the gas in the drainage pipes from underground on the suction side of the pumps;
- ▷ temperature and pressure in the pipe range on the outlet side of the pumps;
- ▷ the temperature of the pump circulating water (feed and return).

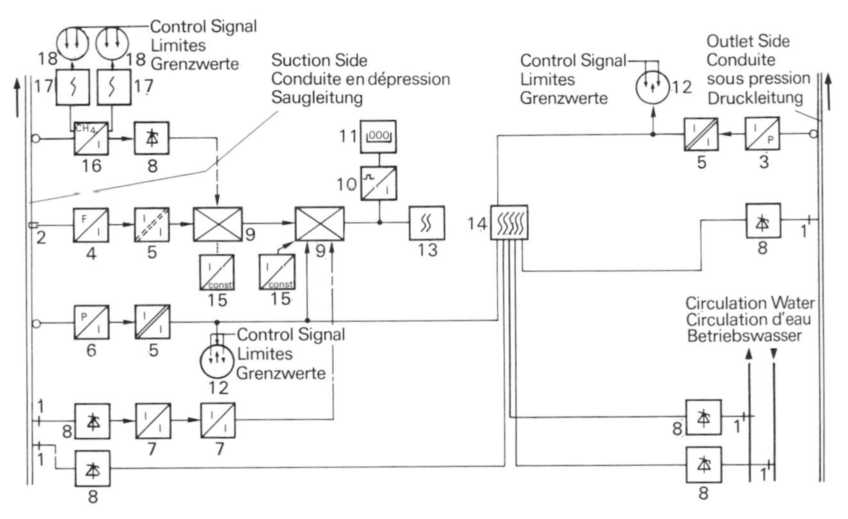

1 Resistance thermometers
2 Inlet orifice plate
3 Outlet pressure monitor
4 Differential pressure monitor for 2
5 Signal conditioner
6 Suction transducer
7 Inlet temperature signal conditioner
8 I.S. Barrier
9 Density, pressure, flow correction processer
10 Signal converter for 11
11 Flow meter
12 Indicator/alarm for suction and pressure
13 Recorder for extracted and utilised gas flows
14 Six channel recorder:
1. Absolute pressure on suction side
2. Absolute pressure on outlet side
3. Extracted gas temperature
4. Water feed temperature
5. Water return temperature
6. Outlet gas temperature
15 Voltage stabiliser for 9
16 Two 0 to 100 % Unor analysers for purity
17 Two recorders for 16
18 Two purity alarm and cut-off switches

Fig. 4.41 Monitoring and Control Circuitry at a German Surface Firedamp Extraction Plant (using Water Seal Pumps).

The control functions cover:

▷ suction, temperature and concentration of methane on the suction side,

▷ pressure on the outlet side,

▷ temperature of the circulation water and any gas discharged to the sump in circulating water.

Reference should also be made to Appendix 3.5 of Chapter 3.

1.2.1 Pressure Measurement

1.2.1.1 Diaphragm Absolute Pressure Transmitter Type CMR 15.741

Principle

In the Hartmann & Braun CMR 15.741, a diaphragm 1, (Figure 4.42) is subjected on the positive (+) side to the pressure being measured, the negative (—) side being sealed under vacuum. As it is deflected, the diaphragm displaces the core of an induction coil 2. Changes in deflection, which are proportional to the pressure being measured produce a d. c. signal which is amplified 3.

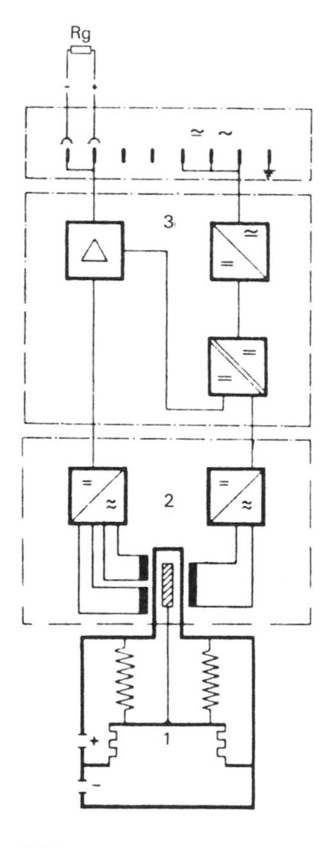

Fig. 4.42 Schematic Diagram of CMR 15.741 and CM 15.240 Pressure Transmitters.

Application

It is used for measuring absolute pressures, principally barometric pressure.

Characteristics

Manufacturer: Hartmann & Braun (GFR)
Dimensions: 285 mm height, 138 mm width, 225 mm depth
Weight: ≈ 8 kg
Scale adjustments: start point 0 to 80 %, end point 100 to 20 %
Output: 4 to 20 mA
Ranges: 0 to 5, 0 to 10, 20 to 40, 70 to 90, 80 to 100, 90 to 110 kPa.

1.2.1.2 Diaphragm Absolute Pressure Transmitter Type 4-385

Principle

In the Bell and Howell type 4-385, the deflection of the diaphragm is measured by a strain gauge which forms part of a Wheatstone bridge.

Application

It is used for measuring absolute pressures, principally barometric pressure.

Characteristics

Manufacturer: Bell & Howell (UK)
Dimensions: 190 mm height, 153 mm width, 89 mm depth
Weight: ≈ 2.5 kg
Scale adjustments: Continuously adjustable zero suppression and 11 : 1 range
Output: normally 0.4 to 2 V d. c., others available
Ranges: normally 85 to 115 kPa, others available.

1.2.1.3 CMR 15.240 Diaphragm Pressure Transmitter

Principle (Figure 4.42)

The diaphragm is connected on the positive (+) side to the higher pressure and on the negative (—) side to the lower pressure; deflection of the diaphragm moves the core of an induction coil. Change in deflection which is proportional to the pressure difference to be measured, produces a d. c. signal which is amplified.

Application

The instrument will measure suction in the range and differential pressure across orifice plates and can be used for very high values.

Characteristics

Manufacturer:	Hartmann and Braun (GFR)
Dimensions:	285 mm height, 138 mm width, 225 mm depth
Weight:	approx 7.4 kg
Start point of measurement:	0 to 90 % of the scale
End point of measurement:	100 to 10 % of the scale
Output:	0 to 20 mA with transmission facilities
Measuring range:	0 to 2, 0 to 2.5, 0 to 6, 0 to 10, 0 to 25, 0 to 40, 0 to 60, 0 to 100, 0 to 200 kPa.

It can be connected directly to a meter or recorder, a controller or a computer.

1.2.1.4 Differential Pressure Transmitter 5 PdH

Principle (Figure 4.43)

The measuring element transmits a force F through a lever L_1 which is pivoted at O_1. This force is transmitted by the tip of the screw V_p to lever L_2, pivoted at O_2. The balancing force F' is obtained from the coil b of a solenoid M, situated in the field of a permanent magnet and through which the output current I passes. A change in pressure causes an imbalance between F and F' and the slight movement of levers L_1 and L_2 is detected by a variable inductance DE. The inductance, which has a 2 kHz supply from an oscillator, controls the magnetic amplifier such that the output current I flowing in solenoid M balances the new force F. The force F' from the solenoid is directly proportional to the current I, which in turn is proportional to the measured value of F.

A sensitivity adjustment of the transmitter is obtained by movement of the tip of the screw V_p, which changes the lengths of the lever arms $O_1 — V_p$ and $O_2 — V_p$. A fine adjustment is obtained using potentiometer Rh. Zero adjustment is provided by the spring Z. This spring can also be used to change the start of the scale up to 50 % of the adjustable scale range.

In one model, a supplementary spring attached to lever L_1 gives a change of $\pm$ 24.5 kPa with a maximum differential pressure of 60 kPa.

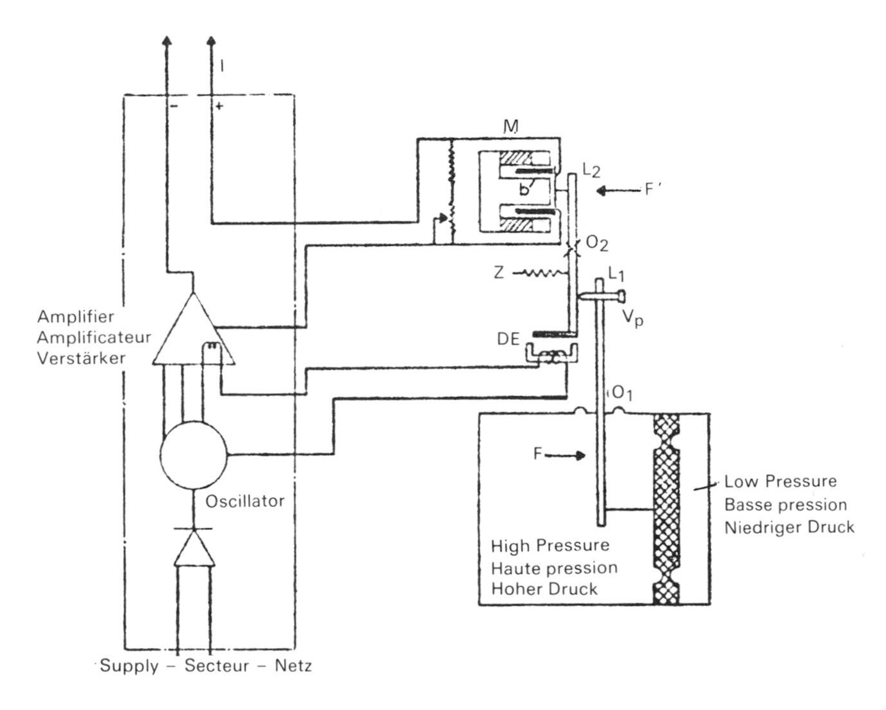

Fig. 4.43 Schematic Diagram of the 5 PdH Pressure Transmitter.

Application

It is used to measure differential pressures at the surface.

Characteristics

Manufacturer:	Schlumberger (France)
Weight:	Transmitter: 15 kg Amplifier: 1.5 kg
Scale Range:	5 to 60 kPa
Maximum Static Pressure:	10 MPa
Output signal:	0 to 10 mA d. c. with a maximum load resistance of 2500 ohms (1500 ± 1000 ohms)
Power supply:	d. c., 48 V (also available 24 V) a. c., 127 to 220 V, 50 Hz (60 Hz also available)
Consumption:	≈ 4 VA

Measuring cell:	Double diaphragm of stainless steel
Measuring cell housing:	Stainless steel
Use:	All liquids or gases
Operation temperatures (surroundings):	— 20 °C to + 60 °C
Movement of zero:	Standard model: + 50 % of scale with scale maximum of 60 kPa
	Model B: ±24.5 kPa with scale maximum of 60 kPa.

1.2.1.5 Differential Pressure Transmitter Type 050

Principle

The transmitter employs a stretched metal diaphragm and operates on a capacitance principle.

Applications

This small sensitive pressure transmitter has been used in the UK at surface firedamp utilisation plants for the measurement and remote monitoring of flow of drained gas. Other similar units are intended for eventual general use in firedamp drainage systems to give remote analogue outputs from suctions, pressures or differential pressures.

Characteristics

Manufacturer:	Furness Controls (UK)	
Dimensions:	125 mm height, 90 mm diameter	
Weight:	0.7 kg	
Ranges:	differential pressure:	0 to 0.5 and 0 to 2 kPa
	vacuum:	0 to 30 and 0 to 60 kPa
	positive pressure:	0 to 35, 0 to 70 and 0 to 140 kPa
Output:	standard 0.4 to 2 volts (live zero at 0.4 volts)	
Power Supply:	standard DC 2 or DC 3/Bat 1 rechargeable battery (both approved intrinsically safe systems).	

Pressure ranges are mechanically set so that the same electrical circuitry is used regardless of range.

1.2.2 Measurement of Methane Concentration

1.2.2.1 General

All methane measuring instruments approved for use underground can also be employed on the surface (for example BM2H, high concentration GTM, UNOR). In addition laboratory type infra red analysers used with Tube Bundle systems (Section 1.2.7.4) are employed for the analysis of high concentrations of methane.

1.2.2.2 Industrial Infra Red Gas Analysers for the Measurement of Combustibles in Drained Gas

In the UK industrial infra red gas analysers are currently used for the measurement of combustibles in drained gas at surface firedamp extraction plants. They are employed on the suction and delivery sides of surface firedamp extraction plants for the monitoring of drained gas purity and plant control.

Principle

The Feedback PSA 401 which is employed already for monitoring and control, is a single path two wavelength analyser, with a solid state infra red detector. The narrow bandwidths at the measurement and reference wavelengths are selected by interference filters. The measuring cell is maintained at a temperature of 318 K by a heater wire wound around the outside, and is thermally insulated and sealed inside plastic bellows. The bellows are connected to a purge system. The optical bench and control unit are housed in separate boxes so that the control unit can be installed remotely. The unit is mains powered, gives a linear response and is provided with four outputs. The conventional range is 0 to 75% combustibles in drained gas. Cross sensitivities of combustible constituents are about 1 : 1. It does not suffer from interference from background gases present in drained gas and gives the high accuracy necessary for monitoring and control of surface firedamp extraction and utilisation plants. Measurements are automatically corrected for variations in atmospheric pressure.

The MSA Lira 202 infra red analyser is of the double beam type with a Luft type detector. The analyser cell is maintained at a temperature of 338 K and separate housings provided for the optical bench and electronic controls. Total combustibles in drained gas are measured, and tests are being carried out at colliery surface firedamp extraction plants.

Characteristics

Manufacturers:	Anatek Instruments, UK (Feedback PSA 401)
	MSA, UK (Lira 202)
Range of measurement:	0 to 75 % combustible gas
Power supply:	mains 110 V
Output:	0.4 to 2 V (analogue signal, continuous current)

Four preset contact relays for operating an alarm and cut-off at high and low concentration levels. Stable instrument, accurate measurement, gradually replacing the Acoustic methanometer at surface extraction plants (Section 1.1.3.8).

1.2.2.3 Uras 2 T-Ex

Principle and Applications

See UNOR (Section 1.1.3.11).

Characteristics

Approval:	Intrinsically safe in the GFR
Manufacturer:	Hartmann and Braun (GFR)
Dimensions:	420 mm breadth, 600 mm height, 270 mm depth
Weight:	40 kg
Range of measurement:	0 to 100 % methane
Flow rate of gas:	30 to 60 l/h (maximum 500 l/h)
Gas pressure:	2 to 100 kPa
Output:	0 to 20 mA

1.2.3 Measurement of Concentration of Gases other than Methane

In addition to that described below, laboratory type infra red analysers used with Tube Bundle Systems (Section 1.2.7.4) are employed for the analysis of carbon monoxide, carbon dioxide and oxygen.

1.2.3.1 Carbon Monoxide: UNOR (Infra-Red)

Principle

The instrument has been described in Section 1.1.3.11. It is necessary to use a detector cell filled with carbon monoxide.

Application

It is used for the measurement and recording of carbon monoxide concentrations in gas at a surface plant. It is necessary to insert a filter in the instrument when high concentrations of methane are present.

Characteristics

Range of measurement: most frequent: 0 to 0.03 % (300 ppm)
lowest: 0 to 0.01 % (100 ppm)

1.2.3.2 Oxygen: Paramagnetic Analysers

Principle

These analysers take advantage of the paramagnetic properties of oxygen which cause the gas to be attracted by a magnetic field. This attraction is inversely proportional to the temperature of the gas.

In the Magnos type of analyser, a horizontal tube A, (Figure 4.44) under the influence of a powerful permanent magnet, receives a mixture whose oxygen content has to be determined. The oxygen is attracted towards the pole tip of the magnet (Figure 4.45) where the gradient of the magnetic field is strongest. At this point also, the mixture is heated by an electric coil. The oxygen in the mixture thus undergoes two successive and contrary effects. It is attracted to the pole tip of the magnet where it is heated by the electric coil; this reduces its paramagnetism and allows it to be displaced by cooler inflowing oxygen which is more powerfully attracted by the magnet. Thus, a continuous circulation of the mixture is generated in the tube (known as a 'magnetic draught') at a speed which is approximately

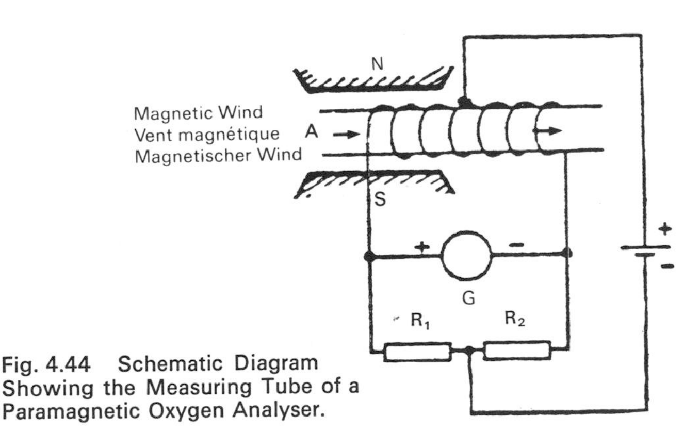

Fig. 4.44 Schematic Diagram Showing the Measuring Tube of a Paramagnetic Oxygen Analyser.

proportional to the oxygen content. The same coil is used to measure the oxygen content (Wheatstone bridge Section 1.1.3.1). The galvanometer G of the bridge is graduated directly in percentage oxygen by volume and the measurement is continuous. The measuring tube A is sealed into a hollow circular tube (Figure 4.45), so that it is symmetrical in relation to the gas inlet and outlet. Consequently, the measurement is virtually independent of the flow of gas in the circular tube because, to avoid the effects of the dead volume of piping, the circular tube receives only a small diverted flow.

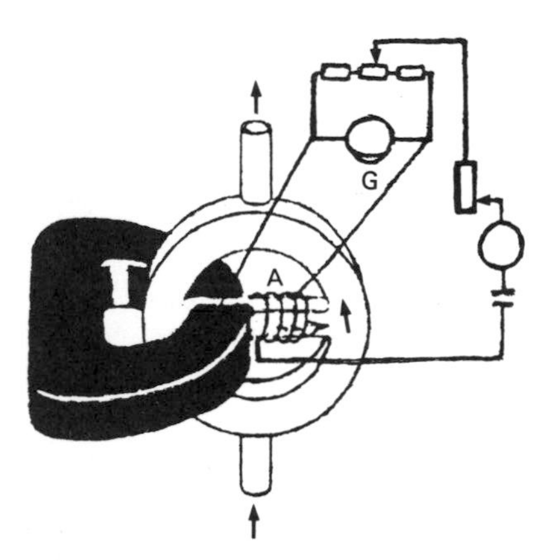

Fig. 4.45 Schematic Diagram of a Paramagnetic Oxygen Analyser.

In the Servomex analyser, a light dumb-bell shaped body is suspended on a platinum-iridium strip in a non-uniform magnetic field. A torque is produced proportional to the magnetic susceptibility of the gas surrounding the dumb-bell shaped body. This torque is counteracted by an opposing force produced by passing a current through a coil wound on the dumb-bell. The current is continuously and automatically maintained by electronic circuitry at the value needed to balance the initial torque. Hence, the current is proportional to the magnetic susceptibility of the sample gas and therefore to the oxygen content.

Applications

It is necessary to set the measuring tube of the Magnos analyser horizontally (Figure 4.45) otherwise in the absence of oxygen, ie 'magnetic draught', there would be an ascensional current in the tube and consequently the measurement would not be zero. The analyser is provided with a level and a regulator screw clearly marked for levelling. It must be firmly fixed to a vertical wall. It is essential to adjust for the mean local barometric pressure when commissioning the analyser. It is necessary also to fit filters, flame traps at the inlet and the outlet (to atmosphere) of the gas, and a water separator in some cases. Because the composition of the gaseous mixture may affect the measurement, the analyser must be calibrated against a standard.

The Servomex analyser is hardly affected by tilting. As the analyser reading is directly proportional to the pressure in the measuring cell, it is important that no restriction is inserted between the cell and atmosphere. Calibration with air automatically compensates for any change in barometric pressure.

Characteristics of Magnos Analyser

Manufacturer:	Hartmann & Braun (GFR)
Dimensions:	Length 380 mm, depth 180 mm, height 380 mm
Weight:	≈ 28 kg
Construction:	Flameproof
Power supply:	220 or 110 volts. Constant voltage transformer delivers 220 V a. c. for the thermostat and 12 V d. c. for the measuring circuit
Measuring scale:	0 to 3, 5, 6, 10, 21, 50, 100 % by volume
Minimum scale:	0 to 2 %
No. of measuring scales:	Two
Measuring error:	$\leqq \pm$ 2 % of full scale
Sensitivity of analyser:	1 % of full scale
Maximum temperature of measured gas:	4 K below that of thermostat
Average gas flow rate in the chamber:	8 to 16 ml/s
Gas pressure:	maximum: 100 kPa minimum: 2 kPa (otherwise pump required)

Characteristics of Servomex Analyser

Manufacturer:	Taylor Servomex (UK)
Dimensions:	Length 305 mm, depth 203 mm, height 216 mm
Weight:	7.7 kg
Construction:	Intrinsically Safe to BASEEFA Standard No. SFA 3007 Class 2a, 2c, 2d and 2e

Power supply:	220 or 110 volts, or others and battery
Measuring scale:	Switched 0 to 10, 0 to 25 and 0 to 100 % oxygen
Minimum scale:	0 to 10 %
No. of measuring scales:	Two
Measuring error:	± 1 % of span on each range
Sensitivity of analyser:	± 0.2 % Oxygen
Maximum temperature of measured gas:	Up to 373 K for limited periods
Average gas flow rate in the chamber:	0 to 2.5 ml/s
Gas pressure:	atmospheric

1.2.4 Flow Measurement

For flow measurement above ground, direct measurements are given by a meter, and indirect measurements by orifice plates.

1.2.4.1 Fluxi Gas Meter

Principle (Figure 4.46)

The Fluxi meter consists essentially of a turbine 1 which is installed in the gas stream and coupled to a counter 2. The turbine is located between upstream and downstream guide vanes 3 within a liner 4 which makes the meter independent of pipe profile. An opposing aerodynamic arrangement 5 and 6 associated with the turbine makes the accuracy independent of pressure and density. The magnetic

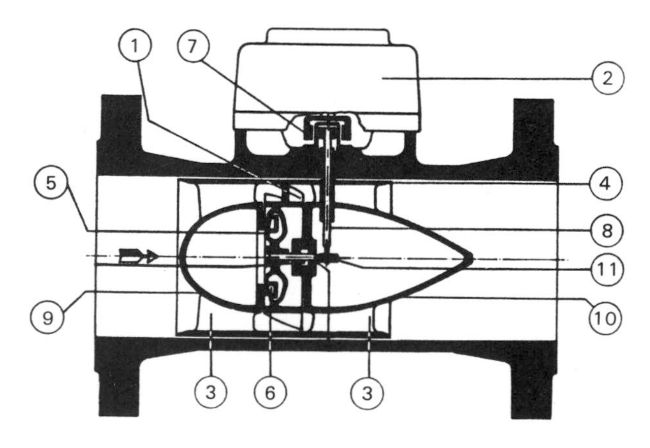

Fig. 4.46 Sectional Drawing of Fluxi Gas Meter.

transmission 7 and 8 is shielded from dust, thereby reducing the frequency of maintenance. The two fairings 9 and 10 reduce the resistance and improve the aerodynamic shape. The upstream fairing produces an aerodynamic restriction. The downstream fairing protects the turbine spindle bearings and gearing 11.

Remote Transmission of Volume Flow Rates

In this case, the counter comprises a low frequency transmitter (frequency less than or equal to 1 Hz) consisting of a thin flexible plate, placed in a sealed glass bulb. The signal is made to cross the bulb by a magnet.

Remote Transmission of Instantaneous Flow

The counter is fitted with a high frequency oscillator which converts the incoming frequency to direct current which in turn is proportional to the instantaneous flow over the whole range of the counters.

Applications

The meter can be installed in any horizontal pipe. For vertical pipes of larger size, special measures are necessary.

The counter must be protected against dust by a filter. If there is a risk of condensation, vertical mounting is advisable. The installation requires to be planned to avoid any liquid running through the meter, eg by installation at a high point, by the use of water traps, etc.

The instrument can be used for temperatures between 243 and 323 K.

Characteristics

Manufacturer:	Schlumberger (France)
Maximum Flow:	70 to 1800 l/s
Pressure Loss:	40 to 60 Pa (density 0.8 kg/m^3)
Advantages:	compact, accurate

The counter may be orientated by hand and has a seven figure digital display, a socket for the remote transmission unit and a mechanical take-off facility for a flexible cable to connect to a correcting unit.

1.2.4.2 Teleperm M 730 Transmitter with Orifice Plate

Principle (Figure 4.47)

A metallic capsule 1 contains a membrane which is deflected by the pressure difference to be measured, causing the lever 3 to pivot, rotating the small lever 7 about a point fixed with respect to the transformer 6, and by further levers, withdrawing the induction core 10 from the permanent magnet 11.

The core 10 is electrically controlled by the transformer 6 via the amplifier 12. This arrangement causes the equilibrium of the system to be re-established as described below.

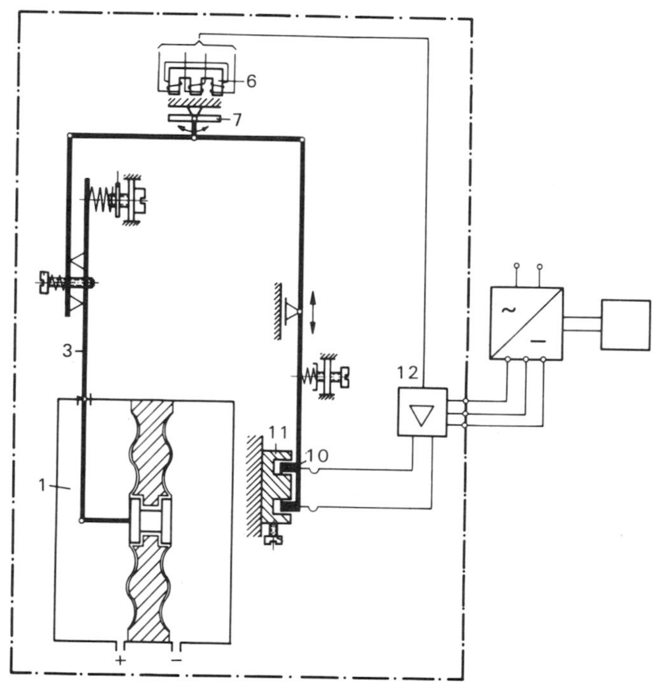

Fig. 4.47 Schematic Diagram of the Teleperm M 730 Differential Pressure Transmitter.

Movement of the small lever 7 causes voltage changes in the secondary windings located in the lateral limbs of the transformer 6 (the primary ones are located in the centre limb) causing a continuous current to flow through the amplifier 12, proportional to the pressure difference to be measured.

This continuous current tends to strengthen the core 10. At a certain stage, equilibrium is reached between the pressure difference exerted through the lever 3 and the reaction on 10 due to the transformer 6.

The magnitude of the direct current at equilibrium is a measure of the applied pressure difference.

Applications

It is used to measure differential pressure across orifice plates for flow measurement. It can be used for indication and recording of flow rates, with an additional special squares or square root facility.

Characteristics

Manufacturer:	Siemens (GFR)
Dimensions:	Height 228 mm, breadth 372 mm, depth 402 mm
Measuring ranges:	0.4 to 2.0, 1.5 to 6.0 kPa or 2.5 to 15, 5 to 64, 50 to 200 kPa
Output:	0 to 20 mA

1.2.4.3 Differential Pressure Transmitter TEC 5 QB

Principle

The principle is the same as that described in Section 1.2.1.3. As the differential pressure to be measured may be very small, the measuring

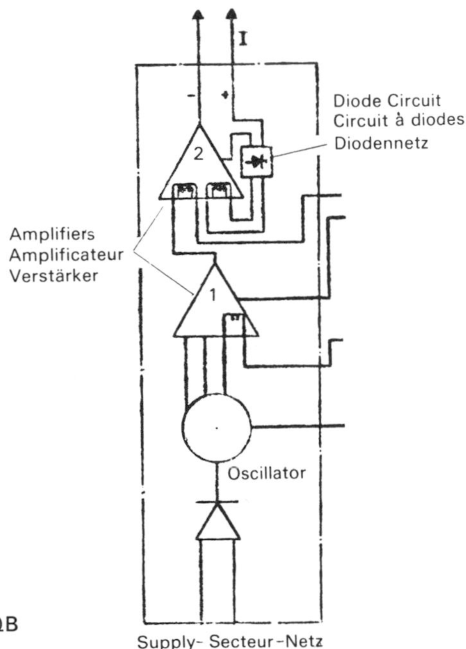

Fig. 4.48 Diagram of the TEC 5 QB Differential Pressure Transmitter.

element is made very sensitive and range adjustments may be made by an adjusting screw.

The transmitter, connected across an orifice plate in the pipe, gives a signal proportional to flow by means of an operational amplifier (Figure 4.48) with a square root output.

Application

The device is used, mainly in France, to measure flow at an orifice plate in surface installations.

It must be fixed in a vertical position.

Characteristics

Manufacturer:	Schlumberger (France)
Weight:	Transmitter: 15 kg Amplifier: 2 kg
Measuring ranges:	Type PdB1: 0.5 to 2.5 kPa Type PdB2: 0.15 to 1.0 kPa
Maximum Static pressure:	200 kPa
Output:	0 to 10 mA d. c. with a maximum load resistance of 2500 ohms (1500 $\pm$ 1000 ohms)
Supply:	d. c. 48 V (also available 24 V) a. c. 127 V, 220 V, 50 Hz (60 Hz also available)
Consumption:	8 VA
Measuring cell:	Mylar diaphragm
Use:	Gases only
Ambient temperature:	253 to 333 K

Zero adjustment $\pm$ 5 kPa independent of pressure difference in three distinct ranges: 0 to $\pm$ 0.5 kPa; $\pm$ 0.5 to $\pm$ 2.0 kPa; $\pm$ 2.0 to $\pm$ 5.0 kPa.

1.2.4.4 Furness Controls Differential Pressure Transmitter Type 050 for Orifice Plates and Venturi Tubes

This small sensitive pressure transmitter, described in Section 1.2.1.5, is used at surface firedamp utilisation plants for the measurement and monitoring of drained gas flow. The ranges are usually 0 to 0.5 kPa or 0 to 2 kPa, differential pressure, the flow ranges depending on orifice or venturi sizes.

1.2.5 Calorific Value or Density of the Gas

1.2.5.1 Reineke Calorimeter (Model 66)

Principle

A given quantity of water is heated by burning a known quantity of gas. The rise in temperature of the water is measured and the calorific

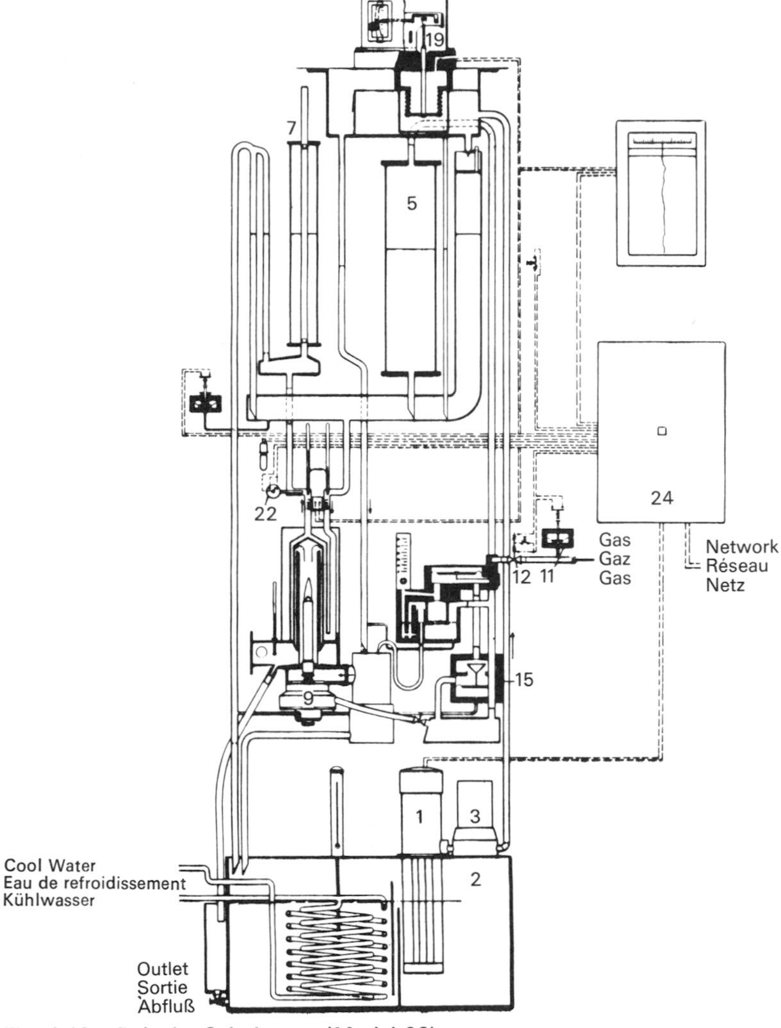

Fig. 4.49 Reineke Calorimeter (Model 66).

value of the gas calculated (in MJ/m^3 under standard conditions). The water is subsequently cooled in a heat exchanger.

Figure 4.49 shows the water circuit which includes a pump 1, a filter 3, a gas burette 5, a water burette 7, a heat exchanger 2 and the burner 9, with compensation for the relative density of the gas and a supplementary supply of gas 15 to maintain the flame between measurements. It also shows the calculator 19, which converts to calorific value and the safety arrangements including the gas pressure controller 11, a magnetic valve 12 which closes the inlet of gas in case of a power supply failure, and a contact thermometer 22 which cuts off the gas if the water circulation or the recooling stop, or if the flame is extinguished.

Application

It is used for the measurement of calorific value of gas at surface extraction plants in Germany and France.

Characteristics

Manufacturer:	Reineke (GFR)
Dimensions:	2000 mm height, 1600 mm breadth, 530 mm depth
Gas Pressure:	0.7 to 2.5 kPa
Gas Consumption:	19 to 28 ml/s
Water Pressure:	100 to 600 kPa
Water Flow:	42 ml/s
Maximum content in gas	
of sulphur:	200 mg/m^3
of hydrogen sulphide:	2 mg/m^3

This apparatus, which employs a naked flame must be kept under close surveillance.

1.2.5.2 Sigma Calorimeter

Principle

The products of combustion of drained gas (burnt at constant flow rate) reach the atmosphere after passing through the interior of a steel tube, itself surrounded by another tube: these tubes are joined at the base. The upper extremity of the external tube is connected to the instrument case whilst that of the inner tube is connected to a mechanism which amplifies the difference in expansion between the tubes.

In these conditions the difference in expansion is a direct function of the calorific value of the gas. A variation in ambient temperature has the same effect on the two tubes.

A very sensitive regulator (a bell-shaped cover in an oil bath, inside a closed chamber) compensates for variations in density, pressure and temperature of the gas.

Application

It is used in the UK in surface extraction plants, only when drained gas is sold to an external customer.

Characteristics

Manufacturer:	Sigma Instrument Co Ltd, (UK)
Dimensions:	1200 mm height, 380 mm breadth, 300 mm depth
Gas Flow Rate:	Corresponding to normal constant flow rate of 50 ml/s (100 kPa, 288 K)
Gas Pressure:	0.25 kPa at the outlet of the first regulator; then adjusted by the sensitive regulator
Range of Measurement:	3 to 37 MJ/m^3 (under normal conditions)
Recorder:	By mechanically driven chart (6.25; 12.5; 25.4 mm/h)

When the calorific value falls below 15 MJ/m^3 the instrument sounds an alarm and shuts off delivery of gas to the customer.

1.2.5.3 Debro Densimeter

The density of firedamp depends on its composition and may be used to determine the methane concentration in drained gas. Density decreases as the calorific value of firedamp rises, and follows an exponential law which may be established statistically from measurements.

Principle

In a centrifugal fan, the outlet pressure is proportional to the density of gas moved. The outlet pressure also depends on the fan speed and the gas density varies with ambient pressure and temperature. Corrections to a measurement for relative density of firedamp must be adjusted for pressure and temperature of the air used for comparison, and brought to a common fan speed.

The Debro Densimeter (Figure 4.50) uses two centrifugal fans mounted on the same motor shaft, one of which runs in air and the other in gas which is at the same temperature, has been previously

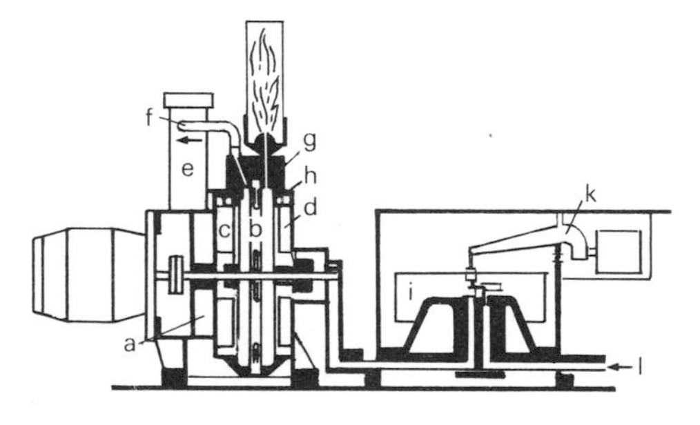

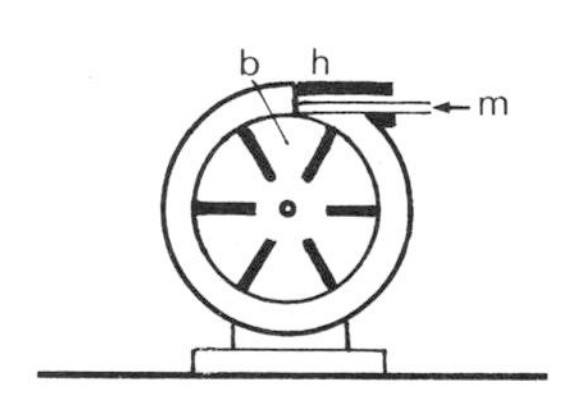

a Air inlet — Entrée d'air — Rücklufteintritt
b Centrifugal Fan — Ventilateur centrifuge — Flügelrad
c Centrifugal Fan (Air) — Ventilateur centrifuge (air) — Flügelrad (Luft)
d Centrifugal Fan (Gas) — Ventilateur centrifuge (gaz) — Flügelrad (Gas)
e Air Dryer — Sécheur d'air — Lufttrockner
f Return Air — Echappement de l'air — Luftrückführung
g Intermediate Chamber — Chambre à gaz intermédiaire — Gaszwischenkammer
h Sensing Head — Capteur — Meßsonde
i Regulating Bell — Cloche régulatrice — Reglerglocke
k Suction Regulator — Réglage de l'aspiration — Saugregler
l Gas inlet — Entrée du gaz — Gaseintritt
m Connection to Density Recorder — Raccordement à l'enregistreur de densité — Zum Dichteschreiber

Fig. 4.50 Diagram of Debro Densimeter.

dried and is at the same inlet pressure (atmospheric). The two delivery pressures (Figure 4.51) act on a balance comprising two bell-shaped chambers submerged in oil. At equilibrium:

$$\frac{p_1}{p_2} = \frac{b'}{a'} = \frac{\text{density of firedamp}}{\text{density of air}} = \text{relative density of firedamp} \quad . \quad [4.13]$$

Variations in ambient pressure and temperature or in fan speed have the same effect on the firedamp as on the air: the equation therefore still applies.

The scale of the recorder is made linear by means of a cam.

Application

The Densimeter is used in surface installations in France (Bassin du Nord). No correction is necessary.

Calibration

It is sufficient to measure the outlet pressures of gas and air using a water manometer; the measurements taken are then compared with those of the instrument.

Characteristics

Manufacturer:	Debro Messtechnik (GFR)
Dimensions:	1450 mm length, 600 mm breadth, 910 mm height
The instrument is fixed	on a frame.
Weight:	100 kg
Maximum inlet pressure:	1.5 kPa gauge
Centrifugal pressure:	0.5 to 1.0 kPa
Gas consumption:	7 ml/s
Relative density measurable:	between 0.1 and 2.5
Accuracy:	+ 1 % of full scale
Measurement:	continuous
Fan motor:	synchronous, flameproof
Balance oil:	7 litres of 'spindle' oil

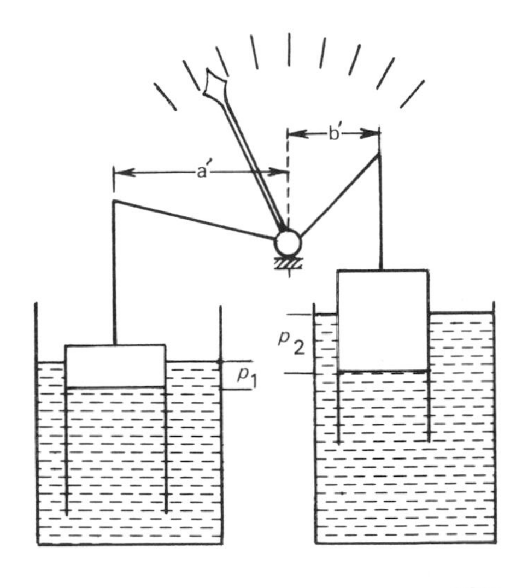

Fig. 4.51 Diagram of the Pressure Balance in the Debro Densimeter.

Recorder:	220 V synchronous motor or 7 day clockwork movement
	chart width: 120 mm
	chart speed: 20 mm/h
	calibrated in relative density (dimensionless): the density in kg/m^3 is obtained by multiplying the relative density by 1.293.
Remote transmission:	electric or pneumatic
Driers:	filled with calcium chloride, renewed every two months for gas; for air in closed circuit renewal practically unnecessary.

1.2.6 Other Monitoring and Control Devices

1.2.6.1 Vacuostat (Figure 4.52)

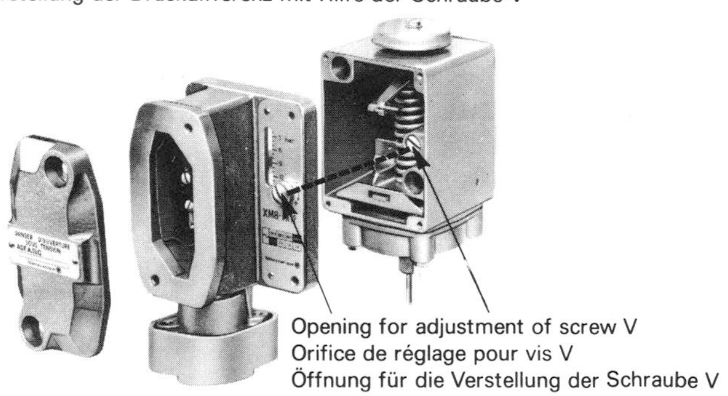

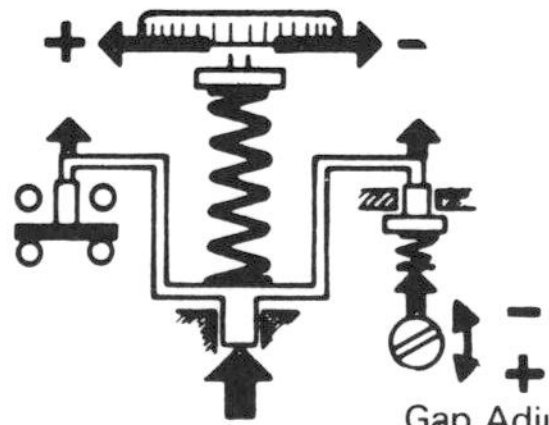

Fig. 4.52 Vacuostat Cut-off and Alarm for Suction.

Principle

When the suction exceeds a pre-set adjustable value, a valve is opened and an electrical contact broken.

Application

The apparatus can provide a general alarm or cut-off of power in case of abnormal suction below a reference level, which is set by adjustment.

Characteristics

Type:	XM8-E
Manufacturer:	Télémecanique (France)
Maximum positive pressure:	+ 100 kPa
Range of setting reference pressure:	— 8 to + 100 kPa
Range of suction for alarm or cut-off adjustable from:	— 6 to — 16.5 kPa

1.2.6.2 Sieger 1350 Atmospheric Alarm (Figure 4.53)

Principle

A Wheatstone bridge is used, operating on the catalytic combustion principle, and measures low methane concentrations in air (Section 1.1.3.5).

Application

It is used for monitoring methane concentrations in the atmosphere in and around the surface extractor plant and to alarm and stop the plant if atmospheric methane concentrations exceed prescribed values, usually about 0.5 % methane.

Characteristics

Manufacturer:	Sieger (UK)
Dimensions:	500 mm width, 400 mm height, 400 mm depth
Construction:	Modular with up to 8 IS detector heads
Measuring range:	0 to 5 % methane

Control unit has a maximum of 8 channels which are used for surveillance of the environment inside the extractor house, in cable ducts, over the external water sumps for surface water seal extractor pumps, near the optical benches of industrial infra-red analysers, rarely in

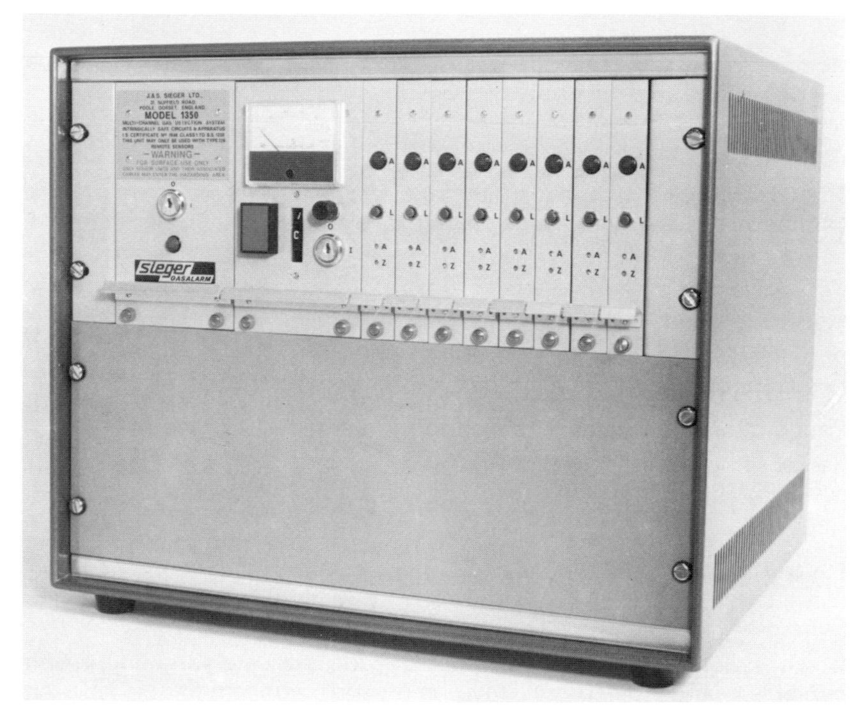

Fig. 4.53 Sieger 1350 Atmospheric Alarm.

Sigma calorimeter rooms, and in the vicinity of certain gas pipes in utilisation plants.

Equipment includes meter, alarm, detector for safety faults, calibration device, testing facilities and individual channel controls.

1.2.7 Remote Monitoring and Control Systems

1.2.7.0 Introduction

These installations collect, process and present at the surface data received from many parts of the mine.

A central station, such as those described below is of great value for the following reasons.

a) It allows the stages of evolution of drainage to be followed continuously at numerous positions, and in particular it allows instantaneous measurement of the effect of changes (regulation by valves, etc.) at all control points and rapid detection of anomalies such as pipe fractures, water blockages, and abnormal pressure losses.

b) It facilitates the organisation and supervision of firedamp drainage service work prior to going underground, the priority of the work frequently being assisted by recorder and/or visual display data.

c) It allows the overall situation to be assessed at the central station by comparing drainage readings with those of general body methane concentration and ventilation from particular parts of the mine. When problems arise it enables assessments to be made as to whether solutions can be found using the firedamp drainage system.

d) It provides a means of assessing system effectiveness and particularly in finding the optimum suction, because data are available on pure methane flow rates, at constant pressure and temperature conditions, giving the conditions of the gas in the pipes.

e) It permits certain on/off and control functions to be achieved.

Such central systems include the CERCHAR central telemethanometry system, the centralised remote control TCC or SCI, with tricapteurs, Time Division Multiplexing (TDM) systems, central Tube Bundle systems and in certain cases systems incorporating underground measuring instruments connected to recorders in a room at the surface. Certain of these central systems such as TCC and TDM can be connected to visual display units, printers, mini-computers and micro-processors.

1.2.7.1 Centralised Telecontrol for Drainage (TCC)

It comprises one module, or more, which interrogates on a cyclic basis the various tricapteurs each of which is provided with a 'coding station'.

Module type ASC 72 B (Figure 4.54)

This model has a local power supply and is self contained with regard to interrogation and recording.

It possesses a telephone connection to the measuring point, call buttons, controller and a loudspeaker (shown at the top of Figure 4.54) and a measuring unit whose principal function is to house the three meters which indicate suction Δp (0 to 40 kPa), methane concentration c (0 to 100 %) and velocity w (with 2 scales, 0 to 9 or 0 to 20 m/s). It also has a switch for manual measurements, a power supply unit (bottom left on the figure) with an on-off switch ("M—A") and five channels (bottom right of the figure) comprising a push button for each of the parameters Δp, c and w, an on-off switch and another switch for selecting velocity range.

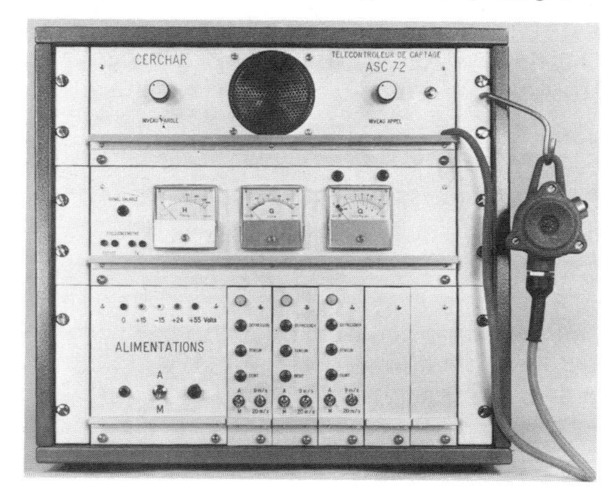

H = Δp
G = c
Q = w

Fig. 4.54 Drainage Centralised Telecontrol (TCC) Module ASC 72B.

Characteristics of the Module

Manufacturer: CERCHAR (France)

Dimensions: 620 mm breadth, 600 mm height, 450 mm depth

Each module deals with five tricapteurs (Section 1.1.5); other monitors can also be handled.

Power supply: 220 V

Coder (Figure 4.34)

The Coder has three connections, one to the tricapteur, a second to the transmission line from the four-wire TCC or to an intermediate station with the more common two-wire transmission system, and a third for a telephone to the TCC. The latter is only suitable for the direct 4-wire transmission system, otherwise the facility has to be provided through an intermediate station. The electronic circuitry of the coder is powered through four wires: the polarity applied to those wires determines which parameter is measured, suction, concentration or flow. This circuitry also powers the thermistors and gives a frequency code to the measurement.

Coder Characteristics

Manufacturer: CERCHAR (France)

Dimensions: 350 mm length, 120 mm breadth, 70 mm height

Weight: 2 kg

Operation of the Unit

Between interrogations, the TCC supplies a current of 30 mA on the line which charges the batteries of the intermediate stations and provides permanent heating of the thermistors. During interrogations, depending on the strength and direction of the signal detected, the intermediate station applies the polarity corresponding to the measurement of Δp, c or w to the coder. The TCC decodes the received frequency signal and displays it on the relevant meter and recorder where appropriate. An interrogation cycle usually takes 4 minutes although 2 minute cycles are sometimes employed.

The flow of pure methane is obtained by multiplying the measured velocity of the pure methane in m/s by a coefficient K, given in Figures 4.55 and 4.56, for the appropriate pipe diameter. Because the flow measurement is only accurate within a certain range of velocities and concentrations in the pipe, it is necessary to choose the nozzle carefully. The velocity must always be kept below 15 m/s using a

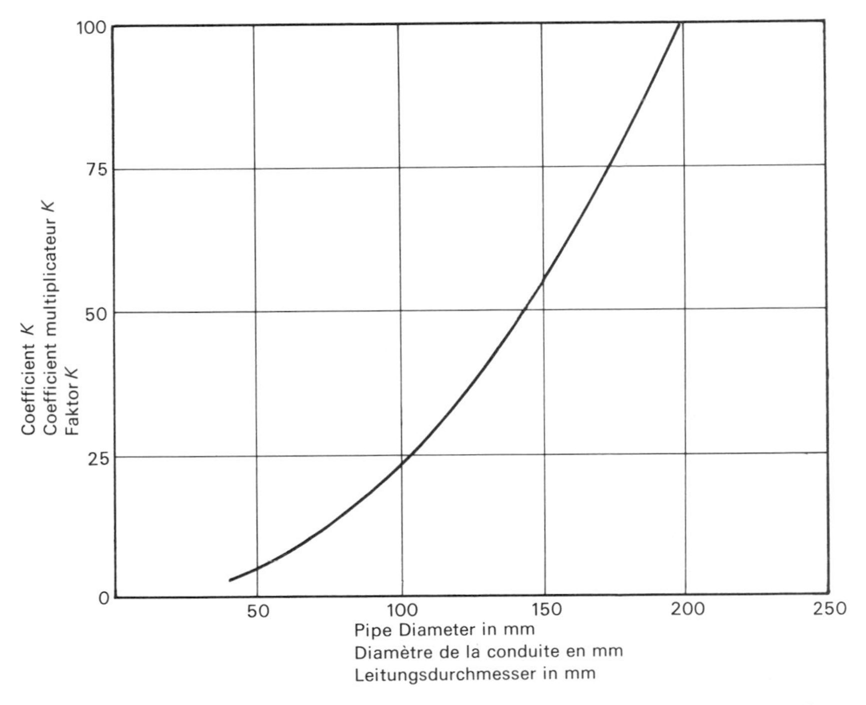

Fig. 4.55 Curve to determine the Coefficient K for a Tricapteur to obtain flow rate in m^3/h in smaller pipes.

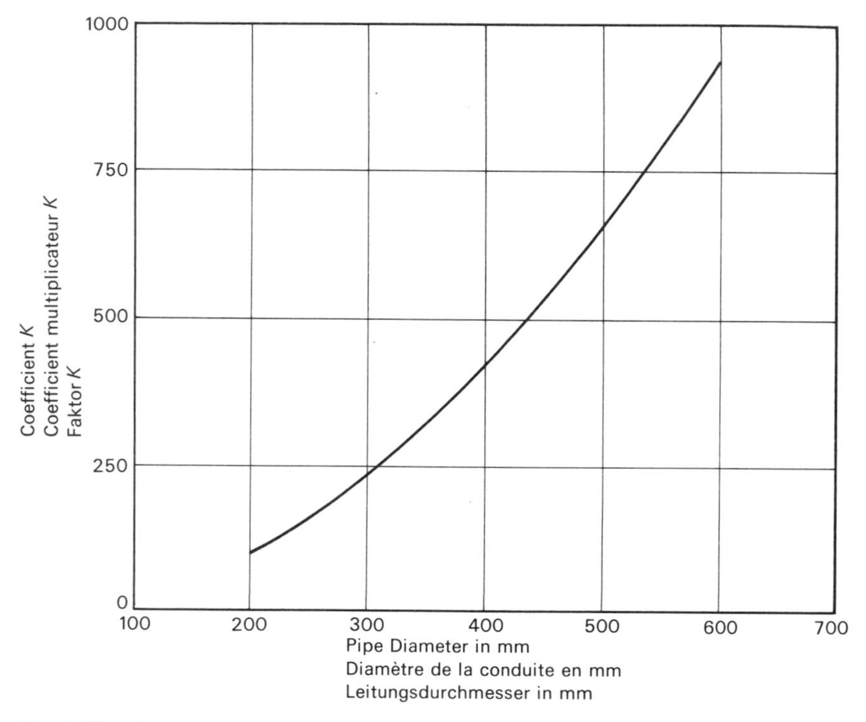

Fig. 4.56 Curve to determine the Coefficient *K* for a Tricapteur to obtain flow rate in m^3/h in larger pipes.

larger diameter pipe at the measuring position if necessary. For an accurate measurement, corrections must be applied to the indicated reading (Figure 4.57). For example if values of methane concentration of 65% and indicated velocity (from meter) of 10 m/s were to be plotted on Figure 4.57 a point would be found between the 10 and 11 m/s lines of constant actual velocity. By interpolation the true velocity is found to be 10.2 m/s. It is important to note that this chart is only applicable between certain concentrations, which in the given example lies between lower limits of 30 and 55%, depending on the indicated velocity, and an upper limit of 90% methane.

1.2.7.2 System SCI 76

This unit provides the interface between the tricapteur and the Funke and Huster TF 24 system which transmits the output signals from the mine to the surface.

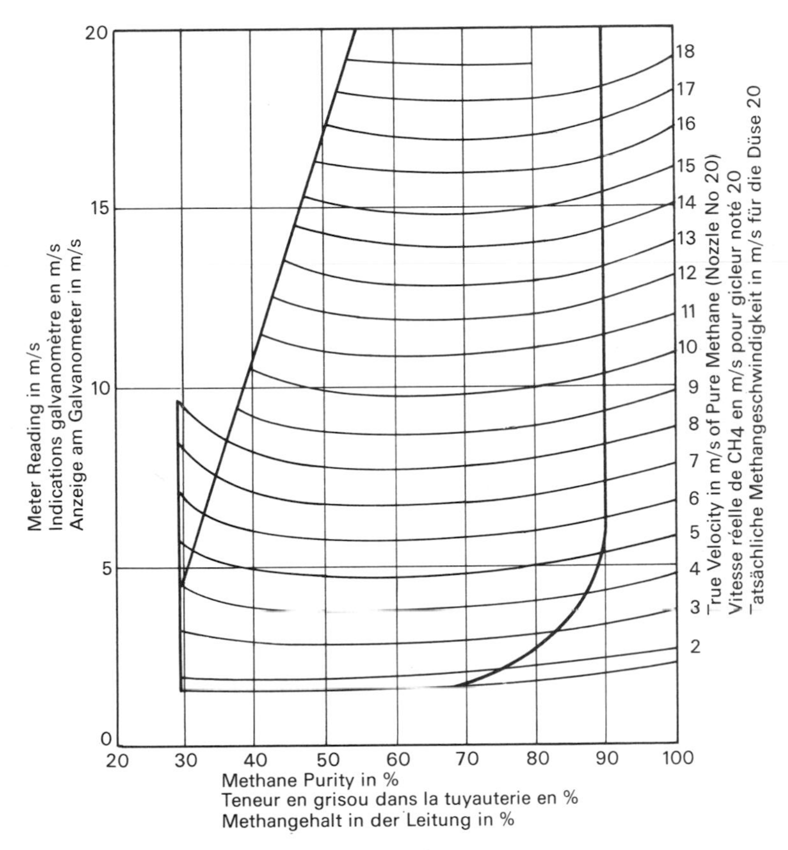

Fig. 4.57 Purity Correction Curves for a Tricapteur.

Principle

During interrogation, a constant current is fed to the tricapteur reference thermistors, the supply current *I* to the measuring thermistor being adjusted until its resistance is restored to the reference value. The current I then represents the value of the parameter being measured. An amplifier circuit gives a 0 to 10 V signal on any 2 of the 4 connections of the TF 24 transmission system according to the parameter being transmitted.

Underground, the system provides a station for power supply, measurement and transmission for each tricapteur, as well as a charger.

Power Supply and Measuring Station (Figure 4.58)

This station is connected to the tricapteur, the charger and the transmission system. It consists of a continuously recharged battery supplying power to the whole station and providing the heating current for the tricapteur thermistors. The stations also contains the electronic clock controlling the interrogation cycle.

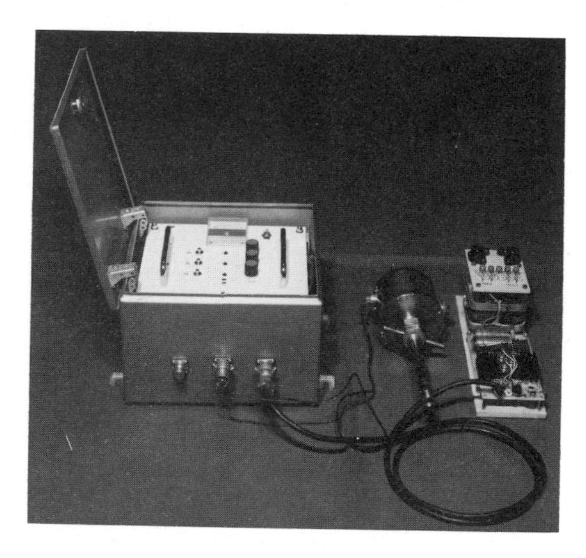

Fig. 4.58 Power Supply and Outstation for the System SCI 76.

The front panel of the station has 3 buttons, for interrogation of the three parameters, each of which overrides the interrogation cycle. There is also a meter which displays the measurement when the button is pressed, together with 3 potentiometers for zero adjustment and an on-off switch.

Characteristics

Approval:	Intrinsically Safe (Belgium)
Manufacturer:	CERCHAR (France)
Life of charged battery:	14 h
Interrogation cycle:	4 min 30 s, made up of 7.5 s for interrogating each parameter at set intervals of 93.5 s, 77 s and 77 s.

Charging Station

It supplies the necessary charging current for the station battery.

Characteristics

Approval: Intrinsically safe (Belgium)
Manufacturer: CERCHAR (France)
Power Supply: 550 or 220 V

It is in a flameproof enclosure. The maximum distance from the supply station is about 500 m.

1.2.7.3 Central Time Division Multiplexing (TDM) Systems
(Figures 4.59 and 4.60)

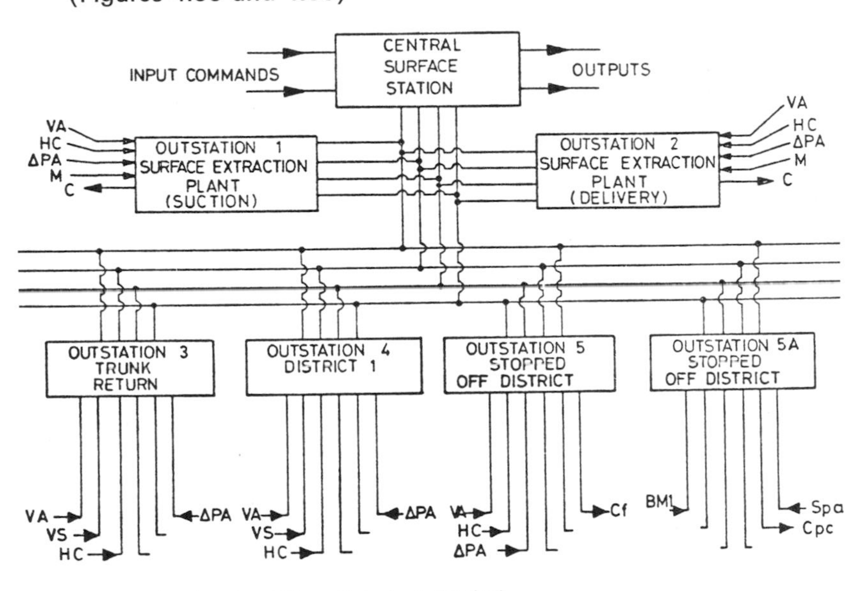

VA Vacuum (analogue) — Vide — Unterdruck (analog)
VS Vacuum Switch (on/off) — Interrupteur à vide — Unterdruckschalter (ein/aus)
ΔPA Differential Pressure (flow) (analogue) — Pression différentielle (débit) (analogique) — Differenzdruck (Volumenstrom) (analog)
HC High Concentration Methane Monitor — Méthanomètre hautes teneurs — Methanmeßgerät für hohe Konzentration
M Multi Head Methane Monitor — Méthanomètre multiple — Mehrfach-Methanmeßgerät
Cf Drained flow Command and Control — Contrôle et surveillance du débit capté — Steuerung und Überwachung des abgesaugten Volumenstromes
BM1 Single Head Methane Monitor (analogue) — Méthanomètre simple (analogique) — Einfach-Methanmeßgerät (analog)
Spa Differential Pressure — Pression différentielle (chambre d'équilibrage — Differenzdruck an einer Druckausgleichskammer
Cpc Pressure Balance Control — Commande de l'équilibrage — Druckausgleichssteuerung

Fig. 4.59 Block Diagram of TDM System for Remote Monitoring and Control of a Firedamp Drainage System.

Fig. 4.60 Surface Control Room for a TDM Monitoring System Incorporating Firedamp Drainage.

Principle

The system consists of a central station, on the surface, from which all the underground and surface outstations are interrogated in turn.

Outstations

The outstations receive from the transducers on/off or standard 0 to 2 V analogue signals which they convert to digital form for transmission purposes. They can also receive commands from the central station.

They are mains powered, with a battery standbye in some cases, and are connected in parallel to the main transmission cable.

There are two types of outstation.

a) If control is not required, an intrinsically safe outstation is used, which contains a number of printed circuit boards to which the incoming transmission line and transducer inputs are connected.

b) If control is needed, a flameproof section is included in the outstation which incorporates a transformer, rectifier and main pilot relay to which is connected a 110 V supply and a contactor panel pilot circuit.

Data transmission and processing

Data are transmitted by modulated electrical pulses on demand from the shift register (on the surface) itself driven by an electronic clock and controlled by a pre-programmed minicomputer.

Each outstation has a unique address (digital code).

Data are presented on a programmed basis on visual display units (VDU) and printers and on demand provide reports on the operating condition of the firedamp drainage giving detailed suction, pressure and flow values and full analysis of drained gas. A secondary computer system may be used to store and process data, access to store being obtained on demand.

Applications

The TDM system provides complete monitoring of the most complex drainage systems. It has the advantage of being flexible (easily and quickly installed and extended). It can indicate alarms and faults and can be programmed to present data as required by mine management. Five such systems are in use (1976). It can also be adapted to Tube Bundle systems (Section 1.2.7.4) controlled by a microprocessor.

Characteristics

Approval: Intrinsically safe in UK

Manufacturers: Transmitton, Hawker-Siddeley Dynamics, Huwood Ltd, and Westinghouse Brake and Signal Company Ltd, (all UK)

Interrogation cycle: every 1 second or longer as required

Transmission distance: at least 13 km

1.2.7.4 Tube bundle system

Principle

At each measuring point in the atmosphere or in the firedamp drainage system, a gas sample is sucked through a tube by a vacuum pump to a surface station for analysis (Figure 4.61). Two tubes in armoured cable are joined in a junction box (Figure 4.62). These boxes also serve to connect several cables in one place, 5 (Figure 4.61) and are located at roadway junctions and intermediate points where long distances are involved.

The gas samples are analysed at the surface by an infra red analyser (principle: Section 1.2.2.2) in a sequence determined by the interrogation cycle. Samples can be analysed for constituent gases, particularly methane and carbon monoxide and results recorded on

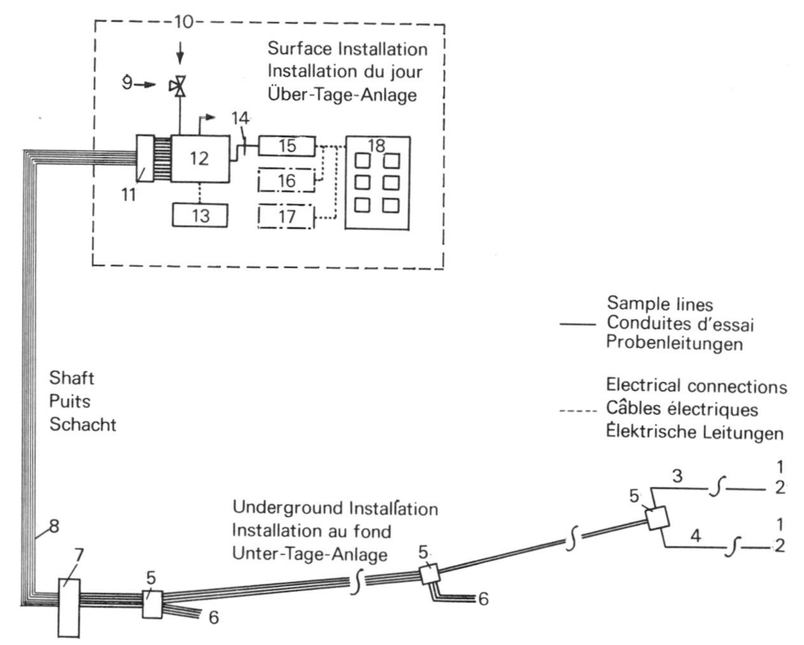

Fig. 4.61 Diagram of Tube Bundle Monitoring System.

chart. Paramagnetic analysers are used to determine oxygen concentrations (Section 1.2.3.2).

One of the most recent developments is a system driven by microprocessor, which has a two analyser tube bundle system to provide for up to 40 general body and 12 firedamp drainage sampling positions. Analytical data and operating status of the colliery equipment can be interrogated from a Regional Laboratory some 40 km away using the Datel 200 Modem method.

This system gives continuous routine drained gas sample results to laboratory standards, automatic warning of potentially dangerous conditions, display of all data (including alarm) on a VDU and by line printer, management information and automatic transfer of microcomputer data to a minicomputer driven system dedicated to the environment.

Automatic features cover analyser range change, zero check and reset, calibration, fault monitoring including methane in the analyser house and sampling flow rates, and automatic alarm data on VDU and line printer.

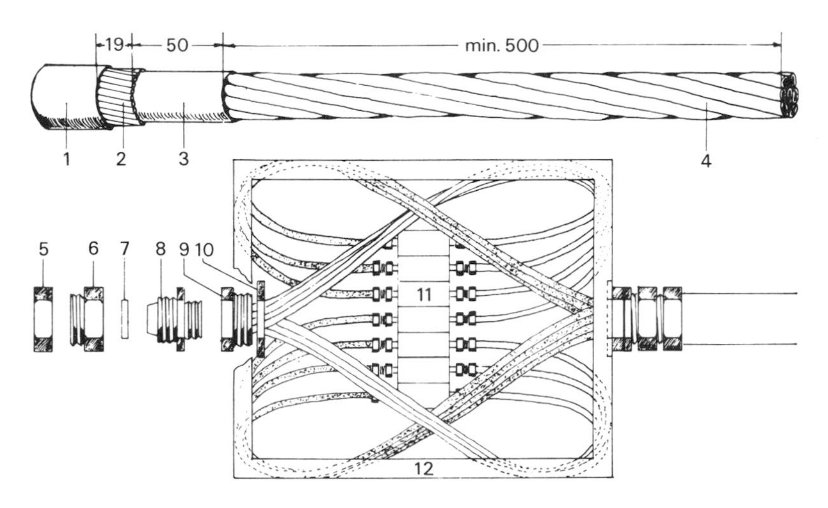

Fig. 4.62 Junction Box for Tube Bundle Monitoring System.

Applications

The tube bundle system is used to determine methane and other combustible gas concentrations in drained firedamp, at the outbye end of roadways, at the surface extraction plant and at stoppings. Sample tubes are connected to drainage pipes using the upstream tapping of an orifice plate.

Characteristics

The advantages include simplicity of the underground equipment and its installation, flexibility and no restrictions due to electrical regulations because the analysers are on the surface of the mine. Surface analysers are easier to maintain and in some cases can be checked from a remote laboratory, and are made rapidly available of drained gas results to colliery management.

Tubes: polyethylene with internal/external diameters 4.3/6.3 mm (for distances less than 3 km) or 6.3/9.4 mm.

Internal Tube Diameter in mm	Maximum number of tubes	Manufactured Lengths in m		
		Roadways		Shaft
		Normal	Maximum	Maximum
4.3	19	500	630	700
6.3	7	500	600	700

Pumps: small vacuum pumps, supplying the analysers in a particular sequence and regulated by valves.

Delays in analysis: as it is necessary to flush out a previous gas sample before accepting another, and as varying distances are involved, the

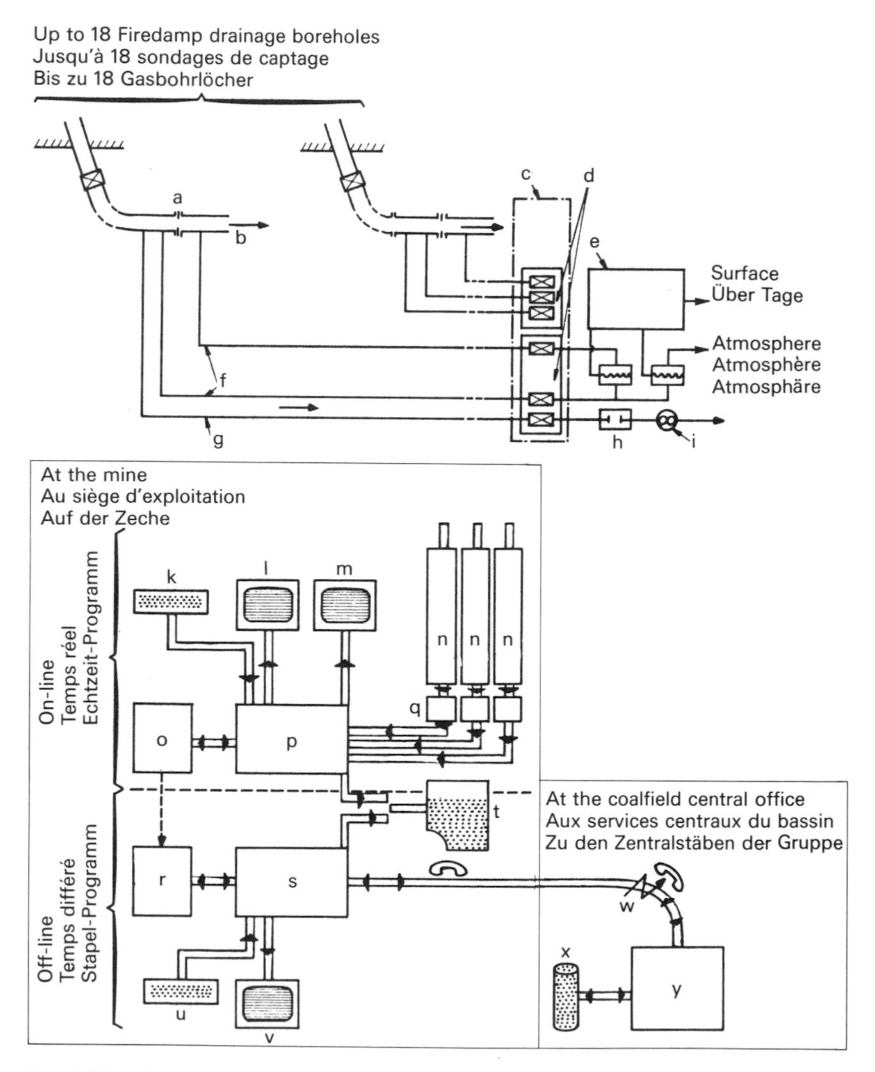

Fig. 4.63 Computer Controlled Firedamp Drainage Monitoring in the Nord Pas de Calais Coalfield. Above: Underground Layout. Below: Surface Layout.

time required to cover all sampling positions in a mine by one analyser usually ranges from 20 to 60 min depending on the distance and the internal diameter of the tube.

The system may have limitations in rapidly changing environmental situations.

1.2.7.5 Transmitted Firedamp Drainage Measurements coupled with a Computer

This system, which was commissioned at a colliery in the north of France in 1977 permits on-line monitoring of the firedamp drainage network and off-line processing of the drainage information. The arrangement for monitoring boreholes along a roadway is shown in Figure 4.63.

Legend for Fig. 4.63:

- a Orifice Plate — Diaphragme — Meßblende
- b To drainage range — Vers réseau — Zum Absaugnetz
- c Groups of electrically operated valves — Groupes d'électrovannes — Gruppen von Elektroventilen
- d Each group of three valves opened in turn — Electrovannes ouvertes cycliquement par groupes de 3 — Elektroventile, die zyklisch in 3er-Gruppen geöffnet werden
- e Outstation for transmission of suction and pressure difference (for calculation of flow) — Télétransmission des dépressions ou du débit (calcul éventuel du débit) — Fernübertragung der Unterdrücke oder des Volumenstromes (evtl. Berechnung des Volumenstromes)
- f Gas in equilibrium with that in the drainage range — Gaz statique en équilibre avec celui de la conduite de captage — Gas im Druckgleichgewicht mit demjenigen in der Absaugleitung
- g Smallflexible tubes (approx. 6 mm bore) — Petits tuyaux souples (diamètre intérieur ⋕ 6 mm) — Kleine elastische Rohre (Innendurchmesser $\approx$ 6 mm)
- h Purity measuring head — tête mesure teneur CH_4 — Meßkopf für Methangehalt
- i Pump — Pompe — Pumpe
- k Key board — Clavier Commande Système — Tastatur zur Systemsteuerung
- l VDU for messages — Ecran Affichage Messages — Bildschirm für Mitteilungen
- m VDU for alarms — Ecran Affichage Alarmes — Bildschirm für Alarmmeldungen
- n Three master stations Oldham CT 63/40 (Cerchar Licence) 120 lines connected to 120 heads underground — 3 Centraux télégrisoumétrie Oldham CT 63/40 Licence Cerchar = 120 lignes reliées aux 120 têtes disposées au fond — 3 Methan-Fernmeßzentralen Oldham CT 63/40, Lizenz Cerchar = 120 Adern zum Anschluß von 120 in der Grube verteilten Meßköpfen
- o 24 hour storage on discs — Stockage (24 h) données sur disque souple — Speicherung der Daten von 24 h auf Floppy Disc
- p Mini computer SPD 10/40 — Mini ordinateur SPD 10/40 CIT Transac — Kleinrechner SPD 10/40
- q Interfaces — Interfaces — Schnittstellen
- r 24 hour storage on discs — Disque souple avec stockage données sur 24 h — Floppy Disc mit gespeicherten Daten von 24 h
- s Mini Computer SPD 10/40 — Mini ordinateur — Kleinrechner SPD 10/40
- t Printer — Imprimante — Drucker
- u Key board — Clavier commande — Tastatur zur Steuerung
- v VDU — Ecran — Bildschirm
- w Connection by telephone — Liaison fil téléphonique — Verbindung über Telefonleitung
- x Files on discs — Fichier sur disque — Plattei
- y Central Computer IBM 370/55 — Ordinateur central du bassin IBM 370/55 — Zentraler Großrechner der Gruppe IBM 370/55

On-line monitoring (Figure 4.63) is achieved using a mini-computer, which receives information at the central station, and provides the following facilities.

a) Storage of information on floppy discs for 24 hours, applying corrections or calculations as appropriate (eg flow rate corrected for suction and purity).

b) Display of information on VDU of current underground data with location, covering on demand the state of the district or complete network, the purities at three points underground for the previous 100 minutes and shift or daily trends from three locations.

c) Selection and display of alarms when pre-selected levels are exceeded as programmed to give location and time, with audible and visual alarms.

d) Printing out on demand any of the above displays.

A second mini-computer is used for off-line data processing (Figure 4.63) which transfers the stored data from the previous 24 h to the central computer (IBM 370/55) once a day, enables existing programs to be modified, communicates with the central computer and carries out certain off-line processes including printing out of reports and other drainage management information (long term, weekly and monthly trends).

1.2.8 Calculators

The three calculators described in Appendix 4.3 facilitate drainage calculations.

2. Commissioning Networks, Connecting Boreholes and Extending Ranges

2.1 Commissioning Networks and Extending Ranges

When starting up a network for the first time (or after a long stoppage), particular attention needs to be given to situations where the gas pressures may be insufficient to overcome the column of air in the shafts. It may be necessary to put the drainage network into service progressively, starting with low suctions at the extractor and discharging directly to atmosphere. The utilisation side must be isolated from the extraction plant during this operation. The purity of drained gas should be monitored at the bottom of the shaft and on the surface during priming.

Once the shaft ranges are primed, buoyancy of the gas becomes operative, particularly for deep mines. An indication of the time required to prime a drainage system can be obtained from the total volume of the pipes and extraction rate.

When extending the range for connecting new boreholes, appropriate safety precautions should be taken. Certain countries have regulations on this matter (Appendix 4.4).

2.2 Connecting Boreholes

In general, connecting new boreholes reduces methane concentrations in air. The effect of connecting the first borehole in a district is shown in Figure 4.64. A new borehole is connected through a valve to pipework already added to the range. If there are already a number of productive boreholes in a district, it is necessary to ensure that there are sufficient valves along the range, particularly if a valve is not provided for each borehole (observe national regulations).

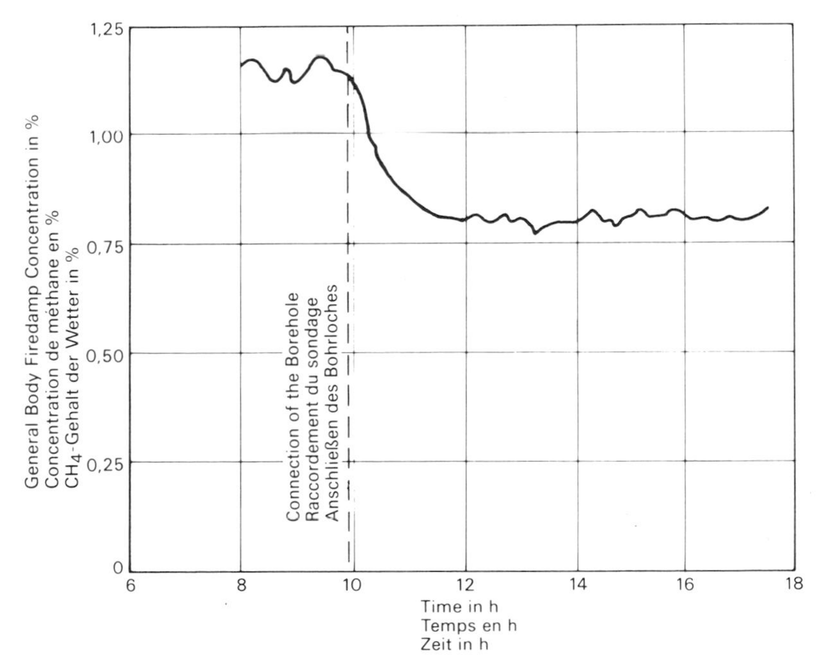

Fig. 4.64 Effect of the First Drainage Borehole on the General Body Firedamp Concentration.

3. Control of Suction

Suction is important as a sensitive means of controlling the concentration and flow in a range. Control of suction is achieved underground by means of valves and on the surface also by changing the number of extractors in service and/or by the use of a by-pass.

In a particular network, the drained flow increases when the suction is increased at a productive borehole, but the purity of gas may decrease as shown in Figure 4.65. In general a position is reached when the flow of pure methane attains a maximum value; thereafter additional suction serves only to increase air inleakage.

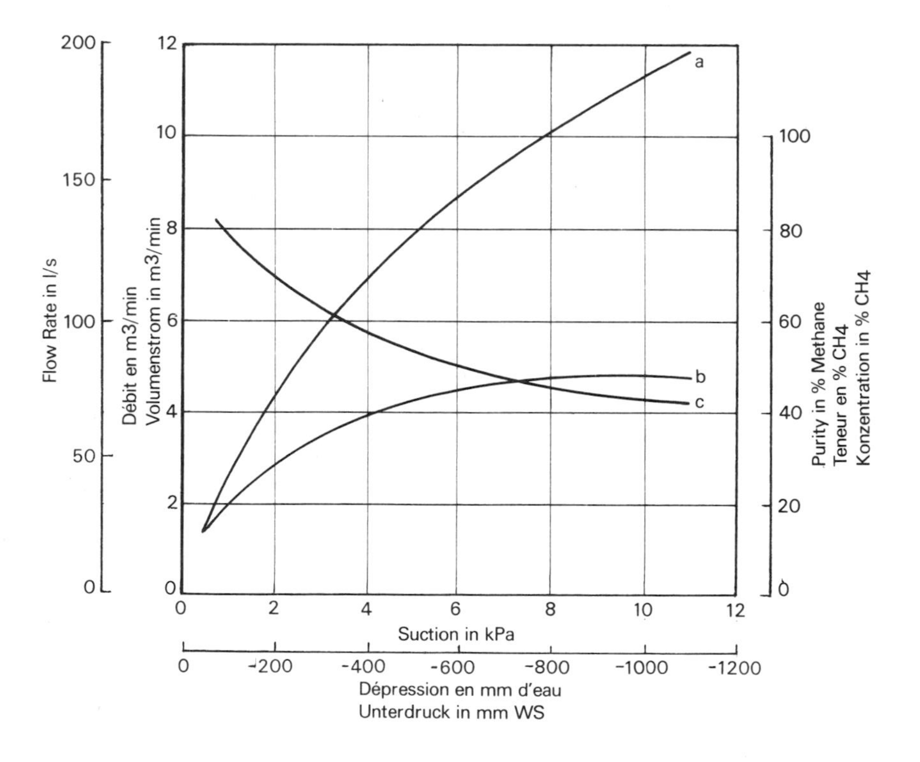

a Mixture Flow — Débit mélange — Gemischstrom
b Pure Methane Flow — Débit CH_4 — Methanstrom
c Purity — Teneur CH_4 — Methankonzentration

Fig. 4.65 Effect of Increasing Suction on Flow and Purity from a Borehole.

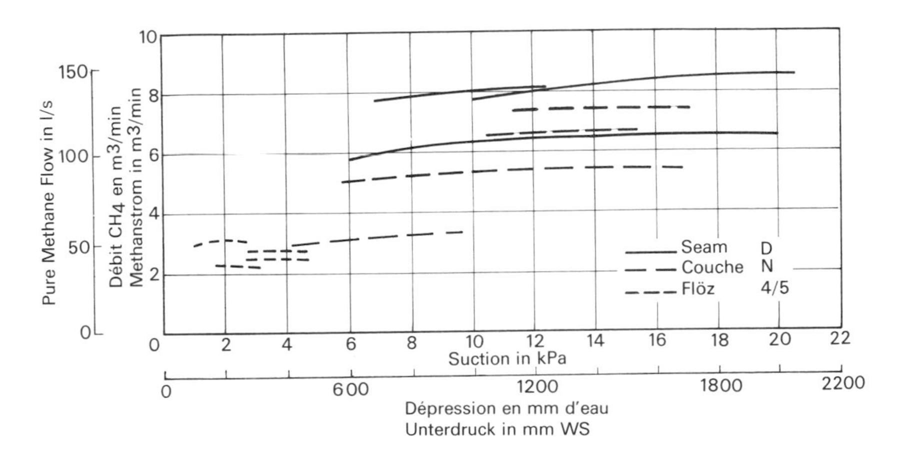

Fig. 4.66 Effect of Increasing Suction on Pure Methane Drained for three Districts.

Two conditions should be recognised:

▷ The suction must not be so high as to cause concentrations to fall to the explosive range. Certain Mining Regulations specify a lower limit of purity (Appendix 4.5).

▷ The suction must not be too low, otherwise some of the drainable gas may not be captured, which in turn may lead to increases in concentrations in air. This implies that the position of 'zero suction' should be well into the borehole.

In general, the suction necessary at a borehole increases with the drainable flow of pure methane (Figure 4.66). It also depends on a number of other factors such as the distance between boreholes, their diameter, flow and natural gas pressures. In general each district has an optimum range of suctions which results in a maximum flow of gas at an acceptable purity. Close control of the suction may sometimes give substantial increases in methane flow, up to 30 or 40 % in some cases. Generally, suctions at boreholes may be up to 10 kPa or more. Certain boreholes, usually those in the floor, may be under positive pressure. Occasionally short term advantages, such as reduced methane concentrations in air can be achieved by temporarily increasing the suction.

Particular note should be taken of the following points:

a) Control can be more difficult when districts being drained are remote from the extraction plant.

b) Control either locally or at the extraction plant may influence the suction at other points in the network but the magnitude of this is generally determined by the layout of the network and the relative position of the workings. For example, three districts in seams D, N and 4/5, were joined by a single drainage network (Figure 4.67). At 1600 h on 19 May 1971 drainage in district N was stopped by closing a valve, resulting in increased suctions in two other districts, and particularly in seam D as shown on the left of the figure. When the valve was re-opened at about 1630 h, the original situation was restored. On another occasion, a reduction of suction in district N on 1 June 1971 produced an increase in suction only in district D, as shown on the right of Figure 4.67.

c) To maintain acceptable concentrations and flow rates allowance needs to be made for the inertia of the system when adjusting district suction.

Because of the importance of suction, the effects of making significant adjustments in the system should be forecast using the network analytical methods (eg computer programs or drainage similators) described in Chapter 3. Close control of suction can be achieved by regulating each borehole. The optimum suction needs to be determined for each case. It is usually impracticable to compare two installations, because optimum values depend on too many factors.

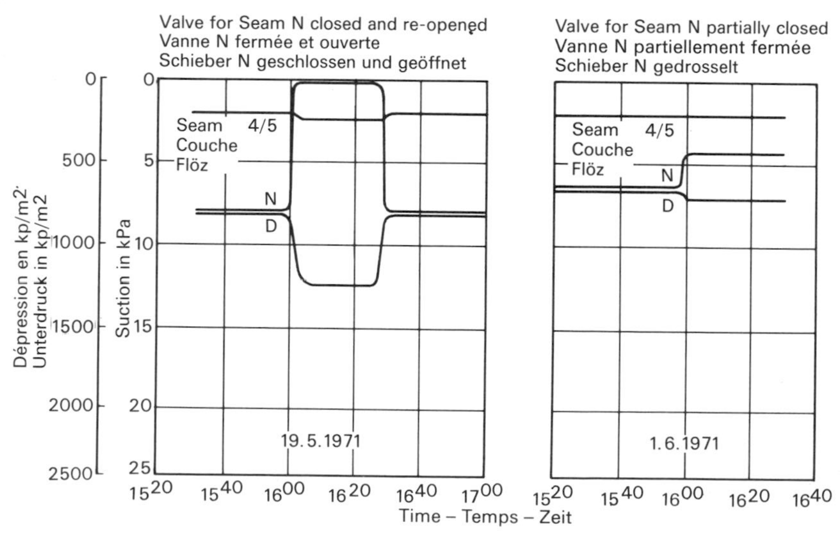

Fig. 4.67 Effect of Regulating a District Firedamp Drainage Suction on three other Districts.

4. Supervision of Network

4.1 Inleakage of Air

It is necessary to ensure that the network is as gas-tight as practicable because air inleakage affects the purity of drained gas. However, if there is leakage from a network under positive pressure, environmental conditions in a roadway may be affected.

4.1.1 Location of Air Inleakages

Abnormal inleakage of air is detected in the whole network by a fall in calorific value at the surface extraction plant (Section 1.2.5) and in district ranges by the fall in concentration, suction, or temperature (Sections 1.1.3, 1.1.1 and 1.1.6). The concentrations and flows can be measured in boreholes, and the positions of methane outflow or air inleakage located for example using the StBV probe (Section 1.1.7).

4.1.2 Leakage at Boreholes

The sealing of a borehole can be judged by its pressure, methane purity, and by probing. If it is well sealed, with the valve closed positive pressures can be measured which rarely exceed 20 kPa, but exceptionally may be 200 kPa in the de-stressed zone. This pressure is generally higher in floorholes, where strata are least fractured.

Inleakage of air can occur in a number of ways:

a) The standpipe seal may deteriorate by progressive opening of fissures around the mouth of the borehole or by the fracture of the standpipe itself.

b) The borehole may be cut off or blocked by strata movement.

c) Additional fissures may be produced for example by underworking, or working an adjacent panel in the same seam.

In case a) the remedial action consists of partially closing the valve, thereby reducing suction on the borehole and inleakage of air, and shutting off the borehole if necessary. However, if the yield has been significant, it may be worth repairing the seal and recommissioning the borehole (Chapter 2, Section 1.1.4.4 and Appendix 2.6). Sometimes, the injection pipe is left in the cement during sealing, and therefore recommissioning is simple. Otherwise it may be necessary to inject cement at a pressure of 1.2 to 1.5 MPa into two or three divergent holes around the borehole. Long standpipes are used in roofholes in the UK.

In case b) a blockage may be removed by inserting a string of rods in the borehole, using a drilling machine, bearing in mind borehole direction and the importance of diameter in weak ground (see Chapter 2, Section 1.1.3.1).

In case c) a second longer standpipe of smaller diameter may be inserted into the existing borehole. It may be necessary in certain cases to improve roadside packs to reduce the fracturing of lower roof and thereby produce a satisfactory seal.

4.1.3 Airtightness of Collecting Ranges

Faults may be due to a defective joint, or to an automatic water trap emptying and remaining open, particularly where sudden increases in suction in the range destroy the water seal. An empty water trap is quickly identified but inleakage of air at joints may be inaudible.

Valves should be located every 500 m or so and near each junction, especially at each branch to a section or a district. A defect may be identified, easily isolated, and corrected, by checking methane concentrations systematically (Chapter 3, Section 3.5) between districts and the shafts.

4.2 Plugs of Water

Plugs of water, because they move about, cause significant and rapid changes in the useful cross-section of the pipe, causing fluctuations in drained gas flow and local variations in pressure.

To detect such rapid changes, it is necessary to use sensitive (low inertia) instruments, providing instantaneous rather then integrated measurements.

Flow is the essential parameter in detecting plugs of water (Figures 4.68 and 4.69).

Suction measurements can also provide information in certain cases, such as over a short length, but in other cases suction pressures may only vary a little, as for example at the beginning of a long roadway. In serious cases, plugs of water can cause reductions in drained gas flows and increases in methane concentration in the general body.

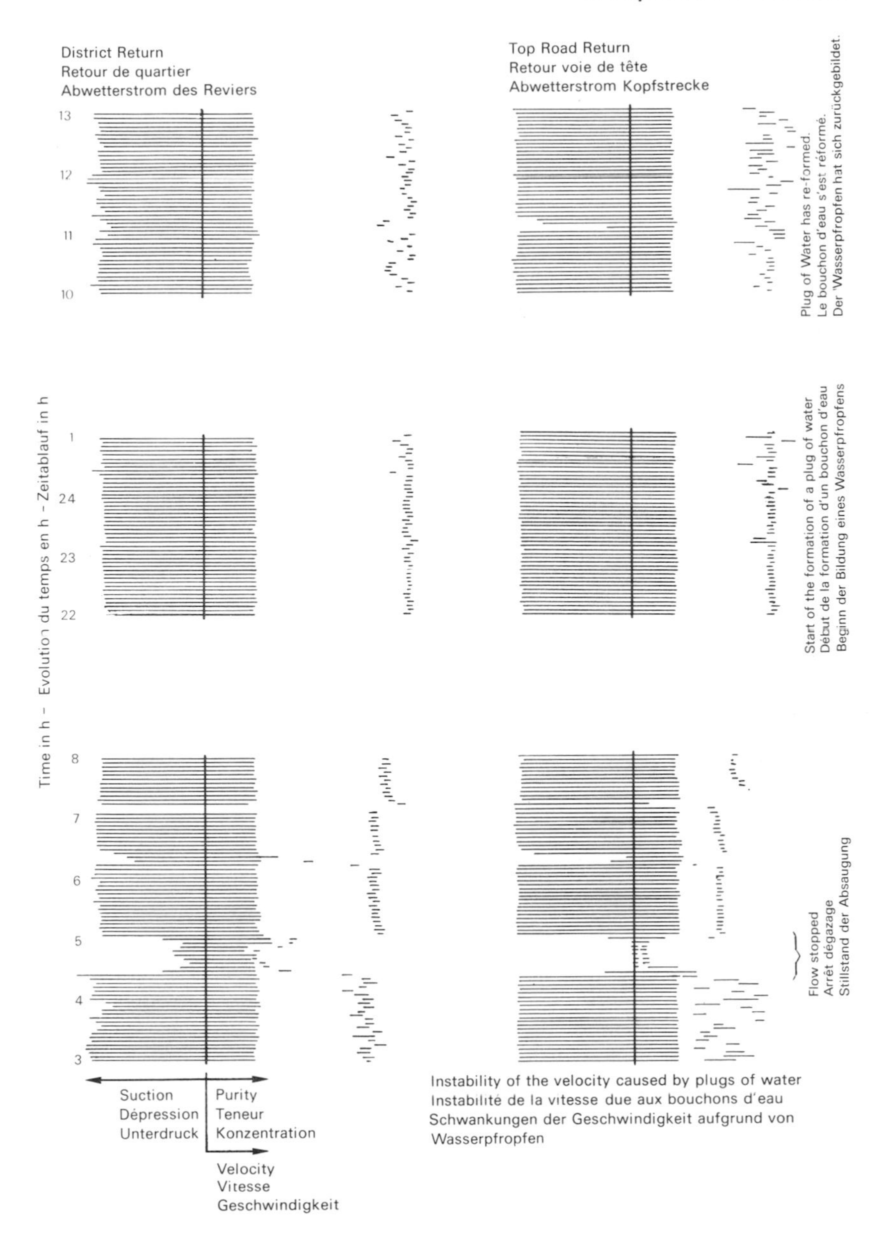

Fig. 4.68 Detection of Water Blockage in a Firedamp Drainage Range.

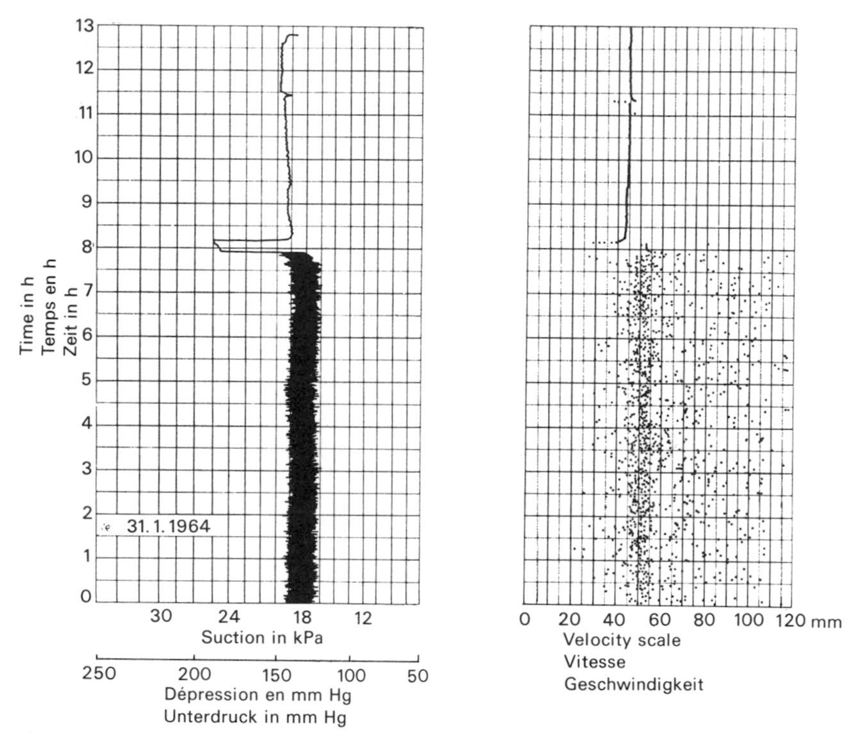

Fig. 4.69 Suction and Velocity Recordings in a Firedamp Drainage Range with Water Blockage.

5. Particular Situations

This section draws attention to a number of difficult points.

a) Drilling and Connecting Boreholes: Methane concentrations in return air may increase unless new boreholes are connected to the range immediately drilling is completed.

b) Interruptions to Drainage: In the event of an interruption to drainage, gas concentrations in air may increase and necessary steps must then be taken to maintain safety. Two typical results for a district are given in Figure 4.70. After drainage was stopped, a quantity of methane equivalent to the drained flow passed into the ventilation, and this caused methane concentrations to increase to a maximum. After drainage was restarted, methane concentrations decreased rapidly following an exponential curve (Appendix 4.6).

Plugs of water can also interrupt drainage with similar effects (Figure 4.71).

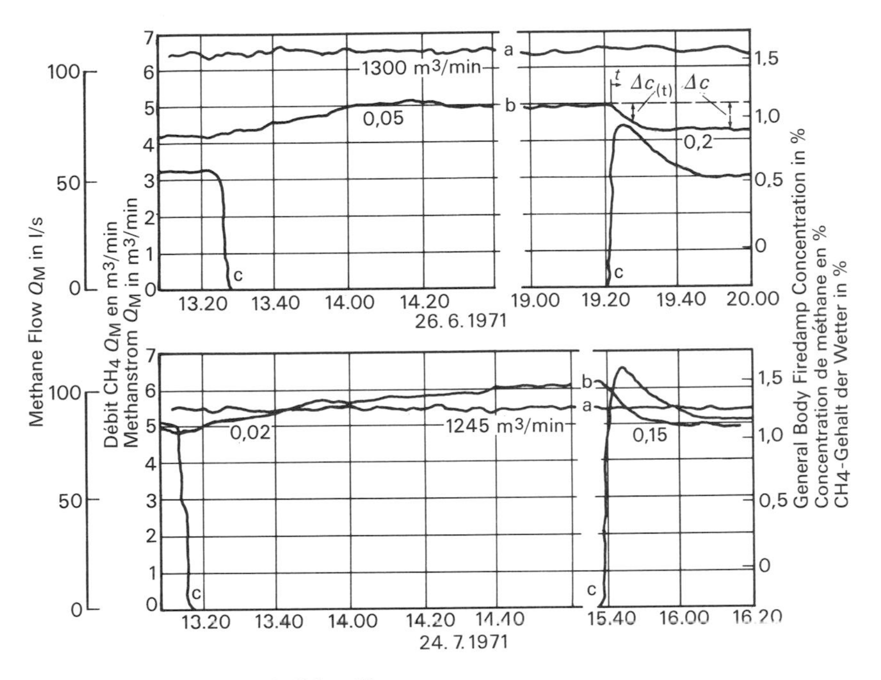

Fig. 4.70 Effect on General Body Firedamp Concentration of Stopping and Restarting the Drainage.

c) Interruption of Ventilation with Drainage Operating: When a fan stops (Figure 4.72) the rise in absolute pressure in the roadways causes a reduction in methane concentrations in air (reduced suction on and pressure gradients across the waste) and in the drainage. During the actual stoppage, these effects decrease. However, when the ventilation is restored, air pressures fall quickly in the return airway causing methane concentrations to rise in the air and sometimes also in the drainage system. The situation then rapidly returns to normal. Drainage should be maintained when main booster or auxiliary fans are stopped.

d) General Power Failure (stoppage of fan and drainage): Surface drainage plant should be restarted before the fan.

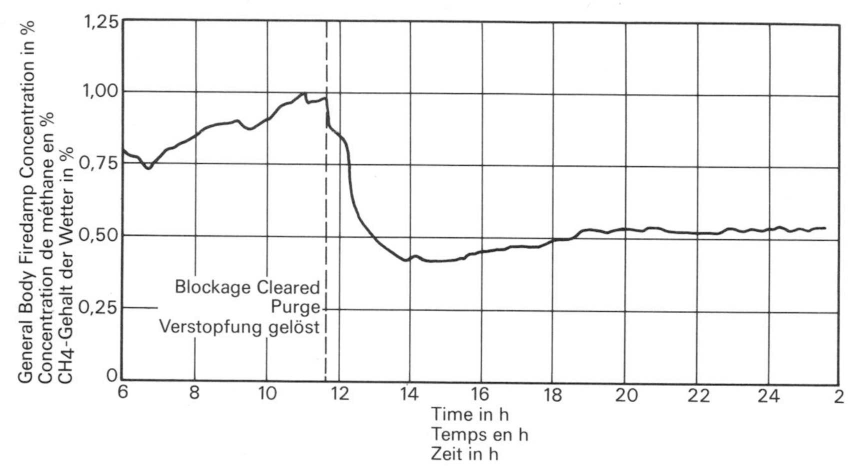

Fig. 4.71 Effect on the General Body Firedamp Concentration of Removing a Water Blockage in the Drainage Range.

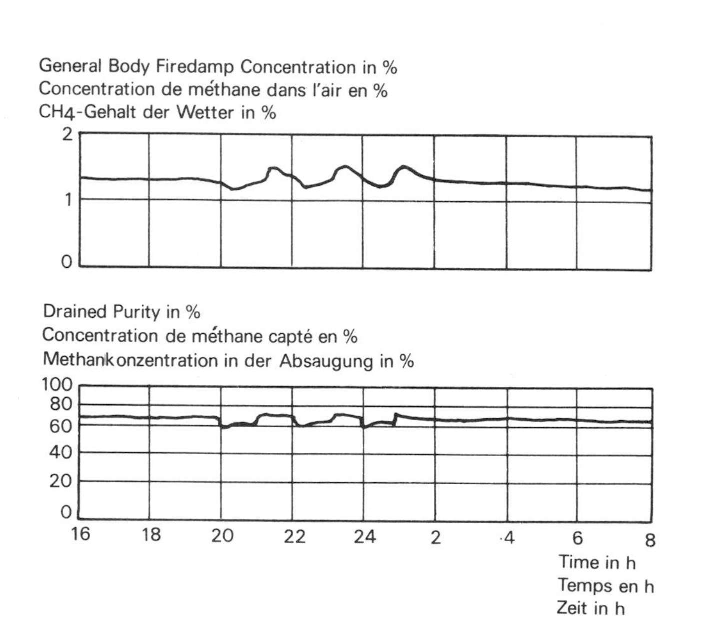

Fig. 4.72 Effect of Fan Stoppage on Drained Purity and General Body Concentration.

6. Drainage Experience

6.1 Factors Influencing Drainage

6.1.1 Applied Suction

The effects of applied suction have already been discussed in Section 3 (Figure 4.65).

6.1.2 Variations in Barometric Pressure

These effects may be difficult to identify since they depend on the case. Ideally if the network was airtight, barometric pressure would have very little effect on methane concentrations, especially where high suctions (of the order of 10 kPa) were applied to boreholes. In practice, however, barometric pressure has a variable influence where suction pressures are low or moderate. In periods of rapid rise in barometric pressure, marked reductions in drained pure methane flow rates have been observed whereas rapid decreases in barometric pressure have the opposite effect.

Variations in barometric pressure are particularly important in drainage from old workings, where applied suctions are generally small. In certain applications, drainage is not operated except in the case of rapid falls in barometric pressure (Chapter 2, Sections 2 and 2.1).

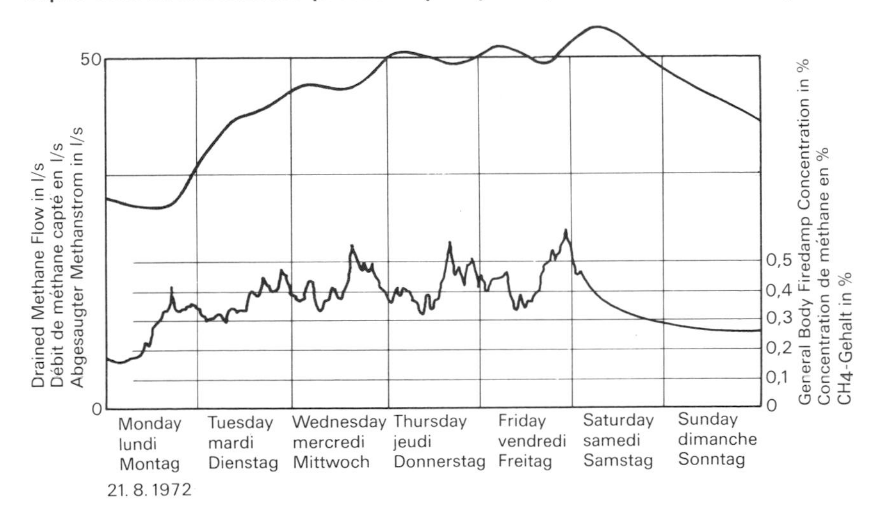

Fig. 4.73 Effect of Production Cycle on Firedamp Drainage and General Body Concentration.

6.1.3 District Coal Production

The coal production cycle, with its characteristic peaks of output, evolution during the week and interruption at the week-end, influences methane emitted into the air stream, and to a lesser extent the flow of drained methane.

In Figure 4.73 the lower curve shows variations in general body methane concentrations in the return of a district working three shifts. Well known daily peaks associated with the cutting cycle can be clearly picked out, as well as the general increase in level during the week and the decrease at the week-end.

The coal cutting cycle also affects the pure methane flow in drained gas (Figure 4.73 upper curve). A daily maximum can be seen here also,

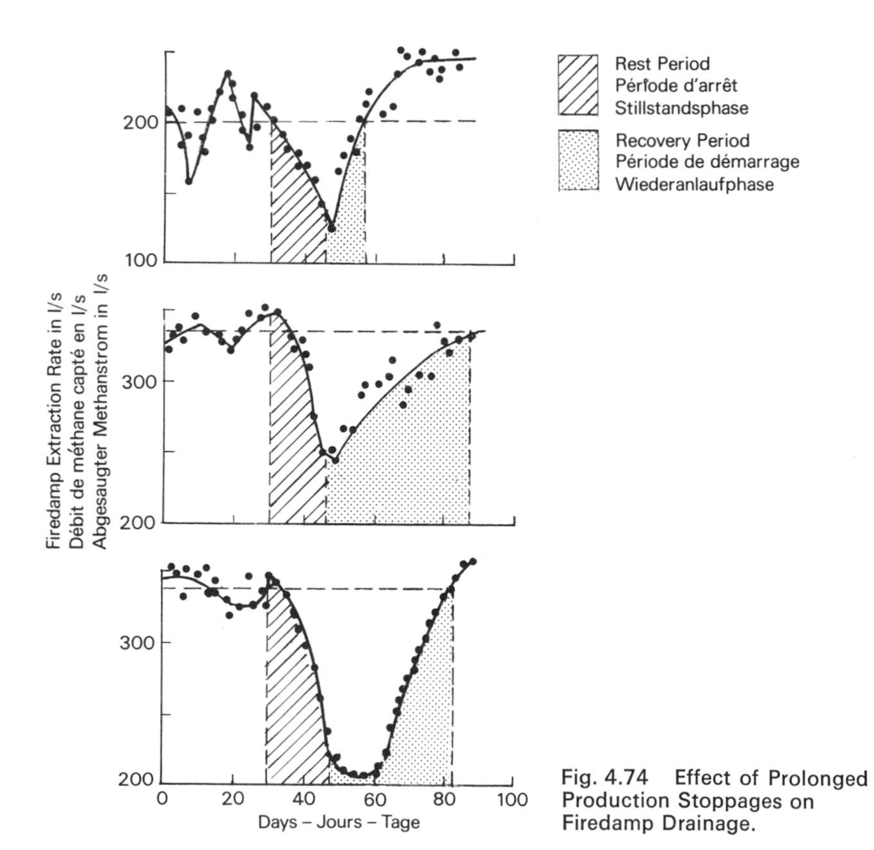

Fig. 4.74 Effect of Prolonged Production Stoppages on Firedamp Drainage.

but is not so pronounced and is delayed relative to peak methane concentrations in air. Variations over the week are also evident.

Weekend stoppages of production mainly affect mines with moderate firedamp emission and drainage flow rates; the effects are smaller in gassier mines with intensive drainage systems.

During prolonged stoppages (annual holidays, for example) methane concentrations and flows of drained gas are modified considerably (Figure 4.74), mainly when there are no floorholes or few of them. The effects vary from mine to mine, and they depend on a number of factors (Appendix 4.7).

6.1.4 Length of Boreholes

The length of borehole depends essentially on the positions of beds emitting gas and low permeability rocks where present (see Chapter 1, Sections 3 and 4 and Chapter 2, Section 1.1.3). In this regard, attention is drawn to the use of the special borehole probe described in Section 1.1.7 which enables easier identification of seams emitting firedamp. Long boreholes may tap gas which would not have reached the district through natural fissures as is suggested in cases where the total emission in a district is higher with drainage than without it.

6.1.5 De-stressing of Strata

The flow of gas is generally much greater from a de-stressed zone than from an undisturbed zone (Chapter 1, Section 3.3). Quiescent boreholes can be reactivated when workings pass underneath them. Borehole flows are less uniform in sandstone formations where fracturing of beds due to working is sporadic and de-stressed zones change suddenly.

6.2 Some Characteristic Features of Drainage in a District

6.2.1 Drainage Flow Rates

These flow rates depend on the characteristic gassiness of rocks. A maximum flow of 140 l/s of pure methane from 6 to 8 boreholes is typical of many districts. Exceptional cases can be quoted as for example a borehole 350 m from the face giving only a methane flow of 4 l/s but a shut-off pressure of 17 kPa.

6.2.2 Actual Effectiveness of Drainage

This parameter has been defined in Chapter 1, Section 4.2.

In numerous cases the actual effectiveness of drainage is considered satisfactory if 50 per cent capture is obtained over a long period. Capture values of 80 per cent have been obtained in a double unit district with 3 roadways (Figure 2.5 of Chapter 2) and of over 90 per cent in formations liable to spontaneous emissions.

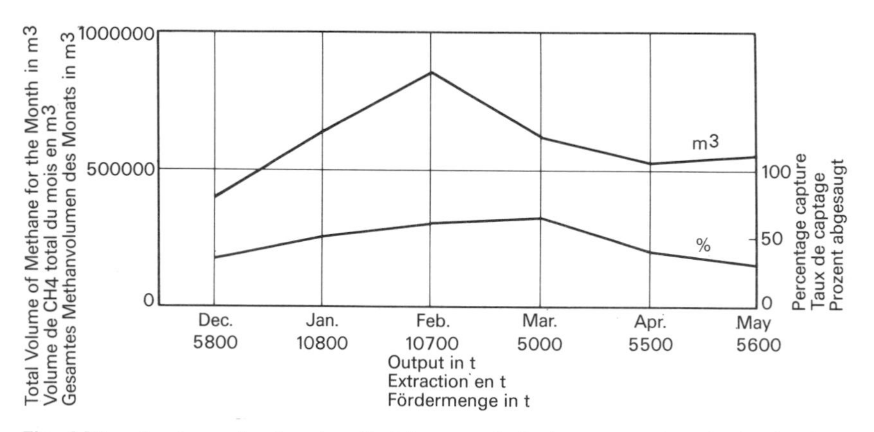

Fig. 4.75 An Example showing that Improved Drainage can be obtained when necessary during Increased Production.

Drainage results may not always reflect the full drainage potential as in general systems are not refined any more than is necessary. It is often possible to improve performance when required, as for example by increasing the number of boreholes. In the example shown in Figure 4.75 drainage in the working was raised to a maximum between December and March during a period of increased coal output.

6.3 Flow Characteristics of Boreholes

Two parameters can be important:

a) The mean quantity of methane drained per borehole varies widely and has ranged between 20 000 and 350 000 m^3/borehole.

b) The quantity of methane drained per metre length during the life of each borehole depends on a number of factors such as strata, length and diameter of boreholes. The range of values can be wide and has varied between 400 and 3600 m^3/m.

Both parameters can be used to compare borehole performance.

6.4 Evolution of Drainage Systems

The number of productive boreholes in a district is usually the same for a given system and regular relaxed zones. Connecting up a new borehole increases the flow initially but subsequently the flow reduces (Figure 4.76) until the next borehole is connected. The decline in drained flow rates shown in the figure for January and February 1970 was due to a stoppage of coal production.

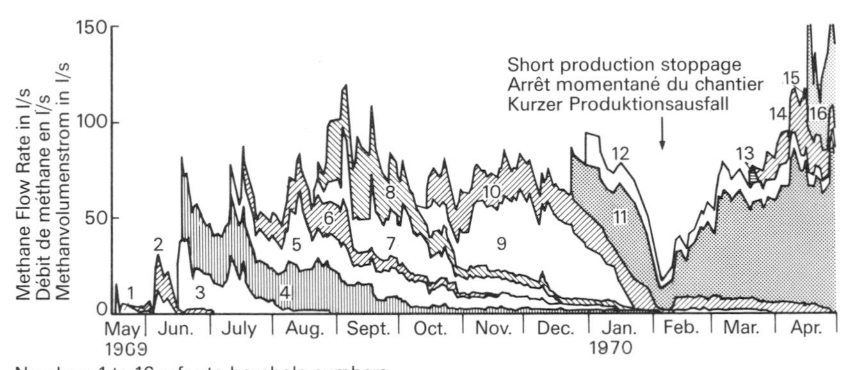

Numbers 1 to 16 refer to borehole numbers.
Les numéros 1 à 16 sont les numéros des sondages.
Die Zahlen 1 bis 16 geben die Bohrlochnummern an.

Fig. 4.76 Borehole and Total Drainage Flow Rates for the First Year in the Life of a District.

6.5 Costs

The costs of a new installation include:

a) The surface extraction plant, which may belong to the colliery or to a distribution company.

b) Main pipe ranges and fittings.

c) Installation of pipes and fittings in shafts and main roadways.

d) Drilling machines, drill rods, bits, standpipes and borehole equipment.

e) Pumps for wet drilling.

These costs depend on a number of factors: depth of shaft, remoteness and number of districts, pipe diameters, method of monitoring and control of the system, etc.

A modern surface installation may cost between £ 100 000 and £ 400 000, depending on size and complexity. This figure could be doubled if underground costs were included.

Around 50 % of running costs may be for salaries and social charges, 45 % for materials (boreholes, extractors, pipes, etc.) and 5 % for energy.

The return on schemes is variable and depends on standing and other charges and particularly the total extraction rate. Gas drained principally for safety reasons, can also provide a valuable source of energy (Chapter 5).

Appendix 4.1

Interferometers

A 4.1.1 Taking the Sample

The interferometer cannot be relied on for direct samples from the range, because the suction falsifies the reading.

Example:

- ▷ Pipe suction 0.49 kPa
- ▷ True concentration 70 % CH_4
- ▷ Actual reading 60 % CH_4

The difference between actual reading and true concentration increases with suction.

The preferred method is by sampling at positive pressure using the arrangement shown in Figure 4.17 with a modified squeeze bulb.

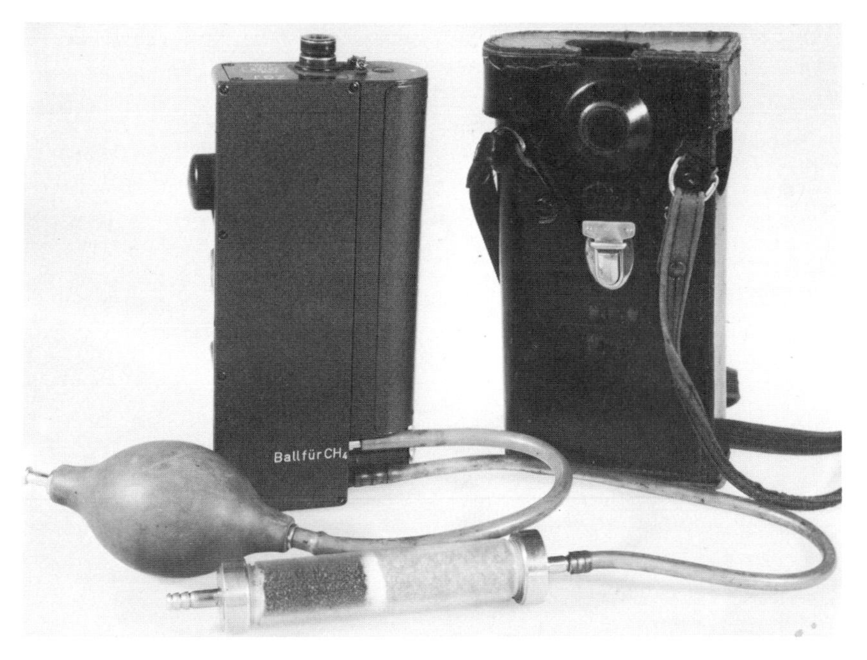

Fig. A 4.1.1 Interferometer with Carbon Dioxide Absorbant.

A 4.1.2 Nitrogen Correction

Because the refractive index of nitrogen is very close to that of air, no correction is necessary.

A 4.1.3 Carbon Dioxide Correction

When the concentration of carbon dioxide exceeds 2 %, the correction is significant because the refractive indices of carbon dioxide and methane are very close. For example a sample containing 60 % methane and 4 % carbon dioxide would give an instrument reading of 62.5 %.

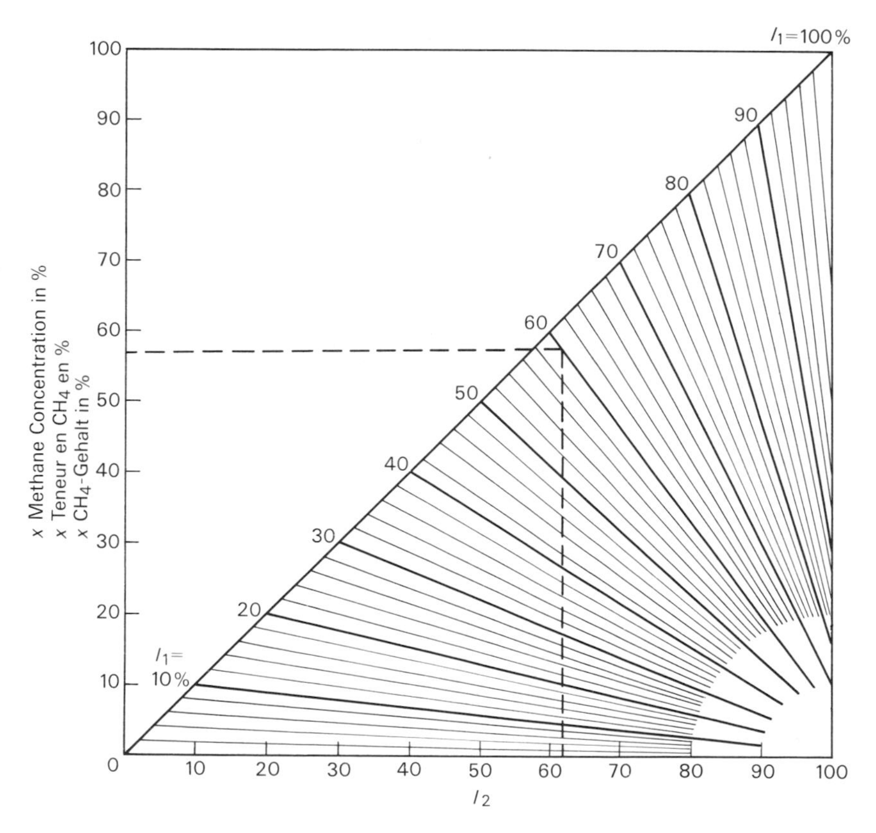

I_1 Reading after absorption of carbon dioxide
I_2 Reading without absorbing the carbon dioxide

Fig. A 4.1.2 Chart for Determining Methane Concentration in a Sample Containing Carbon Dioxide when using a high concentration Interferometer.

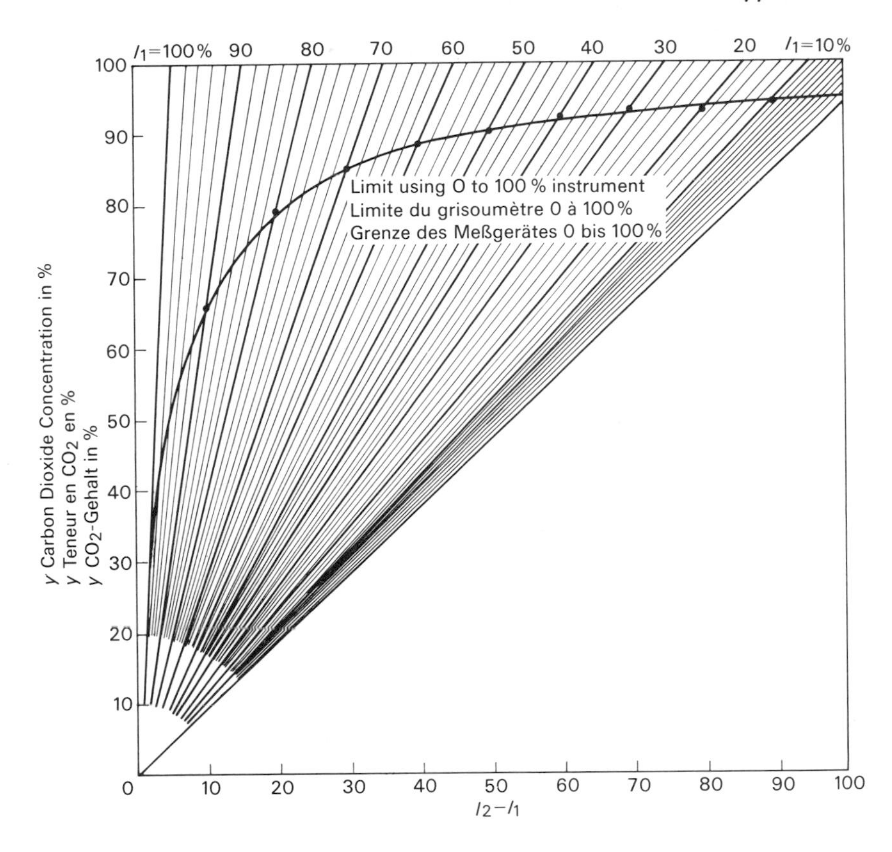

I_1 Reading after absorption of carbon dioxide

I_2 Reading without absorbing the carbon dioxide

Fig. A 4.1.3 Chart for Determining Carbon Dioxide Concentration when $I_2 - I_1$ lies in the range 0 to 100 %.

Two methods of correction may be used.

a) Using an interferometer alone

The reading I_1 is taken, with the sample passing through a cartridge of CO_2 absorbant (Fig. A 4.1.1). The cartridge is then removed and the reading I_2, dependent on both methane and carbon dioxide, is obtained. The graph (Fig. A 4.1.2) gives the methane concentration c as a function of I_2 and I_1. For example if I_1 = 60 % and I_2 = 62 % then c = 57 %.

Additional graphs (Fig. A 4.1.3 and A 4.1.4) give the concentration of CO_2 as a function of ($I_2 - I_1$) and I_1. For example if I_1 = 60 % and I_2 = 62 % then y = 4.4 % CO_2.

The accuracy of the carbon dioxide determination is limited by the lack of precision of $(I_2 - I_1)$.

b) Using a Second Apparatus in conjunction with an Interferometer

In this case the reading I_1 is taken and the carbon dioxide concentration is estimated separately by means of an Orsat or Fyrite apparatus. A graph (Fig. A 4.1.5) gives the methane concentration c as a function of I_1 and the CO_2 concentration (y). For example if I_1 = 60 % and y = 4 % then c = 57.5 %. This compares with 57 % by the first method.

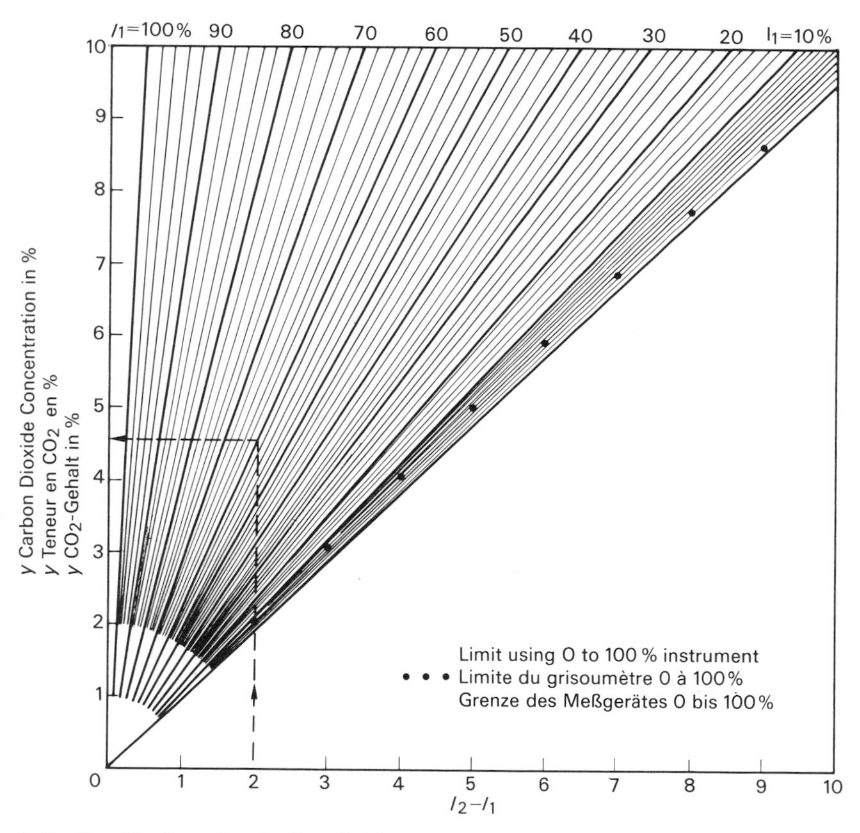

I_1 Reading after absorption of carbon dioxide
I_2 Reading without absorbing the carbon dioxide

Fig. A 4.1.4 Chart for Determining Carbon Dioxide Concentration when $I_2 - I_1$ lies in the range 0 to 10 %.

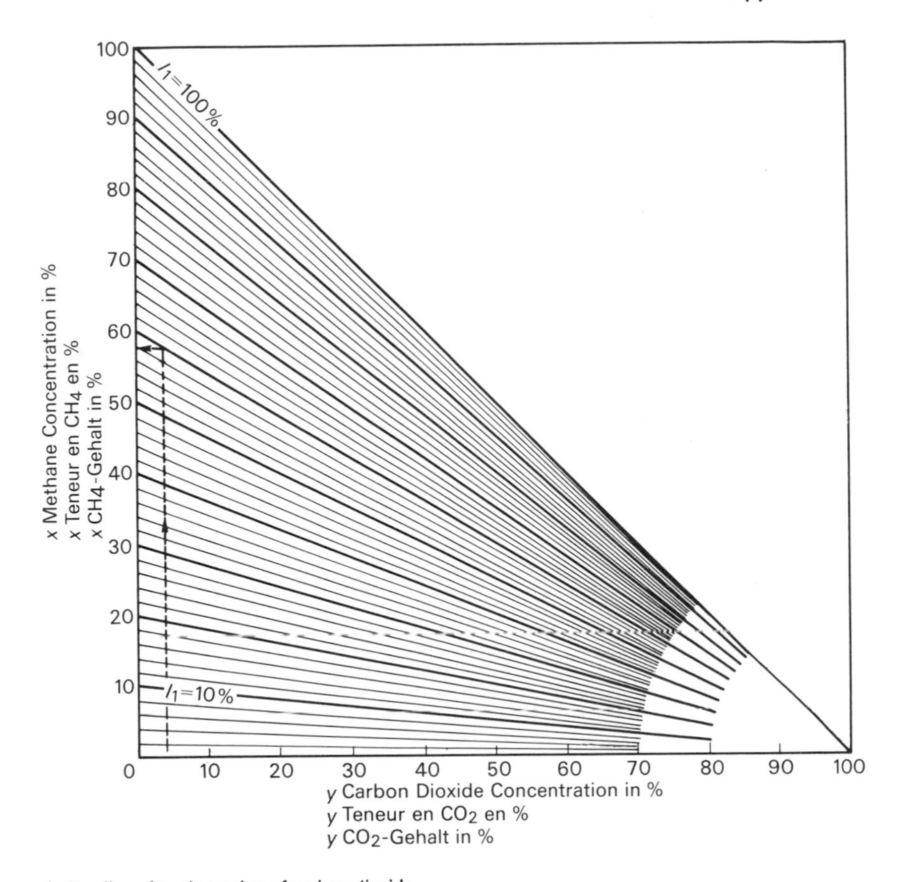

l_1 Reading after absorption of carbon dioxide

Fig. A 4.1.5 Chart for Determining Methane Concentration in a Sample Containing a Known Amount of Carbon Dioxide.

Appendix 4.2

Orifice Plate Formulae

The gas in the pipe can be assumed to be incompressible, because it is subject only to small changes in pressure. In this case, Bernoulli's theorem can be expressed as:

$$p + \varrho \frac{w^2}{2} + \varrho g h = \text{constant} \quad \text{[A 4.2.1]}$$

where:

p the static pressure of gas in the pipe,
ϱ the density which depends on the pressure,
w the mean velocity,
g the acceleration due to gravity,
h the level with respect to a reference.

If the pipe is horizontal, h is taken as zero, in which case the formula reduces to:

$$p + \varrho \frac{w^2}{2} = \text{constant} = p_t \quad \text{[A 4.2.2]}$$

where:

p the static pressure of the gas,
$\varrho \frac{w^2}{2}$ the dynamic pressure and
p_t the total pressure.

Applying formula [A 4.2.2] between points 1 and 2 (Fig. 4.28):

$$p_1 + \varrho \frac{w_1{}^2}{2} = p_2 + \varrho \frac{w_2{}^2}{2} \quad \text{[A 4.2.3]}$$

so that $w_2{}^2 - w_1{}^2 = 2 \frac{(p_1 - p_2)}{\varrho}$ [A 4.2.4]

However, let:

$$\frac{\text{Area } A_2}{\text{Area } A_1} = \frac{w_1}{w_2} = m, \text{ or } w_1 = m\, w_2 \quad \text{[A 4.2.5]}$$

Substituting this in Equation [A 4.2.4]

$$w_2{}^2 (1 - m^2) = 2 \frac{(p_1 - p_2)}{\varrho} \quad \text{[A 4.2.6]}$$

Thus

$$w_2 = \frac{1}{\sqrt{1 - m^2}} \sqrt{\frac{2 (p_1 - p_2)}{\varrho}} \quad \text{[A 4.2.7]}$$

If $$\frac{1}{\sqrt{1-m^2}} = K_E \quad \text{[A 4.2.8]}$$

the approximate flow, Q, in the pipe can be expressed from Equation [A 4.2.7] as:

$$Q = K_C \, K_J \, A_2 \, K_E \sqrt{\frac{2\,(p_1 - p_2)}{\varrho}} \quad \text{[A 4.2.9]}$$

where:

K_C the coefficient of flow, (a function of Reynolds Number and of m) and

K_J an overall correction coefficient (depending on viscosity, roughness and the condition of the edge of the orifice).

Approximate formulae for Q have been established in France for the following average case:

- ▷ methane concentration — 68 %
- ▷ absolute pressure — 625 mm Hg (83 kPa)
- ▷ temperature — 298 K

Orifice Plate d_1/d_2 in mm (Fig. 4.28)	Q	Sphere of Application
82 / 28	$\frac{1}{10}\sqrt{\Delta p}$	10 to 30 m³/h (3 to 8 l/s)
82 / 43	$\frac{1}{4}\sqrt{\Delta p}$	30 to 300 m³/h (8 to 80 l/s)
200 / 117	$2\sqrt{\Delta p}$	250 to 10 000 m³/h (70 to 2750 l/s)

where Q is the approximate flow in the pipe in m³/min under standard conditions of 101.3 kPa and 298 K, and Δp is expressed in mm of water column.

For the two first orifice plates, the use of the formula for the average case gives an error of + 7 %. If the concentration and absolute pressure decrease (in comparison with the average case), the error is increased whereas if concentration and pressure increase, the error will decrease.

Examples:

90 % methane	800 mm Hg (107 kPa)	— 15 % error
68 % methane	625 mm Hg (83 kPa)	+ 7 % error
30 % methane	600 mm Hg (80 kPa)	+ 18 % error

Appendix 4.3

Calculators

There are many types of calculators, three of the more widely used being described here. The first (Hartmann & Braun) and second (Philips) calculators may be used for calculating the quantities expressed by the given general equations; gas flow calculations together with corrections for ambient conditions of temperature etc. come within their scope. The third (National Coal Board) calculator is designed exclusively for firedamp drainage flow calculations.

A 4.3.1 Hartmann and Braun Analogue Calculator CMR TZ A 2
(Figure A 4.3.1)

Principle

Four inputs are provided, 3 current and 1 resistance, so that four different measurement parameters can be dealt with at the same time.

Those parameters entered as current inputs E_i are entered in combination with an added constant K_i. The calculator then allows the following operations: multi-

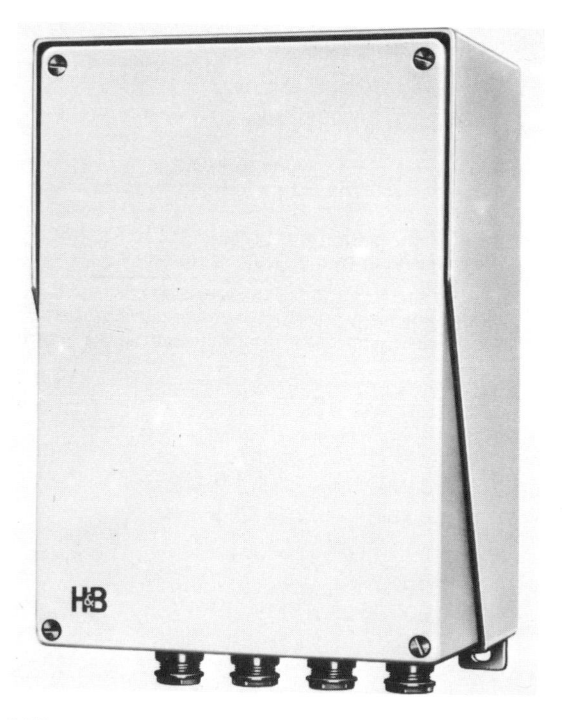

Fig. A 4.3.1
Hartmann and Braun CMR TZ A 2 Analogue Calculator.

plication or division of one parameter by another and the calculation of squares and square roots.

The inverse of the resistance function f (E_4) can be multiplied by the result of these operations on the current parameters and likewise by a standard constant c.

The two basic relationships are:

$$A = c\,(E_2 \pm K_2)\;\frac{E_1 \pm K_1}{E_3 \pm K_3}\,\frac{1}{f\,(E_4)} \quad \text{[A 4.3.1]}$$

$$A = c\,(E_2 \pm K_2)\;\sqrt{\frac{E_1 \pm K_1}{E_3 \pm K_3}\,\frac{1}{f\,(E_4)}} \quad \text{[A 4.3.2]}$$

with:

A	result of operations,
E_1, E_2, E_3	values of parameters entered as current,
E_4	value of parameter entered as resistance,
K_1, K_2, K_3	constant additives of current parameters,
c	standard constant.

Applications

It can be used for the calculation of products, quotients or both, gas flow (velocity × area × concentration of gas) and gas flow, with corrections for pressure, temperature and density.

The necessary programs form 6 plug-in cards. Other operations can be carried out by modifying some connections on the calculator.

Characteristics

Maker:	Hartmann and Braun (GFR)
Dimensions:	200 mm width, 295 mm height, 160 mm depth
Weight:	≈ 5 kg
Supply Voltage:	220 or 24 V
Power consumption:	10 VA
Output resistance:	2 kΩ (at 40 V)
Response time:	≈ 1 s
Linear deviation:	± 0.5 % of maximum value.

A 4.3.2 Philips Control System Calculator (Figure A 4.3.2)

Principle

The PCS calculator has three inputs enabling three parameters to be processed at the same time.

The basic relationship may be expressed as:

$$x_a = a\,x_1\,\frac{b\,x_2}{c\,x_3} \quad \text{[A 4.3.3]}$$

Fig. A 4.3.2
Philips Control System Calculator.

or its square root

$$x_a = \sqrt{a\, x_1 \frac{b\, x_2}{c\, x_3}} \qquad \text{[A 4.3.4]}$$

where:

x_a result of the calculation

x_1, x_2, x_3 values of the parameters fed in

a, b, c constants adjustable between 0.3 and 1.1.

Square roots may be found by means of a circuit which can be connected to one of the inputs or the output.

Application

It can be used for the calculation of products and quotients with or without constant factors, and for the calculation of drainage flow rates. The gas flow rate is first calculated from methane concentration × velocity × cross-sectional area and then corrected for pressure and temperature, for which purpose two calculators are required. Altogether, there is a choice of 30 different operations.

Characteristics

Maker:	Philips (GFR)
Dimensions:	223 mm height, 145 mm width, 120.5 mm depth
Weight:	1.5 kg
Supply Voltage:	110/220 V or 24/42 V (48 to 62 Hz)
Power Consumption:	5 VA
Output Resistance:	0 to 750 Ω

A 4.3.3 NCB Methane Flow Calculator (Figure A 4.3.3)

Principle

The calculator is based on the formula of volumetric flow as a function of the pressure differential Δp measured across an orifice plate (Section 1.1.4.1 and Appendix A 4.2).

$$Q_F = 0.00134\, K_C\, K_Z\, K_E\, d^2 \sqrt{\Delta p} \sqrt{\frac{p_x}{p_{st}} \frac{\gamma_M}{\gamma_F}} \quad \text{[A 4.3.5]}$$

where:

Q_F	the flow of gas in the pipe (l/s, dry, at 101.3 kPa and 288 K),
K_C, K_Z, K_E	constants,
d	the diameter of the orifice in mm,
Δp	the measured differential pressure in Pa,
p_x	the absolute pressure of gas in kPa,
p_{st}	standard pressure = 101.3 kPa,
γ_M	the specific gravity of pure methane (dry),
γ_F	the specific gravity of mixture (dry).

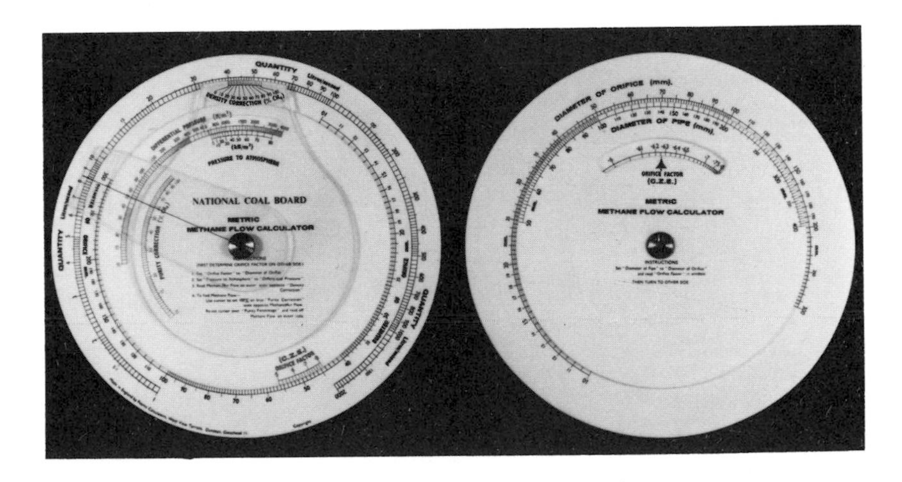

Fig. A 4.3.3 NCB Methane Flow Calculator.

Application

The following parameters are used in the calculation described below:

(1) the diameter of the orifice plate in mm,
(2) the pipe diameter in mm,
(3) the differential pressure in N/m^2 or Pa,
(4) suction in the pipe, ie pressure to atmosphere in kN/m^2 or kPa,
(5) the purity of the gas in % CH_4.

On the reverse side of the disc (on the right of Fig. A 4.3.3) the orifice diameter on the outside circle, is put against the pipe diameter on the inside circle, and the "orifice factor" $K_C\,K_Z\,K_E$ is read in the "CZE" window, 0.625 in the figure.

On the front, of the calculator, this value on the CZE scale is set against the orifice diameter on the inside scale of the outer circle. The suction value on the transparent plastic is then set against the differential pressure on the inside circle.

The "quantity" flow Q_F of the mixture is read in l/s on the outside scale of the outer circle, against the purity on the "density correction" scale (% CH_4).

To find the flow of pure methane, the 100 % line of the "purity correction" scale on the transparent plastic, with the aid of the cursor, is set against the value of Q_F already obtained. The cursor is then rotated to the correct value on the "purity correction" scale, and the flow of pure methane is read in l/s from the same "quantity" scale on the outside circle.

Characteristics

Maker: Fearns Calculators (UK)

No temperature correction.

The disc gives flows of dry gas from measurements made on gas which is assumed to be moist.

This calculator may be used underground and on the surface.

Appendix 4.4

A Method of Purging used in Germany during the Installation or Modification of Firedamp Drainage Ranges

a) During the installation or modification of a drainage range, ie when the range is "broken" or parted, it is necessary to consider any consequent effect upon the ventilation, particularly on the firedamp concentration in the general body while a section is being isolated from the range.

b) When the section of piping is to be removed it must be purged of firedamp using the extractor. To do this, the nearest upstream valve is closed. The range is then opened immediately downstream of the valve and the pipes separated a little to allow air from the roadway to be drawn into the piping by suction thereby purging the pipe section. A particular point to note about purging is that an adequate air velocity in the piping must be used (at least 2 m/s). A minimum duration for purging must also be observed, calculated from the following formula:

$$\text{Minimum purging time in s} = 2\,\frac{\text{length of pipe in m}}{\text{air velocity in the pipe in m/s}} \quad . \; . \; . \qquad [\text{A } 4.4.1]$$

After purging for at least the time indicated above, the nearest valve (Va) downstream of the section to be changed, must be closed and measurements made to verify that no high concentration gas remains in the pipe section. The purged section can be declared clear of gas when the firedamp concentration measured in the upper part of the pipe is no greater than the general body firedamp concentration.

The purged pipe section must be uncoupled only upstream of the valve Va. It is necessary to protect the valves by means of blanks (covers), except when operations are of short duration (eg when replacing few pipes).

c) After completion of installation or replacement it is necessary immediately to reconnect the pipe range on the downstream side.

Appendix 4.5

Limiting Values of Methane Concentrations in Firedamp Drainage Systems in the United Kingdom

Regulation 13 (c) of the Coal Mines (Firedamp Drainage) Regulations (1960) requires that no firedamp drainage system discharges into a utilisation plant firedamp containing less than forty per cent by volume of inflammable gas.

In addition, in general practice, the suction side of surface firedamp extraction plants and underground firedamp extraction plants are usually stopped when methane concentrations in drained gas at the extractor(s) fall to about 20 %.

Appendix 4.6

The Influence of Firedamp Drainage on the Concentration of Methane in the General Body

In three districts of a West German mine, the effect on the firedamp concentration in general body air of stopping and restarting the flow of firedamp drainage has been studied.

When the drainage was stopped on two separate occasions in a district in Seam N (Fig. 4.70) all the flow of methane previously drained ΔQ_M, 3.2 and 5.1 m^3/min respectively, passed into the ventilation (1300 and 1245 m^3/min respectively)*, causing general body firedamp concentration to increase respectively by

$$\frac{3.2}{1300} 100 = 0.25\ \%\ \text{methane and}\ \frac{5.1}{1245} 100 = 0.45\ \%\ \text{methane} \quad [A\ 4.6.1]$$

The increase may be expressed as:

$$\Delta c\ (t) = \Delta c\ (1 - e^{-a\,t}) \quad [A\ 4.6.2]$$

The decrease in concentration when drainage starts up again follows a similar equation:

$$\Delta c\ (t) = \Delta c\ (1 - e^{-b\,t}) \quad [A\ 4.6.3]$$

where:

$\Delta c\ (t)$	the change in general body methane concentration after time t in %,
Δc	the maximum value of this change,
t	the time elapsed since drainage was stopped or started up again in min,
a	the coefficient characteristic of increase in min^{-1},
b	the coefficient characteristic of decrease in min^{-1}.

For the three faces studied it was found that:

$$a \approx \frac{0.15}{Q_M} \quad [A\ 4.6.4]$$

$$\text{and}\ b \approx \frac{0.60}{Q_M} \quad [A\ 4.6.5]$$

Consequently the increase was much slower than the decrease; for instance, for a firedamp flow of 4 m^3/min, more than 60 min was necessary for 90 % of the total increase Δc to be attained whereas only 15 min was required for 90 % decrease of Δc.

* In this district, the total flow without drainage, remained the same as with drainage. In some cases drainage increases the total district flow.

Appendix 4.7

The Effect of Annual Holidays on Quantities of Firedamp Drained

The effects of relatively long breaks in production of coal on firedamp drainage depend largely on the importance of the drainage network, the number of productive districts and old workings being drained, on the intensity of drainage, the duration of the interruption in production and on whether boreholes are in undisturbed or relaxed ground. The effects on both purity and flow can be particularly noticeable where there are few or no floorholes.

The effects of a prolonged stoppage differ from mine to mine. Many mines with average to large emissions of gas are characterised by a 25 to 50 % reduction in quantity drained, a distinct drop (between 3 and 15) % in firedamp concentration and a return to normal flow rates within 7 to 14 days, depending on the configuration of boreholes in roof and floor.

Three examples are shown in Figure 4.74 for coal production stoppages of similar duration.

a) Two districts in a fairly gassy section of a mine gave drained firedamp flows of 80 l/s and 120 l/s respectively during coal production which decreased to minima of 50 l/s and 65 l/s after 19 days. When coal production started up again, the total drained flow reached 240 l/s after 11 days, ie 40 l/s higher than the initial level.

b) At another mine 330 l/s firedamp were drained from seven districts in moderately or highly gassy districts of the mine. Fifteen days after coal production shut-down the drained flow had fallen to 240 l/s, a minimum which was held for five days. The flow only recovered its original value after a further 55 days, so drainage had been affected for a period more than three times the length of the stoppage.

c) At a third mine the flow dropped from 340 to 210 l/s in 22 days and recovered to its original level on the 41st day.

The example in Fig. 4.76 shows a further example of a stoppage (January to February 1970).

Appendix 4.8

Manufacturers and Distributors of Firedamp Drainage Instrumentation

Manufacturers have been grouped according to the type of instrument and hence according to the Chapter paragraph number, and each one is identified by a reference number which allows the reader to retrieve its location and description from the tables that follow. These tables have been prepared from information at our disposal: it is not necessarily exhaustive.

A 4.8.1 France

	Reference Numbers (see following Tables)
1.1 Underground Measurements	
1.1.1 Pressure	
— suction (Tricapteur)	2
— suction (Lugameter)	4
— barometers	9
1.1.3 Methane Concentration	1, 6, 8
1.1.4 Flow Rate	4
1.1.5 Flow Rate (Tricapteur)	2
1.2 Surface Measurements	
1.2.1 Pressure	3
1.2.3 Concentration of Other Gases	
— carbon monoxide	6
— oxygen	10
1.2.4 Flow Rate	3
1.2.5 Density	5
1.2.6 Monitoring and Control (Vacuostats)	
1.2.7 Remote Monitoring and Control Systems	
Central de télégrisoumetrie (CTT)	1
Telecontroleur centralisé de captage (TCC)	2

A 4.8.2 German Federal Republic

	Reference Numbers (see following Tables)
1.1 Underground Measurements	
1.1.1 Pressure	14, 15, 17, 18
— small sensitive barometers	11
— barograph	22
— barometers, Barolux	23, 27
— manometers and inclined manometers	13
— Lugameter	19
1.1.3 Methane Concentration	
— methanometers and alarms	12
— methanometers, borehole probes, Dräger tubes	16
— UNOR gas analyser	25
— interferometer	27
1.1.4 Flow Rate	14, 15, 17
— Lugameter	19
1.1.7 Flow in Boreholes	
— probe	21
1.2 Surface Measurements	
1.2.0 General	
— recorders	20, 24
— transmitters	11, 20, 24, 26, 28
— remote transmission	18
1.2.1 Pressure	20
1.2.2 Methane Concentration	
— Uras	20
1.2.3 Concentration of Other Gases	
— carbon monoxide	25
1.2.4 Flow Rate	28
1.2.8 Calculators	20, 26, 28

A 4.8.3 United Kingdom

	Reference Numbers (see following Tables)
1.1 Underground Measurements	32
1.1.1 Pressure	
— U-tubes, single limb manometers	29, 38, 52
— suction indicators and recorders	31, 46
— Bourdon tube gauges	34, 51, 56
— small portable barometers	36, 51, 60
— alarm and cut-off devices	49
1.1.2 Hand Pumps	47
1.1.3 Methane Concentration	
— hand held	50
— fixed (acoustic, BM2H)	42, 54
1.1.4 Flow Rate	29
— orifice plates	29, 40, 46
1.1.6 Temperature	36, 37
1.1.8 Calculators	43
1.2 Surface Measurements	
1.2.0 General	31, 32, 34, 35, 37, 38, 39, 41, 42, 46, 50, 51, 52, 53, 54, 56
1.2.1 Pressure	
— transmitters	33, 45
1.2.2 Methane Concentration	
— infra-red gas analysers	44, 50
1.2.3 Other gases	
— carbon monoxide	30
— oxygen	57
1.2.4 Flow	45
1.2.5 Calorific Value	55
1.2.6 Monitoring and Control Devices	50, 54
1.2.7 Remote Monitoring and Control Systems	
— TDM system	48, 49, 58, 59
— Tube Bundle system	30
1.2.8 Calculators	43

Table A 4.8.1 **France.**

No.	Manufacturer	Product	Section Reference
1.	Société Française des Produits Oldham 62000 Arras — France	GTM 67 CK 68 Central	1.1.3.7 1.1.3.5 1.2.7.5
2.	CERCHAR 60550 Verneuil-en-Halatte — France	T.C.C.	1.2.7.1
3.	Schlumberger 91302 Massy — France	Fluxi Gas Meter 5 PdH	1.2.4.1 1.2.1.4
4.	Paul Gothe Postfach 908 4630 Bochum — G.F.R.	Lugameter	1.1.4.2
5.	Beri Rue Vercingétorix 141 Paris — France	Debro Densimeter	1.2.5.3
6.	Integra Rue du Cirque 3 Paris — France	UNOR	1.1.3.11 1.2.3.1
7.	Baudot Hardoll Boulevard Port Royal 97 Paris — France	Reineke Calorimeter	1.2.5.1
8.	Codeci Rue Le Brun 13 Paris — France	Fyrite	1.1.3.3
9.	Naudet Rue St-Claude 6 Paris — France	aneroid barometers	1.1.1.8
10.	Hartmann und Braun Postfach 13 61 6000 Frankfurt/Main U/3 — G.F.R.	Magnos oxygen analyser	1.2.3.2

Table A 4.8.2 **German Federal Republic.**

No.	Manufacturer	Product	Section Reference
11.	Conti Elektroindustrie AG Askaniawerk für wissenschaftliche Geräte Grossbeerenstrasse 2—10 1000 Berlin 42	small sensitive barometers transmitters	1.1.1 1.2.0
12.	Auergesellschaft GmbH Friedrich-Krause-Ufer 24 1000 Berlin 65	methanometers and methane measuring systems	1.1.3.1 1.1.3.6
13.	Apparatebau Birkholz u. Co. Postfach 1 07 6148 Heppenheim A.D.B.	U-tubes and inclined manometers	1.1.1.1
14.	Bopp u. Reuther GmbH Carl-Reuther-Strasse 6800 Mannheim, Waldhof	pressure and flow measuring devices	1.1.1 1.1.4
15.	Debrowerk, Paul de Bruyn KG Hansaallee 30 4000 Düsseldorf, Oberkassel	pressure and flow measuring devices	1.1.1 1.1.4
16.	Drägerwerk AG Postfach 13 39 2400 Lübeck	Dräger tubes, methanometers and borehole probes	1.1.3 1.1.7
17.	Dreyer, Rosenkranz u. Droop AG Leisewitzstrasse 26 3000 Hannover	pressure and flow measuring devices	1.1.1 1.1.4
18.	Funke und Huster Postfach 5 29 4300 Essen 1	pressure transducers and automatic cut-off with remote transmission	1.1.1.5 1.2.0
19.	Paul Gothe Postfach 9 08 4630 Bochum	indicating and recording Lugameters	1.1.1.3 1.1.4.2
20.	Hartmann und Braun Postfach 13 61 6000 Frankfurt/Main U/3	Uras, transmitters, recorders, calculators	1.2.0 1.2.1.1 1.2.1.3 1.2.2.3 1.2.8

Table A 4.8.2 (Continued).

No.	Manufacturer	Product	Section Reference
21.	Ernst-Ewald Höntzsch Postfach 13 24 7050 Waiblingen-Stuttgart	borehole probe	1.1.7
22.	Wilhelm Lambrecht KG Postfach 76 3400 Göttingen	barographs	1.1.1
23.	G. Lufft, Metallbarometerfabrik GmbH Postfach 6 92 7000 Stuttgart	barometers	1.1.1
24.	C. O. Mangels KG, Regler- und Messgerätefabrik Brunnenstrasse 3—7 2940 Wilhelmshaven	transmitters, recorders	1.2.0
25.	H. Maihak AG Postfach 60 17 08 Semperstrasse 38 2000 Hamburg	UNOR	1.1.3.11 1.2.3.1
26.	Philips GmbH Postfach 31 03 20 3500 Kassel Wieselweg 5 4300 Essen	transmitter, measuring systems, and calculators	1.2.0 1.2.8
27.	Karl Schierjott, VDI Postfach 23 07 4630 Bochum	Barolux barometers, Riken interferometers	1.1.1 1.1.3.4
28.	Siemens AG, Bereich Grundstoffindustrie Werner-von-Siemens-Strasse 50 8250 Erlangen	transmitter measuring systems, and calculators	1.2.0 1.2.4.2 1.2.8

Table A 4.8.3 **United Kingdom.**

No.	Manufacturer	Product	Section Reference
29.	Airflow Developments Ltd. High Wycombe, Bucks.	manometers, venturis	1.1.1.1 1.1.1.4
30.	Analytical Development Co. Ltd. Pindar Road Hoddesdon Herts EN11 0AQ	Infra-red gas analysers for Tube Bundle systems	1.2.3.1 1.2.7.4
31.	Arkon Instruments Ltd. Whadden Works Cheltenham Glos	Suction and pressure indicators, recorders, integrators and transmitters	1.1.1.2 1.2.0
32.	F. Bamford & Co. Ltd. Ajax Works Whitehill Stockport	water flow indicator and switch	1.1 1.2.0
33.	Bell and Howell Ltd. Lennox Road Basingstoke Hants RG22 4AW	absolute pressure transmitters (surface)	1.2.1.2
34.	Budenberg Gauge Co. Ltd. Broadheath Nr. Manchester	Bourdon and capsule gauges for pressure and suction	1.1.1.5 1.1.1.6 1.2.0
35.	Cambridge Instrument Ltd. Melbown, Royston Herts SG8 6EJ	suction and pressure indicators and recorders	1.2.0
36.	C. F. Casella and Co. Ltd. Regent House Britannia Walk London N1	aneroid barometers dial thermometers	1.1.1.8 1.1.6
37.	Coley Thermometers Ltd. Bryco Works 2—4 London Road Brentford Middlesex	contact type thermometers	1.1.6 1.2.0
38.	Combustion Instruments Ltd. The Causeway Staines Surrey TW18 3AB	single limb manometers	1.1.1.1 1.2.0
39.	Dawson, Mc Donald and Dawson Compton Works Ashbourne Derbyshire DE6 1DB	electric vacuum/pressure gas sampling pumps (surface)	1.2.0

Table A 4.8.3 (Continued).

No.	Manufacturer	Product	Section Reference
40.	Drillfield Equipment Co. Ltd. Manor Road Mancetter Atherstone	orifice plates and borehole equipment	1.1.4.1
41.	Edwards High Vacuum Manor Road Crawley RH10 2LW	electric vacuum/pressure gas sampling pumps (surface)	1.2.0
42.	Electronics Associates Ltd. Norbury Instruments Division 91 Beddington Lane Croydon Surrey	Acoustic Methanometers	1.1.3.8 1.2.0
43.	Fearn Calculators West View Terrace Dunston Gateshead 11	Methane Flow Calculators	1.1.8 1.2.8
44.	Feedback Instruments Ltd. Park Road Crowborough Sussex	Industrial Infra-red High Concentration Analysers (surface)	1.2.2.2
45.	Furness Controls Ltd. Beeching Road, South, Bexhill on Sea TN39 3LJ	Pressure, suction and differential pressure transmitters	1.2.1.5 1.2.4.4
46.	George Kent Instruments Ltd. Luton Beds	Ring balance suction recorders, orifice plates, orifice gas flow indicators, integrators and recorders	1.1.1.2 1.1.4.1 1.2.0
47.	Gresham Engineering Co. Ltd. Old Woking Surrey	Gas sampling hand pumps and capsules	1.1.2
48.	Hawker Siddeley Dynamics Hatfield Herts	TDM data transmission system	1.2.7.3
49.	Huwood Ltd. Gateshead Tyne & Wear NE11 0LP	Vacuum and differential pressure indicators and switches TDM data transmission system	1.1.1.9 1.2.7.3
50.	Mine Safety Appliances Co. Ltd. East Shawhead Coatbridge ML5 4TD	high concentration hand methanometers, industrial infra-red methane analysers (surface)	1.1.3.2 1.2.0 1.2.2.2

Table A 4.8.3 (Continued).

No.	Manufacturer	Product	Section Reference
51.	Negretti and Zambra Stocklake Aylesbury Bucks	suction and pressure indicating and recording gauges, differential pressure gauges, aneroid and portable barometers	1.1.5 1.1.1.8 1.2.0
52.	Paul Poddy 16 Minerva Road London NW10 6HJ	single limb manometers	1.1.1.1 1.2.0
53.	B. Rhodes & Son Ltd. Danes Road Cow Lane Romford Essex	water flow indicators and switches	1.2.0
54.	J & S Sieger Ltd. 31 Nuffield Estate Poole Dorset BH17 7RZ	BM2H High concentration methane monitor, atmospheric alarm Type 1350	1.1.3.9 1.2.6.2 1.2.0
55.	Sigma Instrument Co. Ltd. Letchworth Herts	calorimeter (surface)	1.2.5.2
56.	Smith Industries Ltd. Linkula Works 921 Coventry Road Birmingham 10	Bourdon tube pressure gauges	1.1.1.6 1.2.0
57.	Taylor Servomex Ltd. Crowborough, Sussex	oxygen analyser	1.2.3.2
58.	Transmitton Ltd. Smisby Road, Asbhy de la Zouch Leicester, LE6 5UG	TDM data transmission system	1.2.7.3
59.	Westinghouse Brake and Signal Co. Ltd. Chippenham Wilts	TDM data transmission system	1.2.7.3
60.	T. Wheeler (Scientific Instruments) 19—20 Great Sutton Street London EC1	aneroid and portable barometers	1.1.1.8

Chapter 5

Utilisation of Drained Firedamp

0. Introduction

For over 25 year firedamp drained in West European mines has been utilised in a diversity of ways, both at the mines themselves and in consumer industries such as steelworks, coke ovens, brickworks, glassworks and chemical industries producing plastics. Some time ago it had also been considered for use by gas distributors, because there was at that time a shortage of town gas. Certain manufacturers also investigated the use of high purity drained firedamp with its added convenience. Moreover, applications in internal combustion engines and gas turbines were found. Thus rapid developments in techniques of utilisation of drained gas occurred in the 15 years up to 1965.

The more recent discovery of large reserves of natural gas such as those of Groningen for the Netherlands and of the North Sea for the UK had the effect of reducing the importance of drained firedamp to manufacturers. The distributors of natural gas installed widespread networks throughout Europe and offered gas of high calorific value and constant composition at attractive prices. This was a period of abundant cheap energy. Subsequently at the start of the early 1970s, particularly at the beginning of the energy crisis in late 1973, there was renewed interest in drained firedamp owing to the quintupling of the price of oil and petroleum derivatives.

It is now realised that abundant cheap energy for future generations is not attainable. On assessing known world sources of energy, it is apparent that the resources of natural gas, petrol and coal are limited. Probably by the end of the twentieth century or the beginning of the twenty-first, availability will have decreased so much that it is necessary now to conserve energy and also to develop the use of national resources to the maximum.

Since 1974 colliery companies have endeavoured to utilise firedamp at the pit, in boilers and gas turbines. This has improved the profitability of the collieries and highlighted the potential of such national resources. In the UK for example, the volume of firedamp utilised annually has risen from 108 million m^3 in 1973/74 to 142 million m^3 in 1977/78 and 170 million m^3 are expected to be used in 1981/82; simultaneously the value of this utilised firedamp rose from £ 1 million in 1973/74 to £ 4.5 million in 1977/78 and £ 7.5 million is anticipated. In this period the price per joule has nearly quadrupled.

The need to exploit natural energy resources to a maximum has led to substantial technological progress. For example, significant advances have been made in the construction of boilers and burners, and in the equipment used for their automatic regulation, protection and surveillance. In addition, since more elaborate and more reliable equipment is now available for control and detection, exemptions are being sought in the UK for the utilisation of drained firedamp down to a lower limit of 30 % inflammable gas (equivalent to a calorific value of about 11 MJ/m^3) compared with the current statutory requirement of 40 % inflammable gas (about 15 MJ/m^3). Thus it is anticipated that utilisation of drained firedamp will continue to increase further in the future.

Figures 5.1, 5.2 and 5.3 respectively show quantities of firedamp drained, quantities of firedamp utilised annually, and the proportion of drained gas utilised in the coalmining countries of western Europe for the years 1968 to 1977. For almost 25 years nearly all the drained firedamp has been continuously utilised in Belgium, whereas the proportion for the UK has varied from 33 to 59 % of surface drained

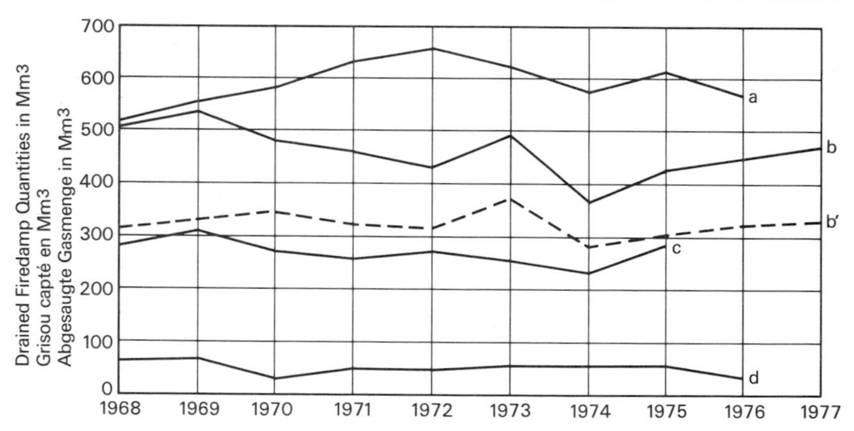

a Federal Republic of Germany — Allemagne fédérale — Bundesrepublik Deutschland

b United Kingdom (total) — Grand-Bretagne — Großbritannien

b' United Kingdom: drained to surface — Grand-Bretagne: grisou capté amené en surface — Großbritannien: zur Tagesoberfläche gefördert

c France — France — Frankreich

d Belgium — Belgique — Belgien

Fig. 5.1 Annual Drained Quantities of Firedamp in the Coalmining Countries of Western Europe.

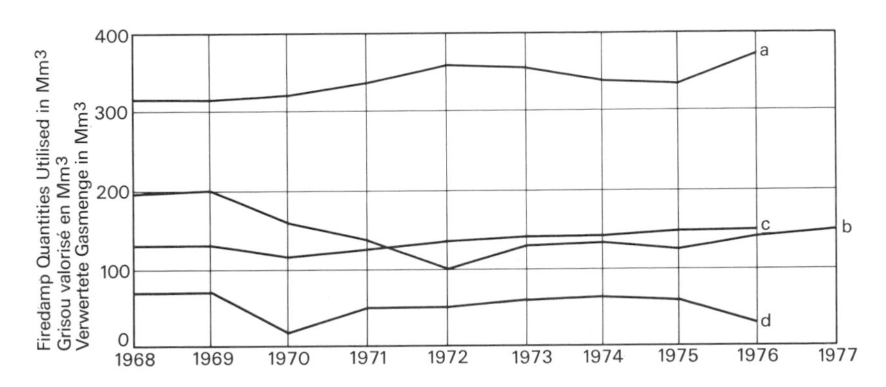

a Federal Republic of Germany — Allemagne fédérale — Bundesrepublik Deutschland
b United Kingdom (total) — Grand-Bretagne — Großbritannien
c France — France — Frankreich
d Belgium — Belgique — Belgien

Fig. 5.2 Quantities of Drained Firedamp Utilised in the Coalmining Countries of Western Europe.

a Federal Republic of Germany — Allemagne fédérale — Bundesrepublik Deutschland
b United Kingdom (total) — Grand-Bretagne — Großbritannien
b' United Kingdom: drained to surface — Grand-Bretagne: grisou capté amené en surface — Großbritannien: zur Tagesoberfläche gefördert
c France — France — Frankreich
d Belgium — Belgique — Belgien

Fig. 5.3 Utilised Firedamp Quantities as a Proportion of Annual Drained Firedamp Quantities in the Coalmining Countries of Western Europe.

firedamp quantities, from 42 to 58 % for France and from 53 to 64 % for Federal Republic of Germany. Only about 70 % of the total quantity drained in the UK is brought to the surface, and only about 50 % of the total drained is available for utilisation for statutory and other reasons. Closure of very gassy mines in the Sud Coalfield of Belgium has already resulted in an important reduction in the volume drained and this trend will continue.

It is difficult now to foresee the construction of a new drained firedamp grid connecting a number of pits of a region or a coalfield. However, it is opportune to recall the diversity of previous applications at a time when further utilisation schemes for drained firedamp in boilers and gas turbines are being evolved. The interconnecting of collieries has the benefit of more consistent and regular supply of drained firedamp to consumers, independent of variations in flow and quality that could occur at a single colliery.

1. Utilisation as Town Gas

In Belgium 25 years ago gas distributors did not have enough town gas to meet demand and became particularly interested in firedamp drained at collieries. Utilisation became most extensive in the Belgian Hainaut Coalfield and in the Saar. In Hainaut Province for example the Société Distrigaz was allowed to collect drained firedamp from collieries and transport and utilise the firedamp, to the benefit of both parties. A collecting grid connects more than 30 mines from the French frontier to Chatelet east of Charleroi (over 100 km). Using this grid the total yield and quality of drained firedamp became very regular, because the firedamp concentration had to exceed 70 % before gas was allowed into the collecting range. Because the calorific value of this gas was greater than that of town gas it had to be reduced to 17.8 MJ/m^3 before being introduced into the distribution network. For this purpose, Société Distrigaz built a central cracking plant at Mont Sainte-Aldegonde, based on two processes namely a vapour cracking process of the Gas Machinery type, and auto-thermal cracking by catalysis in air.

The output of the plant, which followed demand particularly in winter, rose rapidly from 150 000 to 1 million m^3 of reformed gas per day by maximising production and enriching it with propane and butane. In the event of insufficient firedamp, this plant could also crack liquified petroleum gas. In addition, drained gas was mixed with gas of lower calorific value to produce gas comparable with that normally distributed.

Several British Gas Boards have also utilised drained firedamp in town gas distribution systems, notably in Wales and the West Midlands in the years 1956 to 1965.

2. Firing of Furnaces, Kilns and Ovens

At the Gilson à la Croyère Works in Belgium drained firedamp was preferred to town gas for firing certain ovens because it contained no measurable trace of sulphur. Firedamp was utilised at the Martin furnaces, in blooming furnaces, in preheating ovens for large ingots, in heat treatment ovens, in small ovens of the Bolt Division, in non-ferrous foundries etc. In the first three years, the works used more than 50 million m^3 of firedamp, thereby releasing large quantities of town gas for domestic use.

The ceramic industry also utilised firedamp for heating tunnel kilns used for firing porcelain. The atmosphere and temperatures needed in the different zones were obtained by regulating the fuel/air ratio.

Firedamp was utilised in coke ovens in the UK and elsewhere and is still utilised in some cases. Formerly the corresponding quantity of coke oven gas thereby released was sold as town gas. In these cases, investment in pipes for transmission of firedamp paid off, even when distances between collieries and coking plant were large. In the UK, drained firedamp is utilised to fire kilns at a number of brickworks.

3. Chemical Uses

Theoretically firedamp could be used, as is natural gas, as a raw material in the chemical industry. Many chemicals can be made from methane such as carbon black, hydrogen, ammonia, acetylene, chlorine derivatives, nitric acid, methanol, formalin and certain products which serve as a base for plastics and synthetic fibres. However, it seems that these compounds are not made from colliery firedamp because it is relatively impure, the quantities are generally not as large as those from natural gas wells, and supplies are not consistent enough. In Belgium, however, the Société Carbochimique de et à Tertre has used a methane cracking installation to produce hydrogen for synthesis. This utilisation was possible only through the interconnection of five very gassy mines which drained firedamp containing more than 75 % methane.

4. Gas Engines and Turbines

4.1 Gas Engines for Compressor Drives

Société Distrigaz has employed many gas engine compressor groups in its town gas compressor stations requiring very large supplies of energy because of their geographical position and throughput. The large gas engines used to drive the compressors are relatively easy to maintain and have a high efficiency. They are of two types, either 2-stroke engines with injection and scavenging, or 4-stroke engines. The engine cylinders are arranged vertically or in a V-formation and the compressor cylinders are horizontal.

4.2 Gas Engines for Vehicles

During the petrol shortages of World War II and the following decade drained firedamp was utilised as a motor fuel in the Saar and the Ruhr, and after the war was so used in the UK. It was compressed to 30 MPa and bottled at 20 MPa in cylinders of capacity 12 m^3 at 273 K and 101.3 kPa. Compression to 30 MPa was carried out exactly as for natural gas. Such use of drained firedamp is no longer of interest now that propane is available for this purpose.

4.3 Dual Fuel Engines for Power Generation

In the UK dual fuel engines are used to drive alternators. The engine works equally well on drained firedamp or on heavy diesel oil. One installation has run continuously for 12 years on drained firedamp, except for maintenance periods. The exhaust from the engines is used for water heating or steam raising. Since 1972 the most modern and comprehensive installation of this type has been in operation at Manton Colliery. Three water cooled dual fuel Ruston Paxman engines are each coupled directly to a 1.5 MW alternator. The engines are designed to start with a pilot ignition of fuel oil, but are normally run on a 95 % firedamp-air mixture with 5 % oil.

Combustion air is delivered to the cylinders by a small turboblower operated by exhaust gases from the engines. Drained gas is compressed to 210 kPa before delivery to the engines. The three alternators supply 4 to 4.5 MW, equivalent to about 75 % of the maximum power consumption of the mine.

When the demand of the mine is less than the output of the alternators, power is supplied to an external grid, leading to a marked reduction in power, heat and light costs. Each engine consumes 120 l/s of pure methane as well as the oil. Exhaust gases leave the engines at a temperature of 625 K and are passed into three vertical boilers, producing 600 kg of steam per hour at 550 kPa; this steam together with a separate boiler heated directly by drained firedamp, provides the hot water and steam necessary for space heating and for the pithead baths.

4.4 Gas Turbines for Power Generation

Further utilisation of drained firedamp can be effected by a small gas turbine driving an alternator or any other generating machine. The Kongsberg KG 2/3 gas turbine drives a 1.35 MW alternator with a consumption of about 250 l/s pure methane at full load.

A compressor delivers drained gas to the gas turbine at a pressure of 750 kPa. The gas turbine has a rotor speed of 1885 rad/s and is coupled through a precision gearbox which reduces the speed to 157 or 188 rad/s, to an alternator generating at 550 volts, 1.1 or 3.3 kV, as required. The net output available to the grid is 1.15 MW after deducting the power taken by the compressor. Ignition of the gas is by spark. The turbine is intended to work on either drained gas or oil. It starts up on oil and changes over to drained gas as soon as combustion is established about one minute after starting. In event of failure of the drained gas supply, the turbine is switched automatically to oil in 4 s. Exhaust gas from the turbine is utilised in a boiler with a capacity of about 6000 kg of steam and hot water per hour; this is used for surface heating.

A Kongsberg KG 2/3 gas turbine was installed at Point of Ayr Colliery early in January 1978 at a cost of about £ 300 000. This turbine has a number of advantages. It requires little maintenance and has a greatly reduced oil consumption compared with a dual fuel engine because oil is used for only a few seconds on starting; being compact it requires small foundations; it is relatively quiet and free from vibration; it requires a minimum holding of spare parts; it consumes no water, is readily adapted to automatic control and is clean.

5. Thermal Uses including Colliery Boilers

The simplest application of drained gas is in boilers or in coal drying plant at collieries and currently these are the commonest applications. Firedamp has numerous advantages as a boiler fuel; it is clean and can easily be automatically monitored and controlled. The boiler does not require an attendant, needs little cleaning and maintenance, and its output can rapidly be adjusted to the demand, particularly when modern packaged boilers are used. The burners can accommodate wide variations in gas purity and quantity. If necessary, dual fuel (drained firedamp and coal or oil) boilers may be installed.

Boilers commonly take between 35 and 250 l/s pure methane. They supply steam for winding engines, heating of buildings and hot water for pithead baths. Small boilers are used for heating the downcast air of mines in winter.

Considerable progress has been made in the manufacture of boiler accessories, in the design of pipework, valves, valve proving systems, water drainage systems, flame detectors, programmed starting up and automatic surveillance. After a shutdown, restarting is initiated manually and continues on sequence control which includes a programme for testing valves for leakage at working pressures. The supply of gas to burners is not permitted until the system has been tested and proved. During normal operation, surveillance is continuous and covers constant interrogation of pressure, flows and purity of gas being supplied to the pilot and main burners. The concentrations of methane in flue gases are also monitored for reasons of safety and combustion efficiency. Additionally in certain installations the atmosphere near gas trains is monitored continuously. These many advances are being applied to schemes for utilisation of drained firedamp down to a lower limit of 30 % pure methane, under exemption, in the UK.

Investment is rapidly recovered in boiler schemes.

6. The Use of low Concentration Methane in Mine Air for Boilers

The ventilating air in the upcast shaft of gassy mines may have a methane concentration of 0.4 to 0.8 %, which because of the large air flows involved represents a large energy loss to the atmosphere. Utilisation of this air would conserve energy and be a positive gain. The energy in the dilute methane of the return air could be utilised by feeding this air to the boilers, where they are located near to the upcast shaft. Theoretical studies have indicated a possible saving of 6 % in fuel.

Symbols utilised in the Formulae

Page 1

Symbol	Quantity	Units*
A	Cross-sectional area	m^2
A_o	Surface area	m^2
C	Gas content	m^3/t
C_v	"Free" gas i. e. compressed in pores of coal or rock	m^3/t
C_p	Adsorbed gas, held on the coal internal surfaces	m^3/t
$C_{p\infty}$	Adsorption capacity of the coal; C_p at infinite pressure	m^3/t
D	Coefficient of diffusion	cm^2/s
F	Force	N
H	Moisture content	% by weight
I	Scale reading e. g. interferometer	% by volume
K	Correction factor (Reglagaz)	—
M	Thickness e. g. of coal seam	cm
P_o	Daily saleable output of coal	t/d
Q	Volume flow rate (firedamp drainage)	l/s
Q_a	Air quantity flow rate	m^3/s
Re	Reynolds Number	—
R_t	Actual (measured) drainage efficiency	—
S	Actual (measured) specific emission i. e. per tonne of coal worked	m^3/t
S_c	That part of S captured by firedamp drainage	m^3/t
T	Temperature	K
V	Total volume of gas mixture flowing in given time	m^3
V_a	Volume of gas mixture flowing into ventilating air	m^3
V_c	Volume of gas mixture drained	m^3
W	Daily face advance	m
a	Ash content	% by weight
b	Breadth, width	m

* For example.

Symbols utilised in the Formulae (continuation). Page 2

Symbol	Quantity	Units*
c	Methane concentration	% by volume
c_L	Methane concentration limit	% by volume
d	Diameter	mm
Δd	Depth of annular groove (slot)	mm
f	A coefficient of friction	—
g	Acceleration due to gravity	m/s^2
h	Height	m
Δh	Difference in height, head	m
i	Coefficient of irregularity of gas emission	—
k	Roughness	mm
k_s	Absolute roughness characteristic	mm
k_1, k_2	Desorption coefficients	$s^{-\frac{1}{2}}$
k_c	Langmuir equation constant	kPa^{-1}
l	Length	m
m	Velocity ratio or cross-sectioned area ratio	—
n	Index of Airey's desorption equation (also number of days in week cf. n_0)	—
n_0	Number of working days per week	—
p	Absolute pressure	kPa
p_0	Atmospheric pressure	kPa
Δp	Pressure difference	kPa
p_{H_2O}	Saturated vapour pressure of water	kPa
q_1^0 (t)	Desorbable gas content when pressure drops quickly from pressure p_1 to atmospheric pressure p_0 in time t	m^3/t
q_1^0 (∞)	Gas content desorbable between p_1 and p_0 in infinite time	m^3/t
r	Degree of gas emission or desorption	%
r_t	Predicted drainage efficiency	—
s	Calculated (predicted) specific gas emission	m^3/t
s_t	Calculated specific emission from roof strata	m^3/t
s_f	Calculated specific emission from worked seam	m^3/t

* For example.

Symbols utilised in the Formulae (continuation). Page 3

Symbol	Quantity	Units*
s_m	Calculated specific emission from floor strata	m^3/t
s'	Calculated specific emission from the lower 20 m of roof strata	m^3/t
s_{tc}	Calculated specific emission drainable from the roof	m^3/t
t	Time	s
v	Porosity	m^3/t
w	Velocity	m/s
x_0	Distance constant (Airey)	m
y	Ratio of specific heats	—
α	Angle of inclination	degree
α_f	Angle of dip	degree
α_F	Prism angle (Flügge prediction method)	degree
β	Coefficient making allowance for non-working days	—
γ	Specific weight	kN/m^3
δ	Specific gravity (relative density)	—
ζ	Coefficient of resistance/friction (fittings)	—
η	Predicted effectiveness of firedamp drainage	—
η_{th}	Theoretical effectiveness of firedamp drainage	—
ϑ	Temperature	°C
$\varkappa$	Proportion of air in a gas mixture	—
λ	Coefficient of friction/resistance (pipes)	—
μ	Dynamic (absolute) viscosity	Ns/m^2 or Pa s
μ_e	Expansion or contraction factor	—
μ_W	Strata constant (Winter prediction method)	—
ν	Kinematic viscosity	m^2/s
ϱ	Specific mass, density	kg/m^3
τ	Overall effectiveness of firedamp drainage	%
ψ	Inflow factor	—

* For example.

Conversion Tables

Table 1. Conversion Factors for Energy, Work and Heat Units.

	J	kJ	kW h	kcal	hp h	kp m
1 J = (=1 Nm = 1 Ws)	1	0.001	2.78×10^{-7}	2.39×10^{-4}	3.73×10^{-7}	0.102
1 kJ =	1 000	1	2.78×10^{-4}	0.239	3.73×10^{-4}	102
1 kW h =	3 600 000	3 600	1	860	1.34	367 000
1 kcal =	4 190	4.19	0.00116	1	0.00156	427
1 hp h =	2 680 000	2 680	0.746	641	1	274 000
1 kp m =	9.81	0.00981	2.72×10^{-6}	0.00234	3.65×10^{-6}	1

Table 2. Conversion Factors for Pressure Units of Gases, Vapours and Liquids.

	Pa	bar	kp/m^2	atm	Torr
1 Pa = (= 1 N/m^2)	1	10^{-5}	0.102	0.987×10^{-5}	0.0075
1 bar = (= 0.1 MPa)	100 000 = 10^5	1 (= 1 000 mbar)	10 200	0.987	750
1 kp/m^2 =	9.81	9.81×10^{-5}	1	0.968×10^{-4}	0.0736
1 atm = (= 760 Torr)	101 325	1.013 (= 1 013 mbar)	10 330	1	760
1 Torr = (≙ 1 mm Hg)	133	0.00133	13.6	0.00132	1

Conversion Tables (continuation).

Table 3. Conversion Factors for Pressure Units of Liquid Manometers.

	Pa (= N/m^2)	mbar	kPa	bar
1 mm WG =	9.81	0.0981	0.0098	0.000098
1 m WG =	9 810	98.1	9.81	0.0981
1 mm Hg (≙ 1 Torr) =	133	1.33	0.133	0.00133

Table 4. Conversion Factors for Units of Force and Selected Imperial Units.

newton (N) 1 N = 1 kg m/s^2
dyne (dyn) 1 dyn = 10^{-5} N
pond (p) 1 p = 9.81 × 10^{-3} N
kilopond (kp) 1 kp = 9.81 N
pound force (lbf) 1 lbf = 4.45 N
inch (in) 1 in = 25.4 mm
foot (ft) 1 ft = 0.3048 m
pound (lb) 1 lb = 0.454 kg
gallon per minute (gal/min)
1 gal/min = 7.58 × 10^{-2} l/s
cubic foot per minute (ft^3/min)
1 ft^3/min = 4.72 × 10^{-4} m^3/s = 4.72 × 10^{-1} l/s
British thermal unit (Btu) 1 Btu = 1.06 kJ
British thermal unit per cubic foot (Btu/ft^3)
1 Btu/ft^3 = 3.73 × 10^{-2} MJ/m^3
therm (thorm) 1 therm = 106 MJ
inch water gauge (in WG) 1 in WG = 249 Pa
inch mercury (in Hg) 1 in Hg = 3.39 kPa
pound force per square inch (lbf/in^2)
1 lbf/in^2 = 6.89 kPa

Table 5. Conversion Factors for Units of Power, Energy and Heat Flow.

	W	kW	kcal/s	kcal/h	kp m/s	hp
1 W = (= 1 N m/s = 1 J/s)	1	0.001	2.39 × 10^{-4}	0.860	0.102	0.00134
1 kW =	1 000	1	0.239	860	102	1.34
1 kcal/s =	4 190	4.19	1	3 600	427	5.61
1 kcal/h =	1.16	0.00116	0.000278	1	0.119	0.00156
1 kp m/s =	9.81	0.00981	0.00234	8.43	1	0.0132
1 hp =	746	0.746	0.178	641	76	1

Acknowledgements for the Figures

Aerzener Maschinenfabrik: 3.20 / 3.21
Auer: 4.12 / 4.19
Bergbau-Forschung: 4.24 / 4.25
Bergbau-Versuchsstrecke: 3.11 / 3.5.4
Bois Stenuick: 2.26
Charbonnages de France: 2.57
Cerchar: 1.1 / 1.3 / 1.8 / 1.9 / 1.10 / 2.1 / 2.6 / 2.10 / 2.11 / 2.13 / 2.30 / 2.43 / 2.46 / 2.48 / 2.49 / 3.3 / 3.4 / 4.28 / 4.34 / 4.35 / 4.36 / 4.55 / 4.56 / 4.57 / 4.63 / 4.64 / 4.69 / 4.71 / 4.75 / 4.1.2 / 4.1.3 / 4.1.4 / 4.1.5
Cerchar + Oldham: 4.54
Clairax: 4.2
Crown Copyright, S.M.R.E.: 2.50
TU Clausthal: 3.6
Debro: 4.50 / 4.51
Edeco: 2.20 / 2.22 / 2.36
Forschungsstelle für Grubenbewetterung: 1.2 / 1.5 / 1.6 / 1.7 / 1.11 / 1.12 / 1.13 / 1.14 / 2.4 / 2.5 / 2.15 / 2.16 / 2.17 / 2.24 / 2.27 / 2.52 / 2.1.1 / 2.4.1 / 3.1.1 / 3.1.4 / 4.10 / 4.38 / 4.39 / 4.40 / 4.65 / 4.66 / 4.67 / 4.70 / 4.73 / 5.1 / 5.2 / 5.3
Forschungsstelle für Grubenbewetterung + Cerchar: 3.1.2
Fuess: 4.5 / 4.6 / 4.7
Funke und Huster: 4.3
Gaz de France: 3.2
Gesellschaft für Gerätebau: 4.11
Gothe: 4.29 / 4.30 / 4.33
Hamacher: 2.28 / 2.35 / 2.38 / 2.41 / 2.45
Hartmann und Braun: 4.42 / 4.44 / 4.45 / 4.3.1
Hausherr: 2.23
Hemscheidt: 2.25
Huwood: 4.8 / 4.9
INIEX: 2.3 / 2.33 / 4.1 / 4.14 / 4.58 / 4.68 / 4.72 / 4.76
Korfmann: 2.19

Lavallée:	2.34 / 2.40
Maihak:	4.26 / 4.27
Mining Engineer:	4.74
MRDE:	1.4 / 3.1.3 / 3.1.5
MSA:	4.13
Müller-Borggräfe:	2.29 / 2.42
Nash:	3.10 / 3.14 / 3.15 / 3.16 / 3.17 / 3.18 / 3.19
NCB:	2.8 / 2.9 / 2.31 / 2.32 / 2.37 / 2.39 / 2.44 / 2.51 / 2.55 / 2.6.1 / 3.1 / 3.7 / 3.8 / 3.9 / 3.12 / 3.13 / 3.22 / 3.5.1 / 3.5.2 / 3.5.3 / 4.22 / 4.23 / 4.59 / 4.60 / 4.61 / 4.62 / 4.3.3
Oldham:	4.18 / 4.20 / 4.21
Philips:	4.41 / 4.3.2
Preussag:	2.54
Prüfstelle für Grubenbewetterung:	2.2 / 2.12 / 2.14 / 4.31 / 4.32
Reineke:	4.49
Richard:	4.4 / 4.37
Ruhrkohle AG:	3.5
Saarbergwerke AG:	2.7 / 2.47 / 2.56 / 2.58
Schlumberger:	4.43 / 4.46 / 4.48
Schmidt-Kranz:	2.53
Sieger:	4.53
Siemens:	4.47
Télémecanique:	4.52
Total:	3.5.5
Turmag:	2.18
Victor:	2.21
Zeiss:	4.15 / 4.16 / 4.17 / 4.1.1

Selected Bibliography

English Bibliography

1. *Clough, R. H.,* and *J. Carver:* A Study of the Movement of Methane/Air Mixtures in the Wastes of Longwall Workings. Trans. Instn. Min. Engrs. 116 (1956/57) p 131.

2. *Potts, E. W.,* and *W. S. Foster:* An Experiment in Firedamp Drainage from a Retreating Longwall Face at Horden Colliery. Trans. Instn. Min. Engrs. 116 (1956/57) p 363/88.

3. *Nicholls, G.:* The Use of Methane in Dual-Fuel Internal Combustion Engines at Point of Ayr Colliery. Trans. Instn. Min. Engrs. 116 (1956/57) p 499.

4. *Wood, J. E.,* and *D. C. Yates:* Controlled Drainage of Firedamp from Old Workings into a Firedamp Drainage System. Trans. Instn. Min. Engrs. 117 (1957/58) p 3.

5. *Dobson, A.,* and *W. Challenor:* Firedamp Risks in Modern Mining. Trans. Instn. Min. Engrs. 118 (1958/59) p 163.

6. *Hird, W. T., S. L. Wright* and *G. H. Thomas:* The Collection, Transmission and Utilisation of Methane from the Afan Valley. Trans. Instn. Min. Engrs. 118 (1958/59) p 606/27.

7. *Bromilow, J. G.:* The Drainage and Utilisation of Firedamp in Great Britain. Coll. Guard. 199 (1959) p 61/68, 97/100.

8. *Carver, J.,* and *L. F. Louth:* Firedamp Drainage from Sealed Areas and Adjacent Wastes of Longwall Retreating Faces in a Seam Liable to Spontaneous Combustion. Trans. Instn. Min. Engrs. 118 (1958/59) p 23.

9. *White, E.,* and *A. Wright:* Methane Drainage in the Barnsley Seam of South Yorkshire, with Particular Reference to Investigations at Maltby Colliery. Trans. Instn. Min. Engrs. 119 (1959/60) p 725/43.

10. *Steele, E.,* and *D. C. Yates:* The Development and Application of Methane Drainage in the North Staffordshire Coalfield. Min. Engr. 119 (1959/60) p 214/28.

11. *Jolliffe, G. V.,* and *W. E. Raybould:* The Application of Pressure Balancing Chambers to Control Air Movement in Sealed Areas. Trans. Instn. Min. Engrs. 120 (1960/61) p 861.

12. *Morris, I. H.:* Firedamp Drainage in Mines. Proc. Nat. Assoc. Coll. Managers 58 (1961) p 394/423.

13. *Robertson, W. M.:* Methane Drainage and Spontaneous Combustion. Min. Engr. 121 (1961/62) p 253.

14. *Moore, D. R.:* Drainage and Use of Methane from Mines. Min. Engr. 121 (1961/62) p 344/45.

15. *Wharton, P. B.:* Some Observations on Drainage and Emission of Firedamp. Min. Engr. 121 (1961/62) p 577.

16. *Yates, D. C.:* Drainage of Methane from Sealed Areas. Steel and Coal, London, September 14th 1962.

17. *Morris, I. H.:* Firedamp Drainage. The Min. Electr. Mech. Engr. 43 (1962/63) p 175/93.

18. *Carver, J., L. J. Purdy* and *M. Spedding:* Special Techniques of Firedamp Drainage. Min. Engr. 122 (1963) p 861/64.

19. *Harley, A.:* Some Observations on the Behaviour and Dispersal of Firedamp in Longwall Faces. Trans. Instn. Min. Engrs. 123 (1963/64) p 10.

20. *Baxter Brown, J. McD.:* An Analysis of the Flow of Gases into Cross-Measures Methane Drainage Boreholes. Trans. Instn. Min. Engrs. 123 (1963/64) p 472.

21. *Rhydderch, L. D.,* and *D. C. Yates:* Outbursts of Firedamp in the North Staffordshire Coalfield. Trans. Instn. Min. Engrs. 124 (1964/65) p 168.

22. *Hinsley, F. B.,* and *Others:* The Estimation of the Firedamp Content of Coal Samples. Trans. Instn. Min. Engrs. 124 (1964/65) p 591.

23. *Morris, I. H.:* Some Factors Affecting Rates of Methane Extraction. Min. Engr. 125 (1965/66) Nr. 62 p 72/94.

24. *Kelly, M. V.,* and *B. J. Quick:* Methane Utilisation. Min. Engr. 125 (1965/66) p 198/212.

25. *Robinson, R.,* and *W. Holding:* Re-opening of Second South District, Low Main Seam, Easington Colliery. Min. Engr. 125 (1965/66) p 263/77.

26. *Highton, W.:* Methane Problems Experienced in Lancashire and their Relationship with the Technique of Methane Drainage. Coll. Guard. 215 (1967) p 445/54.

27. *Ahmed, M.:* Development of an Integrated Control System for Mine Ventilation and Firedamp Drainage. Min. Eng. 127 (1967/68) p 382.

28. *Highton, W.,* and *J. J. Cunliffe:* Retreating Longwall Faces at Sutton Manor Colliery. Min. Engr. 127 (1967/68) p 403/18.

29. *Airey, E. M.:* Gas Emission from Broken Coal: Experimental and Theoretical Investigation. Int. J. Rock Mech. 5 (1968) p 475/94.

30. *Daines, M. E.:* Apparatus for the Determination of Methane Sorption on Coal at High Pressures by a Weighing Method. Int. J. Rock. Mech. 5 (1968) p 315/23.

31. *Dunmore, R.:* Gas Flow through Underground Strata. Colloquium on Firedamp Measurement and Control, Isleworth, 3rd May 1968. Min. Engr. 128 (1969) p 193/99, p 216/24.

32. *Davies, J. T.,* and *C. Jones:* The Prevention of Waste Gas Flushings in the Blackshale Seam at Markham Colliery. Colloquium on Firedamp Measurement and Control, Isleworth, 3rd May 1968. Min. Engr. 128 (1969) p 200/06, p 216/24.

33. *Wolstanholme, E. F.:* Methane Detection. Coll. Guard. 217 (1969) p 47.

34. *Swift, R. A.:* Firedamp Drainage in Great Britain. Coal Age 75 (1970) p 94/99.

35. *Morris, I. H.,* and *W. Highton:* Excessive Firedamp Emissions in Current Practice. Min. Engr. 130 (1970/71) p 276/80, 321/39.

36. *Morris, I. H.:* Some Current Firedamp Emission Problems. In: Access, University of Wales Mineral Exploitation Society 1970. p 8/20.

37. *Morris, I. H.,* and *R. A. Swift:* Combating Sudden Gas Emissions from the Floor of Coal Seams. Proc. Conf. on the Control of Firedamp Emission and Improvement of Mine Atmosphere, Luxembourg, 24th and 25th February 1971. p 327/52.

38. *Kimmins, E. J.:* Firedamp Drainage in the North Western Area. Coll. Guard. Ann. Rev. 1971. p 39/45.

39. *Airey, E. M.:* A Theory of Gas Emission in Mining Operations. Internat. Conf. of Safety in Mines Research, Donezk, U.S.S.R. 1971. Paper A. 16.

40. *Shillingford, H. S.:* The Automatic Monitoring System for the Haig Colliery Methane Drainage Scheme. Min. Engr. 131 (1972) p 290/309.

41. *Morris, I. H.,* and *R. Williams:* Emissions and Outbursts in Coal Mining. In: Proc. Sympos. Environm. Engng. Coal Min., Harrogate 1972. p 101/16.

42. *Tube Bundle Techniques.* National Coal Board, Scientific Control. Harrow 1972.

43. *Turner, C. W.,* and *J. J. Mallen:* Methane Drainage and Utilisation at Manton Colliery. Min. Engr. 132 (1972/73) p 225/35.

44. *Chamberlain, E. A. C.,* and *Others:* The Continuous Monitoring of Mine Gases: the Development and Use of a "Tube Bundle" Technique. Min. Engr. 133 (1973/74) p 239.

45. *Morris, I. H.:* Substantial Spontaneous Firedamp Emissions. Min. Engr. 133 (1973/74) p 407/27.

46. *Morgan, B. G.:* Developments in Methane Drainage Techniques in the South Wales Area. Min. Engr. 134 (1974/75) p 81/95.

47. *Dunmore, R.:* A Theory of Emission of a Mixture of Methane and Ethane from Coal. Proc. Int. Mine Ventilation Congr. Johannesburg 1975. p 117, 145.

48. *Harrison, N.:* Recent Developments in the Tube Bundle System of Air Monitoring in the United Kingdom. Proc. Int. Mine Ventilation Congr. Johannesburg 1975. p 179.

49. *Jones, K.:* The Environmental and Remote Control System for Manton Colliery. Min. Engr. 135 (1975/76) p 169.

50. *Morris, I. H.:* Monitoring of the Mine Environment. Symposium on Monitoring. The Polytechnic of Wales, January 1976.

51. *Bexon, I.:* Remote Control of Colliery Operations by Computer. Int. Conf. on Remote Control and Monitoring in Mining. Birmingham 1977. Vol. 1 p 5.1—5.17.

52. *Cooper, L. R.:* Sensors and Instruments for Control and Monitoring in Coal Mines. Int. Conf. on Remote Control and Monitoring in Mining. Birmingham 1977. Vol. 1. p 9.1—9.11.

53. *Morris, I. H.,* and *G. W. Gray:* Environmental Monitoring and Control in Mines. Int. Conf. on Remote Control and Monitoring in Mining. Birmingham 1977. Vol. 1. p 10.1—10.16.

French Bibliography

1. *Chiche, P.:* La fixation des gaz par la houille. Publication Cerchar N° 1044. Document intérieur Cerchar. Avril 1960, 54 p.

2. *Codet, P.:* Emploi des grisoumètres interférentiels pour l'analyse des gaz de captage. Publication Cerchar N° 1258. Documents Techniques N° 8. 1962, 10 p.

3. *Codet, P.:* Instruments de mesure utilisables pour le contrôle du captage du grisou au fond. Publication Cerchar N° 1285. Documents Techniques N° 8. 1962, 15 p.

4. *Gunther, J.:* Etude de la liaison gaz-charbon. Publication Cerchar N° 1572. Revue Ind. Min. Vol. 47, N° 10, p. 693/708.

5. *de Vergeron, M., P. Codet* et *B. Bruyet:* Observations systématiques du dégagement du grisou de plusieurs quartiers d'exploitation par tailles. Publication Cerchar N° 1573. Revue Ind. Min. 1965. Vol. 47, N° 9, p. 673/83.

6. *de Vergeron, M., P. Codet* et *B. Bruyet:* Observations sur le dégagement du grisou. Publication Cerchar N° 1587. Documents Techniques 11/65, p. 677/96.

7. *Gunther, J.:* Mécanisme et prévision du dégagement grisouteux. Publication Cerchar N° 1588. Documents Techniques 11/65, p. 697/703.

8. *de Vergeron, M.* et *P. Codet:* Les bouchons d'eau dans les conduites de captage de grisou. Conception d'un purgeur. Publication Cerchar N° 1589. Documents Techniques N° 11/65, p. 705/11.

9. *Gunther, J.:* Le dégagement des gaz contenus dans le charbon. Col. International CNRS sur les phénomènes de transport avec changement de phase dans les milieux poreux ou colloïdaux, Paris 18 à 20 avril 1966. Publication Cerchar N° 1640. Publication CNRS, p. 181/86.

10. *Gunther, J.:* Dégagement du grisou dans les chantiers d'exploitation. Publication Cerchar N° 1718. Ann. Min. Belg. 1967, p. 151/61.

11. *Gunther, J.* et *J. Belin:* Prévision du dégagement de grisou en taille pours les gisements en plateure. Publication Cerchar N° 1757. Revue Ind. Min. 1968. Vol. 50, N° 1, p. 41/54.

12. *Bertard, C., B. Bruyet* et *J. Gunther:* Détermination de la concentration en gaz désorbable des charbons (méthode directe). Publication Cerchar N° 1778. Documents Techniques 12/67, p. 665/86.

13. *Gunther, J.:* Etat actuel de nos connaissances de base sur le dégagement du grisou en taille. Publication Cerchar N° 1814. Documents Techniques 3/68, p. 81/84.

14. *Bertard, C.:* Introduction au captage du grisou en longue taille peu pentée. Publication Cerchar N° 1816. Documents Techniques 3/68, p. 115/28.

15. *Gunther, J.* et *J. Belin:* Mesure de la concentration en grisou des charbons et prévision du dégagement grisouteux dans les exploitations houillères. Publication Cerchar N° 1859. Communication C. 12 présentée à la Conférence Internationale sur l'aérage des mines profondes, Jachymov (Tchécoslovaquie), 13 à 16 janvier 1969.

16. *Bertard, C.* et *J. J. Liabeuf:* Le captage du grisou dans le mur des longues tailles peu pentées. Publication Cerchar N° 1970. Communication présentée à la Conférence Internationale des Directeurs de Stations d'Essais, Tokyo, novembre 1969. Revue Ind. Min. 1970. Vol. 52, N° 8, p. 541/48.

17. *Bruyet, B.:* L'irrégularité du dégagement de grisou et sa mesure: définition, utilisation et valeurs du coefficient d'irrégularité. Publication Cerchar N° 2041. Revue Ind. Min. 1970. Vol. 52, N° 4, p. 258/64.

18. *Bertard, C., B. Bruyet* et *J. Gunther:* Determination of desorbable gas concentration of coal (direct method). Int. J. Rock. Mech. Min. Sci. 1970. Vol. 7, p. 43/65.

19. *Belin, J.:* Mesure de la concentration en gaz des couches de charbon (méthode directe) Publication Cerchar N° 2122. Communication aux journées d'information Grisou CECA — Luxembourg, 24 à 25 février 1971. Document EUR. 4670 d, f, p. 39/56.

20. *Liabeuf, J. J.:* La prévision du dégagement de grisou dans les tailles en plateure. Résultats acquis en France avec la méthode Cerchar. Publication Cerchar N° 2126. Communication aux journées d'information Grisou CECA — Luxembourg, 24 à 25 février 1971. Document EUR. 4670 d, f, p. 171/92.

21. *Bruyet, B.* et *J. J. Liabeuf:* Etude de la circulation du grisou dans le mur des tailles en plateure: Application au captage. Publication Cerchar N° 2127. Communication aux journées d'information Grisou CECA — Luxembourg, 24 à 25 février 1971. Document EUR. 4670 d, f, p. 257/80.

22. *Bordonne, G.:* Progrès dans le captage du grisou aux Houillères de Lorraine. Communication aux journées d'information Grisou CECA — Luxembourg, 24 à 25 février 1971. Document EUR. 4670 d, f, p. 281/301.

23. *Boutonnat, M., C. Froger, C. Gagniere* et *A. Monomakhoff:* Appareils de surveillance de l'aérage et du captage d'une mine grisouteuse. Publication Cerchar N° 2125. Communication aux journées d'information Grisou CECA — Luxembourg, 24 à 25 février 1971. Document EUR. 4670 d, f, p. 355/72.

24. *Bruyet, B.:* Le mécanisme du captage du grisou au mur de couches en plateure et ses conséquences pratiques. Publication Cerchar N° 2172. Communication à la XIVè conférence des Stations d'Essais — Doneck 1971. Revue Ind. Min. 1971. Vol. 53, N° 12, p. 781/97.

25. *Belugou, P., J. Belin* et *M. Boutonnat:* Télécontrôle du captage du grisou. Publication Cerchar N° 2171. Communication à la XIVè conférence des Stations d'Essais — Doneck 1971. Revue Ind. Min. 1971. Vol. 53, N° 12, p. 798/810.

26. *Bruyet, B.* et *J. J. Liabeuf:* Calcul automatique des reseaux de captage de grisou. Documents techniques Août/Sept. 1976.

27. *Jeger, C.* et *C. Froger:* Modification de la permeabilité de veines par des exploitations sus-jacent — Application au predegazage. 18e conference internationale "Recherche sur la securité dans les mines". Dubrovnik 1979.

28. *Jeger, C.:* Degazement de grisou dans les tailles à faible pendage — Nouvelles connaissances sur la zone degazée au mur et au toit et sur les limites de detente — Nouveau schema de prevision de degazement. (En préparation).

29. *Jeger, C.:* Degazement de grisou dans les traçages. Cas de veines permeables et detendues. Prevision et methodes de lutte. (En préparation).

Belgish Bibliography

Publications (revues, journées d'information)

1. *Boxho, J.:* Maîtrise des dégagements grisouteux. Ann. Min. Belg. 1976. p 919/93.

2. *Cremer, J.:* Perfectionnements des méthodes et divers. Dans: Captage et utilisation du méthane des charbonnages. O.E.C.E. Paris 1958. p 65/105.

3. Règles essentielles pour l'obtention d'un grisou à haute teneur en méthane lors du captage du grisou. Ann. Min. Belg. 1961. p 60/66.

4. *Degueldre, G.,* et *J. Boxho:* Conditions de travail dans les chantiers d'abattage à haute performance. Dans: Chantiers d'abattage à haute performance dans les charbonnages. Journées d'information. Luxembourg 1976. Vol. 1. p 319/99.

5. *Josse, J.:* Le captage de méthane sur puits abandonnés. Dans: Maîtrise du dégagement grisouteux. Amélioration du climat dans les mines. Journées d'information. Luxembourg 1971. p 313/23.

6. *Stassen, P.,* et *J. Venter:* Captage et utilisation du grisou. 6ème Conférence Mondiale de l'Energie. Melbourne 1962. Sous-section II. 3. Rapport 107. II 3/5. 12 p. Ann. Min. Belg. 1963. p 439/46.

7. *Vandeloise, R.,* et *P. Rosen-Meyer:* Le captage et la valorisation du grisou en Belgique. Geologie Mijnb. 1962. p 87/94.

8. *Vandeloise, R.:* Gisement et dégagement du grisou. Rapport de synthèse des études de l'INIEX, financées par la C.C.E. 1969/1972. Ann. Min. Belg. 1974. p 705/52.

Bulletins techniques «Mines» (INICHAR)

1. et 2. *Stassen, P.* et *Y. de Wasseige:* Le captage du grisou. Perfectionnements apportés aux techniques de captage et essai d'explication du dégagement du grisou dans les exploitations. 1958 N° 64 novembre p 1327/49.
1958 N° 65 décembre p 1351/73.

Bulletins techniques «Mines et Carrières» (INIEX)

1. *Vandeloise, R., J. Bernard* et *F. Jadin:* Le captage du grisou des vieux travaux à la S. A. des Houillères d'Anderlues. 1969 N° 119 janvier. 36 p.

German Bibliography

Fachbücher

1. *Albring, W.:* Angewandte Strömungslehre. 4. Aufl. Dresden: Th. Steinkopf Verlag 1970.

2. *Eck, B.:* Technische Strömungslehre. 8. Aufl. Berlin: Springer Verlag 1978.

3. *Herning, F.:* Stoffströme in Rohrleitungen. 4. Aufl. Düsseldorf: VDI-Verlag 1966.

4. *Prandtl, L.:* Führer durch die Strömungslehre. 6. Aufl. Braunschweig: F. Vieweg 1965.

5. *Richter, H.:* Rohrhydraulik. 5. Aufl. Berlin: Springer Verlag 1971.

6. *Schlichting, H.:* Grenzschicht-Theorie. 5. Aufl. Karlsruhe: G. Braun 1965.

7. *Schwaigerer, S.:* Rohrleitungen. Theorie und Praxis. Berlin: Springer Verlag 1967.

8. *Truckenbrodt, E.:* Strömungsmechanik. Berlin: Springer Verlag 1968.

Veröffentlichungen in Fachzeitschriften

9. *Baar, C. A.:* Unfallschutz bei Bohrungen in gasführendem Gebirge. Schlägel u. Eisen 1961 S. 468/69.

10. *Barth, W., u. a.:* Vorausgasung von Steinkohlenflözen durch hydraulische Rißbildung. Bergbauwiss. 17 (1970) S. 7/11.

11. *Bartknecht, W.:* Zünddurchschlagsicherungen für die über Tage befindlichen Ausblasleitungen von Grubengasabsaugeanlagen. Schlägel u. Eisen 1961 S. 323/31.

12. *Bartknecht, W.:* Entwicklungen und Prüfungen von explosionstechnischen Einrichtungen für Grubengasabsaugeanlagen. Schlägel u. Eisen 1964 S. 162/77, 243/44, 260, 322/25.

13. *Bartknecht, W.:* Gasexplosionen in Rohrstrecken. Bergfreiheit 31 (1966) S. 101/17.

14. *Bartknecht, W.:* Explosionen in Rohrstrecken und Maßnahmen zur Verhütung schädlicher Explosionsauswirkungen. Moderne Unfallverhütung 1966 S. 65/76.

15. *Bormuth, Ph.:* Ermittlung der Temperaturerhöhung in Roots-Gebläsen. Konstruktion 13 (1961) S. 21/23.

16. *Brändle, E.,* und *A. Wefers:* Der Einfluß der Gasabsaugung auf die Abbauführung. Glückauf 110 (1974) S. 324/28.

17. *Busche, H.:* Probleme der Ausgasung bei steigenden Fördermengen im Abbau. Glückauf 109 (1973) S. 205/07.

18. *Düpre, G.:* 25 Jahre Grubengasabsaugung im Saarrevier. Glückauf 111 (1975) S. 1162/67.

19. *Dürr, R.:* Verfahren und Einrichtungen zur Grubengasabsaugung. Gas- u. Wasserfach, Ausg. Gas 109 (1968) S. 165/71.

20. *Externbrink, W.:* Herstellen und Abdichten der Bohrlöcher für die Gasabsaugung. Glückauf 100 (1964) S. 1028/34.

21. *Fauth, G., u. a.:* Ferngespeister Klein-Unor und Gasleitungssonde für die Methanüberwachung. Glückauf 112 (1976) S. 1163/65.

22. *Feyferlik, H.:* Die Grubengasabsaugung beim Strebrückbau in Fohnsdorf. Berg- u. hüttenm. Mh. 103 (1958) S. 41/51.

23. *Flügge, G.:* Die Anwendung der Trogtheorie auf den Raum der Zusatzausgasung. Glückauf-Forsch.-H. 32 (1971) S. 122/29.

24. *Flügge, G.:* Beispiele verstärkter Zusatzausgasung und Möglichkeiten ihrer Bekämpfung. Glückauf 108 (1972) S. 337/41.

25. *Giesel, W., u. a.:* Messungen der Gasspeicherung und Gaswanderung im Steinkohlengebirge des Saarkarbons auf der Grube Luisenthal. Bergbauwiss. 15 (1968) S. 201/12.

26. *Graumann, K.:* Modellversuche über die Dichteschichtung in strömenden Medien. Glückauf-Forsch.-H. 33 (1972) S. 211/21.

27. *Hetzel, K. W.:* Nachweis und Bestimmung von häufig vorkommenden Gasen bei Reparaturarbeiten an Gasleitungen. Moderne Unfallverhütung 1966 S. 120/26.

28. *Hilgenstock, D.:* Vereinfachte Berechnung von Methanleitungen im Untertagebetrieb. Glückauf-Forsch.-H. 36 (1975) S. 110/13.

29. *Janas, H.:* Ermittlung des Gasinhalts vor Ort mit dem Desorbometer. Glückauf 112 (1976) S. 1159/61.

30. *Jungnitz, G.:* Das Betriebsverhalten von Drehkolbengebläsen zur Grubengasabsaugung. Glückauf 98 (1962) S. 1208/11.

31. *Kaffanke, H.:* Praktische Erfahrungen der Ausgasungsvorausberechnung auf Ruhrzechen. In: Beherrschung der Ausgasung in Grubenbetrieben. Informationstagung der Kommission der Europäischen Gemeinschaften, Luxemburg 1971. S. 217/32.

32. *Kegel, K.-H.:* Probleme der Ausgasung. Glückauf 99 (1963) S. 512/22.

33. *Keienburg, F.:* Das Gusanon-Verfahren. Bergbau-Rdsch. 13 (1961) S. 336/39.

34. *Keienburg, F.:* Praktische Winke für die Gasabsaugung im Abbau. Bergbau 15 (1964) S. 138/44.

35. *Kesseler, G.:* Ortsfeste Gasanalysengeräte für die Wetterüberwachung. Glückauf 100 (1964) S. 1425/35.

36. *Kesseler, G.,* und *H. Müller:* Methan-Handmeßgeräte im deutschen Steinkohlenbergbau. Glückauf 104 (1968) S. 127/35.

37. *Keysselitz, H.,* und *G. Joswig:* Der Betrieb von Dieselgasmaschinen zur Verwertung von Grubengas. Glückauf 97 (1961) S. 198/204.

38. *Klauer, F.:* Die Entwicklung neuzeitlicher Methanometer. Glückauf 103 (1967) S. 379/83.

39. *Kneuper, G.,* und *R. Müller:* Grubengas muß abgesaugt werden. „Frac" heißt das neue Verfahren. Schacht u. Heim 15 (1969) S. 4/6.

40. *Knobling, K.:* Kenngrößen in der Gasdynamik. VDI-Z. 114 (1972) S. 1206/10.

41. *Koppe, U.:* Der Ausgasungsgrad von Begleitflözen im Liegenden der flachen Lagerung. Glückauf-Forsch.-H. 36 (1975) S. 138/44.

42. *Koppe, U.:* Vorausberechnung der Ausgasung von Abbaubetrieben. Glückauf 112 (1976) S. 1154/56.

43. *Krau, P.:* Erhöhung der CH_4-Konzentration bei der Gasabsaugung. Bergfreiheit 23 (1958) S. 162/67.

44. *Linsel, E.:* Entstehung und Freiwerden des Grubengases. Vortrag. Informationstagung „Das Grubengas und seine Bekämpfung" der Europäischen Gemeinschaft für Kohle und Stahl, Hohe Behörde. Luxemburg 1963. Ann. Min. Belg. 1963 S. 1045/55. Geol. Mijnb. 42 (1963) S. 384/93.

45. *Luft, K., F.:* Der „Unor", ein neues Gasanalysengerät für den Bergbau. Glückauf 98 (1962) S. 493/95.

46. *Luft, K. F.,* und *G. Kesseler:* Analysenmeßtechnik unter Tage. VDI-Berichte 1966 S. 93/100.

47. *Luft, K. F.,* und *W. Langner:* Der neue eigensichere Klein-Unor. Glückauf 110 (1974) S. 125/28.

48. *Maercks, J.:* Die bergmännische Gewinnung von Grubengas. Bergbau 10 (1959) S. 154/62.

49. *Mücke, G.:* Ergebnisse der Methanabsaugung im deutschen Steinkohlenbergbau. Glückauf 107 (1971) S. 93/96.

50. *Mücke, G.,* und *G. Tschersich:* Steuerung der Grubengasabsaugung durch Änderung des Unterdrucks in den Sammelleitungen. Vortrag. 15. Internationale Konferenz für Grubensicherheit. Karlsbad 1973.

51. *Mücke, G., K. Renner* und *W. Stegmanns:* Verfahren zur Strömungsmessung in Gasbohrlöchern und in Gasabsaugeleitungen. Glückauf-Forsch.-H. 36 (1975) S. 1/6.

52. *Mücke, G.:* Gasstrommessungen in Bohrlöchern. Glückauf 112 (1976) S. 1165/67.

53. *Müller, R.,* und *G. Kneuper:* Fraccen — Hydraulisches Aufbrechen des Steinkohlengebirges auf Grube Luisenthal. In: Beherrschung der Ausgasung in Grubenbetrieben. Informationstagung. Luxemburg 1971. S. 305/14.

54. *Noack, K.:* Das Absaugen von Methan aus abgedämmten Grubenbauen. Glückauf 100 (1964) S. 1226/27.

55. *Noack, K.:* Untersuchungen über Form und Größe des Ausgasungsraumes um Abbaubetriebe in flacher oder mäßig geneigter Lagerung des Ruhrkarbons. Glückauf-Forsch.-H. 31 (1970) S. 121/32.

56. *Noack, K.:* Untersuchungen über den Ausgasungsraum von Abbaubetrieben. In: Beherrschung der Ausgasung in Grubenbetrieben. Informationstagung. Luxemburg 1971. S. 153/67.

57. *Noack, K., A. von Treskow* und *G. Tschersich:* Die Methanausgasung im bundesdeutschen Steinkohlenbergbau für das Jahr 1970. Glückauf 108 (1972) S. 1077/83.

58. *Noack, K.,* und *P. Hubig:* Die Methanausgasung im bundesdeutschen Steinkohlenbergbau 1975. Glückauf 112 (1976) S. 1374/80.

59. *Otto, G.:* Ergebnisse der Überwachung zweier Abbaubetriebe mit hoher Ausgasung. Glückauf 98 (1962) S. 1286/98.

60. *Pacher, F.:* Die Bekämpfung des Grubengases. Mont.-Rdsch. 14 (1966) S. 43/51, 69.

61. *Paul, K.:* Die Ermittlung des freiwerdenden Teils vom Gasinhalt im Steinkohlenbergbau. Ann. Min. Belg. 1967 S. 134/51, 219/28.

62. *Paul, K.:* Begrenzung der Betriebspunktfördermenge durch die Methanausgasung. Glückauf 105 (1969) S. 1154/58.

63. *Paul, K.:* Gasdruck- und Gasinhaltsmessungen in Steinkohlenflözen. In: Beherrschung der Ausgasung in Grubenbetrieben. Informationstagung. Luxemburg 1971. S. 19/37.

64. *Paul, K.:* Verringerung des Gasinhalts im Bauflöz durch Gasabsaugung mit flözgängigen Bohrlöchern. Glückauf 112 (1976) S. 1170/72.

65. *Schenk, S.:* Die Bedeutung der Ausgasung für Hochleistungsstreben. Glückauf 105 (1969) S. 535/40.

66. *Schilling, H. D., u. a.:* Die Sorptionskinetik von Methan an Steinkohlen als Grundlage des Ausgasungsprozesses. Glückauf-Forsch.-H. 27 (1966) S. 203/14.

67. *Schilling, H. D.:* Chemisch-physikalische Aspekte der Entstehung, Speicherung und Entbindung von Grubengasen. Bergfreiheit 35 (1970) S. 111/17, 131/37.

68. *Schmidt-Koehl, W.,* und *G. Kneuper:* Geologische und lagerstättenkundliche Untersuchungen über die Herkunft, das Auftreten und die Bekämpfung des Grubengases im saarländischen Steinkohlengebirge. Glückauf 110 (1974) S. 193/97.

69. *Schroeder, W.:* Grubenmethan in zwei Verteilernetzen. Schacht u. Heim 3 (1957) S. 9/11.

70. *Schubert, E.,* und *H. Eicker:* Sicherheitliche Grundsätze für die Ausführung und den Einsatz von Gasmeßgeräten im Steinkohlenbergbau. Glückauf 112 (1976) S. 153/56.

71. *Schulz, P.:* Das Entwicklungsbild der Grubengasabsaugung. Bergfreiheit 23 (1958) S. 51/57.

72. *Schulz, W.:* Begriffe der bergmännischen Bohrtechnik. Z. Erzbergb. Metallhüttenw. 17 (1964) S. 211/21.

73. *Schuster, F.:* Das Grubengas in Europa. Gas- u. Wasserfach, Ausg. Gas 109 (1968) S. 1326/30.

74. *Siefke, H.:* Erfahrungen bei der Herstellung von Entgasungsbohrlöchern auf der Zeche Osterfeld. Bergbau 15 (1964) S. 372/78.

75. *Siefke, H.:* Erfahrungen mit der CH_4-Ausgasung, der Überwachung und Abwehrmaßnahmen auf der Zeche Osterfeld. Bergbau 18 (1967) S. 245/59; S. 289/94; S. 318/27.

76. *Siefke, H.:* Die CH_4-Ausgasung im Steinkohlenbergbau und der wirtschaftliche Einfluß der Gasabsaugung auf die Steinkohlengewinnung in den Flözen der Fett- und Gaskohlen. Bergbau 20 (1969) S. 1/9; 34/42.

77. *Siefke, H.:* Betriebsstudien über den Ausgasungsverlauf in Bohrlöchern für Grund- und Zusatzabsaugung und deren Bedeutung für die Wirtschaftlichkeit der Steinkohlengewinnung. Bergbau 24 (1973) S. 226/38.

78. *Thar, R.:* Grubengasabsaugung aus abgedämmten Feldesteilen und aus dem Alten Mann dreier Rückbaustreben in einem zur Selbstentzündung neigenden Flöz. Glückauf 99 (1963) S. 1472/73.

79. *Treskow, A. von,* und *B. Wagener:* Ergebnisse der Auswertung der wettertechnischen Fragebogen 1966 zur Ausgasung in Abbaubetrieben der flachen und der mäßig geneigten Lagerung. Glückauf 105 (1969) S. 216/20.

80. *Treskow, A. von:* Die Methanabsaugung im deutschen Steinkohlenbergbau im Jahre 1970. Glückauf 107 (1971) S. 761/62.

81. *Treskow, A. von:* Methangasabsaugung im deutschen Steinkohlenbergbau im Jahre 1971. Glückauf 108 (1972) S. 742/43.

82. *Treskow, A. von,* und *G. Fitzner:* Methangasabsaugung im deutschen Steinkohlenbergbau im Jahre 1972. Glückauf 109 (1973) S. 877/78.

83. *Treskow, A. von,* und *G. Fitzner:* Das Absaugen von Methan im deutschen Steinkohlenbergbau im Jahre 1973. Glückauf 110 (1974) S. 738/40.

84. *Treskow, A. von,* und *G. Fitzner:* Das Absaugen von Methan im deutschen Steinkohlenbergbau im Jahre 1974. Glückauf 111 (1975) S. 928/29.

85. *Treskow, A. von,* und *G. Fitzner:* Das Absaugen von Methan im deutschen Steinkohlenbergbau im Jahre 1975. Glückkauf 112 (1976) S. 928/29.

86. *Trouvain, A.:* Grube Luisenthal — Modellfall der Entgasung? Bergfreiheit 25 (1960) S. 219/27.

87. *Trouvain, A.:* Entgasung durch Gasstrecken oder Bohrlöcher? Bergfreiheit 26 (1961) S. 226/35.

88. *Ufer, W.:* Grubengasabsaugung mit Flüssigkeitsring-Gaspumpen. Glückauf 112 (1976) S. 1168/70.

89. *Winter, K.:* Gasabsaugung. Bergbau 9 (1958) S. 187/202.

90. *Winter, K.:* Ausspülen von Rohrleitungen mit Gasen. Moderne Unfallverhütung 1966 Nr. 10 S. 58/65.

91. *Winter, K.:* Die Anwendung statistischer Verfahren als Grundlage für die Vorausberechnung der Ausgasung. Glückauf-Forsch.-H. 32 (1971) S. 220/28.

92. *Winter, K.:* Reichweite der Ausgasung im Einwirkungsbereich des Abbaus. Glückauf-Forsch.-H. 37 (1976) S. 22/27.

93. *Wunsch, H.:* Erfahrungen mit Diamantkronen neben Hartmetallschneiden und Rollenmeißeln beim Gasbohren auf der Zeche General Blumenthal. Glückauf 95 (1959) S. 265/73.

94. *Wunsch, H.:* Gasbohrungen mit Diamantkronen auf der Zeche General Blumenthal. Erdöl-Z. 76 (1960) S. 86/95.

95. *Wunsch, H.:* Sauganlage für Grubengas, insbesondere Methangas. Bergbau-Rdsch. 9 (1957) S. 457/58.

96. Empfehlungen für die Herstellung von Bohrlöchern für die Gasabsaugung mit Hilfe des Trockenbohrverfahrens. Glückauf 104 (1968) S. 145.